CATALOGUE OF GEORGIAN
AND OTHER CAUCASIAN PRINTED BOOKS
IN THE BRITISH MUSEUM

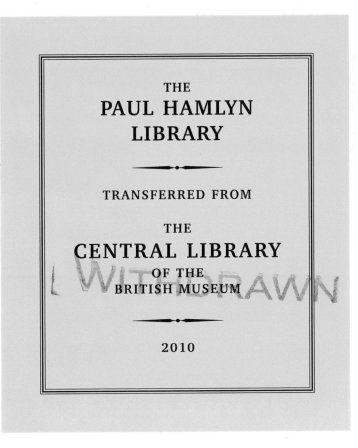

CATALOGUE OF
GEORGIAN
AND OTHER CAUCASIAN
PRINTED BOOKS
IN THE
BRITISH MUSEUM

COMPILED BY

DAVID MARSHALL LANG, M.A., D. LIT.

READER IN CAUCASIAN STUDIES
UNIVERSITY OF LONDON

PUBLISHED BY

THE TRUSTEES OF THE BRITISH MUSEUM
LONDON
1962

Sold at the BRITISH MUSEUM, London, W.C. 1

and by

CAMBRIDGE UNIVERSITY PRESS
200 Euston Road, London, N.W. 1

H.M. STATIONERY OFFICE
York House, Kingsway, London, W.C. 2

KEGAN PAUL & CO., LTD.
43 Great Russell Street, London, W.C. 1

BERNARD QUARITCH LTD.
11 Grafton Street, London, W. 1

©

BRITISH MUSEUM
1962

Printed in Germany by J.J.Augustin, Glückstadt

PREFACE

This Catalogue, like the recently published *Catalogue of Syriac printed books and related literature in the British Museum*, stands as something of a landmark in the development of oriental studies. In it for the first time a major collection of Georgian books in a Western library is catalogued and described for the benefit of those interested in the literature and history of Georgia and in the related languages and cultures of the Caucasus. The Georgian collection in the British Museum is of moderate size and makes no claim to be exhaustive, but it is rich in early printed books acquired by the British Museum Library before the foundation of a separate Department of Oriental Printed Books and Manuscripts, and it has been very considerably augmented during the past ten years through the efforts of Dr. D. M. Lang. To him also is due the credit for including in the present Catalogue a selection of reference books compiled by European specialists, as well as a wide range of books and periodical articles in Western languages relating to Caucasian languages and literatures. These, it is hoped, will greatly enhance the usefulness of the Catalogue to Georgian scholars, for in this way the relevant holdings of the Department of Printed Books as well as those of the Department of Oriental Printed Books and Manuscripts are brought together within the covers of a single volume.

The thanks of the British Museum are due to Dr. Lang for giving so generously of his time and labour in compiling this Catalogue and seeing it through the press.

K. B. GARDNER

Keeper,

Department of Oriental Printed Books
and Manuscripts

January, 1962

INTRODUCTION

The Georgians and the Armenians are the only indigenous nations of the Caucasus to possess original and ancient literatures, the history of which extends in both cases over a period of fifteen hundred years.

The invention of the Georgian and Armenian alphabets, together with that of the Caucasian Albanians, is to be assigned to the fifth century after Christ. Its immediate purpose was the propagation of the holy scriptures among the recently converted peoples of the Caucasus. The Gospels and Psalms were rendered into Georgian at an early date, and were rapidly followed by many other sacred and liturgical texts. The first original works of Georgian literature were lives of Saints, beginning with that of Saint Shushanik, written at the end of the fifth century. Monastic chroniclers soon began to write histories, which were subsequently arranged in connected form under the general title of *K'art'lis tskhovreba* ("The Life of Georgia"). Contact with the Islamic civilization of Persia encouraged the growth of a secular romance literature and the cultivation of lyric and epic poetry. The masterpiece of the mediaeval "Golden Age" of Georgian literature is Shot'a Rust'aveli's romantic epic *Vep'khis-tqaosani* ("The Man in the Panther's Skin"), ascribed to the reign of the Georgian Queen T'amar, who ruled from 1184 to 1213.

The earliest Georgian printed books, published in Rome under the auspices of the Sacra Congregatio de Propaganda Fide from 1629 onwards, were grammars and devotional manuals for the use of Roman Catholic missionaries. Printing was introduced into Georgia itself by King Vakhtang VI, who set up a press at Tiflis in 1709, on which a number of Church books were printed, as well as the *editio princeps* of Rust'aveli's epic (1712). The Turkish invasion of 1723 drove King Vakhtang and his followers into exile. A Georgian press was then set up in Moscow, on which the first complete Georgian Bible was printed in 1743 under the editorship of Prince Vakhushti. The Tiflis press was reopened in 1749 by King Erekle II, but destroyed by the Qajar ruler of Persia, Āghā Muhammad Khān, when he sacked the city in 1795. The Georgian kingdom of K'art'lo-Kakhet'i was annexed by Russia in 1801, the other Georgian principalities later.

Whereas a few Georgian books were produced at K'ut'aisi in Western Georgia and Mozdok in North Caucasia, the publication of works in the Georgian vernacular remained for several decades at a low ebb. However, the first half of the nineteenth century saw the appearance of a number of Georgian devotional books, dictionaries and scholarly works, published in Paris, Saint Petersburg and Moscow. By 1840, the regular publication of books in Georgian had been resumed in Tiflis. Later in the century, a national revival took place, led by such outstanding writers as Ilia Tchavtchavadze and Akaki Tseret'eli. The output of novels, dramas, poetry, historical and other scholarly books, as well as newspapers and journals, reached impressive dimensions. The foundation of Tiflis State University in 1918, and of the Academy of Sciences of the Georgian S. S. R. in 1941, led to a further increase in the volume of published work on literary, historical and scientific subjects. Outside the Soviet Union, books have been published in Georgian at Constantinople, Berlin, Munich, Paris, Louvain, New York, Buenos Aires, Santiago and other centres.

Closely related to Georgian are two other K'art'velian or South Caucasian languages, Svanian and Mingrelo-Laz. Speakers of these normally employ Georgian as a literary medium, except that the Laz domiciled in Turkey use Turkish. However, there exist collections of folk-tales and other texts written down in the Svanian, Mingrelian and Laz vernaculars, for which a modified form of Georgian script is employed.

The affinities of the two other principal groups of Caucasian languages with Georgian, as with each other, remain somewhat obscure. The groups in question comprise the Adyghe/Abkhaz or North-West Caucasian languages, and the Chechen/Daghestanian group (Checheno-Lezgian or North-East Caucasian languages). The main constituents of the Adyghe family are Circassian, Kabardian, Abaza and Ubykh, with the addition of Abkhazian. The Abkhaz, through long residence in Transcaucasia, have acquired linguistic and cultural affinities with the Georgians and Mingrelo-Laz. Until the Russian conquest, neither the Adyghe nor the Checheno-Lezgian languages had been reduced to writing, except for a few works in Avar written in Arabic characters, dating from the 18th century. Being Muslims, the Circassians and Daghestanis used Turkish, Arabic or Persian for written communication, these languages being widely understood and employed in the Caucasus even at the present time.

Daghestan was finally brought under Russian suzerainty in 1859, Circassia in 1864. Russian scholars then collaborated with native informants with a view to providing alphabets for the principal Caucasian languages. In the Circassian group, some attempt was made to evolve a "common Adyghe" literary language, endowed with the Arabic or the Cyrillic character. In this connexion, one may cite the manual of the Adyghe language by ʿUmar Besney, published in 1855, the alphabet of Atazhukin (1865) and the grammar and dictionary of Lopatinsky (1891; 1896). Prior to the pioneer work of D. I. Gulia (1874–1960) the Abkhaz had no literary language, though in 1862 Baron P. K. Uslar had devised a Cyrillic script for them, which was embodied in works relating to Abkhazian published by Lt.-General I. A. Bartholomaei. During this same period, thorough first-hand investigations were made by Baron Uslar into Chechen and the main languages of Daghestan. Detailed descriptions of these languages based on Uslar's materials were published by F. A. von Schiefner in the Memoirs of the Imperial Academy of Sciences at Saint Petersburg. Alphabets modelled largely on Cyrillic were provided during the 1860's for Chechen, Avar and Lak (Kazikumuk), but these failed to take root and scarcely any literary works were composed in these tongues before the Revolution of 1917, although a rich oral literature continued to be handed down by word of mouth.

Following the Revolution, the old tsarist Russification policy was abandoned in favour of a programme of cultural autonomy for the constituent peoples of the U.S.S.R. There was a systematic effort to promote literacy among the smaller peoples of the Caucasus. From 1923 until 1928, this policy entailed the linguistic unification of Daghestan round a Turkic language, either Azeri Turkish or Kumuk. It was thought at that time to be useless to attempt to create a literature in the Avar, Dargwa, Lak and other local tongues, for the use of a few thousand people. "It is infinitely simpler," wrote the Daghestan Communist leader Samursky, "to teach them a real language of civilization." A change of orientation occurred in 1928, when a special commission for the development of Daghestan languages, formed by the Central Committee of the All-Union Communist Party, recommended the use of indigenous languages for teaching in primary schools. In 1930, the Daghestan Communist Party published a list of eleven official languages for the region: Russian, Kumuk, Azeri, Avar, Lak, Dargwa, Kiuri (Lezgian), Tabasaran, Chechen, Tat and Nogay. Today, the languages of instruction at the new Daghestan University of Makhach-Kala are Avar, Dargwa, Lezgian and Kumuk, while Lak and Tabasaran also have the status of literary languages. The Checheno-Ingush were deported from North Caucasia to Siberia by Stalin's order in 1944. Following their repatriation in 1957, newspapers and books are now appearing both in Chechen and the closely related Ingush language.

Soviet policy towards the Adyghe or Circassian peoples is apparently directed against their consolidation into a single, unified Adyghe nation. Accordingly, both Kabardian and West Circassian have been made into literary languages, as has the language of the relatively insignificant kindred tribe of the Abazas. Mention must also be made of the Ubykh, a now fast disappearing Adyghe people who migrated *en masse* to Turkey following the Russian conquest in 1864. Georges Dumézil and Hans Vogt have done important work in collecting specimens of Ubykh folklore and making systematic studies of Ubykh grammar and phonetics.

A once important literary language of the Caucasus, now extinct, was that of the vanished nation of the Caucasian Albanians. This people, well known to the Classical geographers, had a distinctive alphabet from the fifth century A.D. onwards. Later they came under Armenian hegemony and were virtually submerged by the Seljuk invasions of the eleventh century. Their remnants, it is thought, may survive today as the small tribe of the Udi, who inhabit three villages on the borders of the Georgian and Azerbaijan Soviet Socialist Republics. Specimens of the old Albanian language have come to light in ancient manuscripts and inscriptions, a few publications relating to which are included in the present catalogue.

The other leading literary idioms of the Caucasus, Armenian and Ossetic, both belong to the Indo-European family and cannot properly be classed among the Caucasian languages as such. The Museum's extensive collection of Armenian books is described in a separate catalogue, at present in manuscript form. Publications in Ossetic are listed in the Museum's manuscript catalogue of works in secondary Iranian languages.

Although there is a dearth of reference books and bibliographies of Caucasian languages and literatures, much useful information is contained in concise form in *Peoples and Languages of the Caucasus:*

A Synopsis, by Bernard Geiger and others, published at The Hague in 1959 in the series "Janua Linguarum". On the Muslim peoples of North Caucasia, information will be found in *The Evolution of the Muslim Nationalities of the USSR and their Linguistic Problems* by A. Bennigsen and C. Quelquejay (London, 1961). For Georgian, a comprehensive chronological bibliography under the title: *K'art'uli dsigni: Bibliograp'ia* ("The Georgian Book: A Bibliography") was compiled under the editorship of G. I. Kiknadze for the Book Centre (*Dsignis palata*) in Tiflis. Only the first volume of this publication, issued in 1941, and covering works published between 1629 and 1920, was available during the compilation of the present catalogue; a second volume, covering the years 1921 to 1945, was published at Tiflis in three fascicules between 1950 and 1954. Also valuable for reference is the bibliography of publications of the Academy of Sciences of the Georgian S.S.R. (formerly the Georgian Filial of the Academy of Sciences of the U.S.S.R.) compiled by E. Zhuzhunadze and covering the period 1937 to 1956.

The present catalogue contains descriptions of Georgian and other Caucasian books received at the British Museum up to July, 1960. Works in Caucasian languages, as well as translations of such books into European languages, are for the most part kept in the Department of Oriental Printed Books and Manuscripts. Although quite numerous, the collection is far from complete, being especially deficient in works published in the Adyghe languages and those of Daghestan. To present to scholars as comprehensive a range of material as possible, it was decided also to include in this catalogue a selection of grammars, dictionaries and bibliographies compiled by European specialists, as well as a number of texts and monographs relating to the Caucasian languages and literatures and published in periodicals and publications of learned societies. This seemed all the more necessary because the writings of M.-F. Brosset and N. Y. Marr appeared largely in the organs of the Imperial Academy of Sciences at Saint Petersburg and other journals. Important Georgian hagiographical texts, edited and translated by the late Father Paul Peeters, appeared over the years in *Analecta Bollandiana*, and many others have been published in *Le Muséon* by Professor G. Garitte. Material of this nature has been collected on a highly selective basis from the sets of periodicals kept in the General Library of the British Museum.

It should be noted that to avoid the need for extensive cross-references, the old geographical designations of Saint Petersburg and Tiflis have been retained, instead of the modern Leningrad and T'bilisi. It is intended, however, to adopt the modern forms for subsequent catalogues, which will be concerned for the most part with publications of recent and of future date.

In conclusion, the compiler thanks all those who have assisted in the preparation of this catalogue. The Central Scientific Library of the Academy of Sciences of the Georgian S.S.R., Tiflis, which supplied on an exchange basis many of the Georgian publications in the Museum's collection, has assisted also by checking authors' names and supplying their correct and complete forms; thanks are also due to Alexandra Kavkasidze of the State Republican Library named after Karl Marx, Tiflis, and to Monsieur Kale Salia, who gave valuable assistance in the same connexion. Professor G. Garitte of Louvain and Professor Ilia Abuladze, Director of the Institute of Manuscripts of the Georgian Academy of Sciences, were kind enough to read the proofs and point out a number of errata. Any remaining errors and omissions are the sole responsibility of the compiler.

DAVID MARSHALL LANG

Reader in Caucasian Studies in the
University of London

BRITISH MUSEUM

January, 1962

TABLES OF TRANSLITERATION

1) *Georgian*

The Georgian alphabet exists in three forms: the older Khutsuri or "priestly hand", which exists in both majuscule and minuscule series, and the modern Mkhedruli or "knightly hand". The Mkhedruli script was evolved from the minuscule form of Khutsuri during the eleventh century A. D. No capital letters are used in the Mkhedruli script, even for geographical or personal names.

In the table below, the first column contains the majuscule form of the Khutsuri script; the second, the Mkhedruli or modern alphabet; and the third, the transliterations.

Khutsuri	Mkhedruli	Translit.	Khutsuri	Mkhedruli	Translit.	Khutsuri	Mkhedruli	Translit.
Ⴃ	ა	*a*	Ⴌ	ნ	*n*	Ⴗ	ყ	*q*
Ⴁ	ბ	*b*	Ⴢ	ჲ	*y*	Ⴘ	შ	*š [sh]*
Ⴂ	გ	*g*	Ⴍ	ო	*o*	Ⴙ	ჩ	*č [ch]*
Ⴃ	დ	*d*	Ⴎ	პ	*p*	Ⴚ	ც	*c [ts]*
Ⴄ	ე	*e*	Ⴟ	ჟ	*ž [zh]*	Ⴛ	ძ	*dz*
Ⴅ	ვ	*v*	Ⴐ	რ	*r*	Ⴜ	წ	*c̣ [ds]*
Ⴆ	ზ	*z*	Ⴑ	ს	*s*	Ⴝ	ჭ	*č̣ [tch]*
Ⴡ	ჱ	*ey*	Ⴒ	ტ	*t*	Ⴞ	ხ	*ḫ [kh]*
Ⴇ	თ	*t'*	Ⴓ	უ	*u*	Ⴤ	ჴ	*ḥ [kh]*
Ⴈ	ი	*i*	Ⴣ	ჳ	*w [vi]*	Ⴟ	ჯ	*j*
Ⴉ	კ	*k*	Ⴔ	ფ	*p'*	Ⴠ	ჰ	*h*
Ⴊ	ლ	*l*	Ⴕ	ქ	*k'*	Ⴥ	ჵ	*ho [oy]*
Ⴋ	მ	*m*	Ⴖ	ღ	*ġ [gh]*			

2) *Kabardian*

The alphabets created or adapted for the use of the North-East Caucasian (Chechen/Daghestanian) and North-West Caucasian (Adyghe/Abkhaz) groups of languages are of synthetic origin, being modelled on the Arabic, Russian, Latin or Georgian scripts as the case may be. In some cases, the evolution of these alphabets is still at the experimental stage.

Below is reproduced a comparative table of the various alphabets used or proposed for Kabardian, a leading literary language of the Adyghe group. The table is taken from the monograph by A. H. Kuipers: *Phoneme and Morpheme in Kabardian*, published in 1960 by Messrs. Mouton of The Hague. Thanks are expressed to both the author and the publishers for kindly permitting the use of this copyright material.

KABARDIAN ALPHABETS

(upper correspondence table — numbered columns 1–9)

1	2	3	4	5	6	7	8	9
k'	к, ч	ḥ	k	(ʃ)ꟾ	к	ʒ	k	q̇ (q̇')
x'	х	x	x	(ʃ)ꟾ	x	x	x	ḥ
g'	дж	g	g	ꟾ	г	g	g	ḓ (ḡ)
ɣ'	г	k̯'	ʒ	ꟾ	ꟾ	gh	ꟾ	ɣ
k̯'	кI	k̯'	k̯'	ꟾ	k̯'	cv	k, ky	ṭ (k̯')
k°	ку	kv	ku	ꟾ	ку	ku	k°	q°
x°	ху	xv	xu	ꟾ	xу	xu	x°	ḥ°
g°	гу	gv	gu	ꟾ	гу	gu	g°	g̊°
k̯°'	кIу	k̯°	k̯,u	ꟾ	к̯'у	kvu	k°, k°y	ḵ°
q	кхъ	q	qh	ꟾ	к̄	q	q, qy	q
x̣°	хъ	x	x̌	ꟾ	x̄	xh	x̄°	q̇°
ǧ	гъ	ʒ	ꟾ	ꟾ	ʒ	qh	ꟾ°	g̈°
q̯'	къ	q	q	ꟾ	к	qu	q°, q°y	k̯°
x̣°	кхъу	qv	qhu	ꟾ	к̯'у	xhu	x̄°	ḥv
ǧ°	хъу	xv	x̌u	ꟾ	x̄у	qhu	ꟾ°	ǯ
q̯°'	гъу	qv	qu	ꟾ	5у	qu	h	y̆
ʔ	къу	у	у	ꟾ	ку	h	v	у
ʔ°	хь	h	ꟾh	ꟾ	к̄	vu	ꟾ	e
j	I	j	j	ꟾ	ꟾ·y	y	ꟾ	e
w	Iу	v	у	ꟾ	x̄·y	y	E, Е	iꟾ, ẽy
e	й(е,я)	ь	e	ꟾ	ы	w	e, Е	ē, ey
a	ы	e	e	ꟾ	e	i	eꟾ	eꟾ
ā	э	e	yj, i(j)	ꟾ	бій, й	e	ne	ꟾ°
ej	е, ей	ej	ej	ꟾ	e	é	eu	eu
aj	ꟾу, у	v	yu, u	ꟾ	бу	u	o	o̅u, e̅°
ew	эу, о	o	eu, o	ꟾ	бу, о	o	a, A	a
aw	а	a	a	—	a	a		

KABARDIAN ALPHABETS

(lower correspondence table)

Phonemic (1)	Official 1937/8-present (2)	Official 1928-1937 (3)	Official 1923-1928 (4)	Official Until 1923 (5)	Logatinskii Sbornik Mat. (6)	Kube Csaban (Syria, Jordan) (7)	Yakovlev 1927 (8)	Marr's Japhetidolog. Transcription (9)
p	п	p	p		п	p	p	φ
f	ф	f	f		ф	f	f	f
b	б	в	b		б	b	b	b
v	в	w	v		в	w	w	v
p'	пI	г	ph		пʼ	pv	p, py	p̣
f'	фI	ḟ	fh		ф̣	fv	f, fy	φ̣
m	м	m	m		м	m	m	m
t	т	t	t		г	t	t	ʒ̇·ʒ̣
c	ц	c	c		ц	ts	c	s
s	с	s	s		с	s	s	p̣·ɸ̣
d	д	d	d		д	d	d	z
z	з	ʒ	ʒ		з	dz	ʒ	t̳
ʒ	дз	z	z		з	z	z	n
n	тI	t̨	th		гʼ	tv	t, ty	r
r	цI	ꟾ	ꟾ		пʼ	tsv	c, cy	ŝ
š	н	n	n		н	n	n	ž̄
ž	р	r	r		р	r	r	š
x	ш	ƶ	š		ꟾ	zh	ꟾ, ꟾ	j
l	ж	ž	ž		ж	cv	ꟾ	l
	жь	ꟾ	ch		ꟾ	cs	ꟾ	l
	шI	ꟾ	š		ꟾ	j	l	lh
	л	ꟾ	z		л	tl	l, ly	
	лъ	ꟾ	l		ꟾ	l		
		ꟾ	lh		ꟾ°	tlv		

CATALOGUE OF GEORGIAN BOOKS

A., R. [Trans. 'Internationali da sabtchot'a Ruset'i'.] *See* KAUTSKY (C. J.)

ABAEV (VASILY IVANOVICH). О некоторых осетинских элементах в грузинском языке. pp. 437–41. *Москва*, 1956. 8⁰. [*Труды Института Языкознания.* том 6.] **Ac. 1125. sf**

ABAKAROV (AḣmAD-Khān). Даргала поэзияла антология. [An anthology of poetry in the Dargwa language of Daghestan. Compiled by Aḣmad-Khān Abakarov, under the editorship of a committee of scholars.] (Антология даргинской поэзии.) pp. 285. *Даг'истанна Книгабала издательство*: [*Махач-кала,*] 1958. 8⁰. **17075. c. 35**

ABASHELI (ALEK'SANDRE BESARIONIS-DZE). [General edit. of complete works of Vazha-P'shavela.] *See* VAZHA-P'SHAVELA, *pseud.*

—— [Joint edit. of selected works of Vazha-P'shavela.] *See* VAZHA-P'SHAVELA, *pseud.*

—— ერთტომეული. [Ert'tomeuli. Collected poems in one volume.] pp. 318. 1 *plate.* სახელგამი [*State Publishing House: Tiflis,*] 1955. 8⁰. **17075. c. 10**

—— *and others.* დიდება სტალინს. [Dideba Stalins. Glory to Stalin. A collection of poems by various hands in honour of Stalin, including a number trans. from various languages of the Soviet Union and of countries abroad. Edit. by I. Abashidze and others.] pp. 286. 1 *plate.* [თბილისი. *Tiflis,*] 1952. 8⁰. **17075. d. 25**

—— *and others.* Гамарджвеба. Стихи грузинских поэтов, 1941–1944, под редакцией П. Скосырева и С. Чиковани. [An anthology of Georgian patriotic poetry in Russian trans., with a foreword by B. D. Zhghenti.] pp. 143. *Москва*, 1944. 12⁰. **17075. d. 34**

—— *and others.* ქართული საბჭოთა პოეზიის ანთოლოგია. [K'art'uli sabtchot'a poeziis ant'ologia. Anthology of Soviet Georgian poetry. Edited by R. M. Gvetadze and others.] pp. 381. თბილისი [*Tiflis,*] 1947. 8⁰. **17075. c. 26**

—— *and others.* Великому Сталину. [Poems by various authors translated from Georgian. Edited by A. Abasheli, B. Zhghenti and others. With a portrait.] pp. 254. *Тбилиси*, 1949. 4⁰. **11587. d. 9**

ABASHIDZE (GRIGOL GRIGOLIS-DZE). Георгий Шестой. Поэма. [A historical ballad concerning the war between Tīmūr-Leng and King Giorgi VI of Georgia. Trans. into Russian by R. Ivnev.] pp. 77. *Тбилиси*, 1944. 12⁰. **17075. d. 19**

—— ლექსები, პოემები: ერთტომეული. [Lek'sebi, poemebi: ert'tomeuli. Verses and poems, one-volume edition.] pp. 543. 1 *plate.* თბილისი [*Tiflis,*] 1953. 8⁰. **17075. d. 17**

—— На южной границе. Стихи и поэмы. (სამხრეთ საზღვარზე. ლექსები და პოემები. [Samkhret' sazghvarze. Lek'sebi da poemebi. On the southern frontier. Poems, trans. into Russian with a critical essay by G. Natroshvili.]) pp. 194. *Тбилиси*, 1950. 8⁰. **17076. b. 3**

—— Стихотворения. Перевод с грузинского. [Translations by various hands. With a portrait.] pp. 138. *Москва*, 1951. 8⁰. **11588. f. 32**

—— *and others.* Грузинская советская поэзия. [An anthology of Georgian Soviet poetry, translated into Russian by various hands, and edited by G. G. Abashidze and others.] pp. 429. *Тбилиси*, 1954. 4⁰. **11588. t. 2**

ABASHIDZE (IRAKLI BESARIONIS-DZE). [Joint edit. 'Dideba Stalins'.] *See* ABASHELI (A. B.) *and others.*

ABASHIDZE (*cont.*)

—— საბავშვო ლექსები და პოემები. [Sabavshvo lek'sebi da poemebi. Verses and poems for children.] pp. 259. თბილისი [*Tiflis*,] 1953. 8⁰.   **17075. d. 18**

—— *and others*. [Edit. anthology 'Sabtchot'a Ukrainas—K'art'veli mdserlebi'.] *See* RUSSIA.— *Ukrainian Soviet Socialist Republic.*

—— *and others*. Антология грузинской поэзии. (Редакционная коллегия: И. Абашидзе, К. Симонов, Н. Тихонов, С. Чиковани.) ქართული პოეზიის ანთოლოგია. [K'art'uli poeziis ant'ologia. Anthology of Georgian poetry, in Russian trans. by various hands.] pp. 802. *Москва*, 1958. 4⁰.   **17075. c. 21**

ABASHIDZE (VASO ALEK'SIS-DZE). [*Biography*.] *See* P'AGHAVA (A.)

ABAZA LANGUAGE. [For 'Русско-абазинский словарь':] *See* CHERKESSK.—*Cherkessky Nauchno-Issledovatel'sky Institut.*

—— [For 'Абазинский язык':] *See* GENKO (A.N.)

ABESADZE (TSISANA NIKOLOZIS-ASULI) *and others*. სპილენდ-ბრინჯაოს მეტალურგიის ისტორიისათვის საქართველოში. [Spilendz-brinjaos metalurgiis istoriisat'vis Sak'art'veloshi. Studies in the history of Georgian copper and bronze metallurgy. With summaries in Russian and English.] (К истории медно-бронзовой металлургии в Грузии.) pp. 112, 12. 26 *plates*. თბილისი [*Tiflis*,] 1958. 4⁰.   **17080. e. 7**

ABITA (MUKHAB LUKMANOVICH). *See* ABITOV (M. L.)

ABITOV (MUKHAB LUKMANOVICH). [Joint compiler of 'Грамматика кабардино-черкесского литературного языка'.] *See* NAL'CHIK.— *Кабардино-балкарский научно-исследовательский институт.*

—— Инкорпорация в кабардино-черкесском языке. pp. 262–70. *Москва, Ленинград*, 1949. 8⁰. (*Известия Академии Наук СССР. Отделение литературы и языка*. том 8. no. 3.]   **Ac. 1125/44 (11)**

ABKHAZIA. [For 'Народное хозяйство и социальные отношения в Абхазии в XIX веке':] *See* DZIDZARIA (G. A.)

—— [For 'Абхазия':] *See* GURKO-KRYAZHIN (V.A.)

—— [For 'Абхазскій культъ и бытъ, в предѣлахъ Абжу':] *See* JANASHIA (N. S.)

—— [For 'The Religious Beliefs of the Abkhazians':] *See* JANASHIA (N. S.)

—— [For 'Религіозныя вѣрованія абхазовъ':] *See* JANASHIA (N. S.)

—— [For 'Исторія термина "абхазъ"':] *See* MARR (N. Y.)

—— [For 'О религіозныхъ вѣрованіяхъ абхазовъ':] *See* MARR (N. Y.)

—— [For 'D. Gulias sakhelobis Ap'khazet'is enis, literaturis da istoriis institutis shromebi':] *See* SUKHUMI.—*Abkhazian Linguistic, Literary and Historical Institute.*

—— [For 'Les sources des notices du Patriarche de Jérusalem Dosithée sur les rois d'Aphkhazie':] *See* T'AQAISHVILI (E. S.)

—— [For 'Chronology of the Kings of Abasgia, etc.':] *See* TOUMANOFF (C. L.), *Prince.*

ABKHAZIAN DIALECTS. [For 'Ashkharuli dialek'ti':] *See* LOMT'AT'IDZE (K'. B.)

ABKHAZIAN FOLK-SONGS. [For 'Gesänge russischer Kriegsgefangener. III. Band: Kaukasusvölker, etc.', including Abkhazian folk-songs:] *See* LACH (R.)

ABKHAZIAN LANGUAGE. [*Alphabet*.] *See* BARTHOLOMAEI (I. A.) *Lt.-General.*

—— [For 'Краткая священная история переведена на абхазскій языкъ, etc.':] *See* BARTHOLOMAEI (I. A.) *Lt.-General.*

ABKHAZIAN LANGUAGE *(cont.)*

—— [For 'Объ отношеніи абхазскаго языка къ яфетическимъ':] *See* CHARAYA (P. G.)

—— [For 'Абазинскій языкъ':] *See* GENKO (A. N.)

—— [For 'Абхазскій вокализмъ':] *See* GENKO (A. N.)

—— [For 'Абхазско-русскій словарь':] *See* MARR (N. Y.)

—— [For 'Изъ лингвистической поѣздки въ Абхазію':] *See* MARR (N. Y.)

—— [For 'Къ вопросу о положеніи абхазскаго языка среди яфетическихъ':] *See* MARR (N.Y.)

—— [For 'Кавказовѣдѣніе и абхазскій языкъ':] *See* MARR (N. Y.)

—— [For 'Original Vocabularies of Five West Caucasian Languages', including Abkhazian:] *See* PEACOCK (D. R.)

—— [For 'Ausführlicher Bericht über des Generals Baron Peter von Uslar Abchasische Studien':] *See* SCHIEFNER (F. A. von).

ABKHAZIAN TALES. [For 'Абхазские новеллы':] *See* LAKERBAI (M.)

ABO, *Saint and Martyr, of Tiflis.* [For 'Das Martyrium des heiligen Abo von Tiflis', trans. by K. Schultze from the Georgian life by Ioane Sabanisdze:] *See* SABANISDZE (I.)

—— [For 'Les Khazars dans la Passion de S. Abo de Tiflis':] *See* PEETERS (P.)

—— [*Life.*] *See* SABANISDZE (I.)

ABRAMISHVILI (TʻAMAR IASONIS-ASULI). XIII–XIV სს. დასავლურ-ქართული ფული, კირმანეუ-ლი. [XIII–XIV ss. dasavlur-kʻartʻuli pʻuli, kirmaneuli. The Western Georgian coinage of the 13th–14th centuries, known as 'Kirmaneuli'. Geor-

gian text with Russian summary, figures in the text, and a map.] pp. 158. *7 plates.* თბილისი [*Tiflis,*] 1959. 8⁰.   **17078. a. 2**

—— [Another copy.]   *Dept. of Coins and Medals.*

ABULADZE (ILIA VLADIMERIS-DZE). [Edit. 'Balavarianis kʻartʻuli redakʻtsiebi'.] *See* BARLAAM, *Saint, of India.*

—— [Joint editor of 'Kʻartʻuli enisa da mdserlobis istoriis sakitʻkhebi'.] *See* JAVAKHISHVILI (I. A.)

—— [Joint compiler of 'Dzveli kʻartʻuli literatura'.] *See* SHANIDZE (A. G.) *and others.*

—— [Joint edit. of Catalogue of Georgian manuscripts in the Georgian State Museum.] *See* TIFLIS. —*Museum of Georgia.*

ABULADZE (IUSTINE IRAKLIS-DZE). [Edit. of Georgian version of the Shāhnāmeh.]. *See* ḤASAN (ABUʼL-ḲĀSIM), called FIRDAUSĪ, *Ṫūsī.*

—— [Edit. of Shotʻa Rustʻaveli's epic, 'The Man in the Panther's Skin'.] *See* RUSTʻAVELI (SHOTʻA).

ABUSERIDZE, *of Tbetʻi.* [For text and translation of treatise on the Calendar by Abuseridze:] *See* BROSSET (M.-F.). Études de chronologie technique. 1868. 4⁰.   **Ac. 1125/3**

—— Traité géorgien du comput ecclésiastique... traduit par M. Brosset. pp. 420–51. *St.-Pétersbourg,* 1866. 8⁰. [*Mélanges Asiatiques de l'Académie des Sciences.* tom. 5. livr. 4.]   **Ac. 1125/11**

ABZIANIDZE (GIORGI NIKOLOZIS-DZE). [Joint edit. of 'Kʻartʻuli literaturis istoria, otʻkh tomad'.] *See* TIFLIS.—*Academy of Sciences of the Georgian S. S. R.*

—— [Chief editor of complete works of Akaki Tseretʻeli.] *See* TSERETʻELI (A. R.) *Prince.*

ADAM, *the Patriarch.* [For the Georgian version of the Testament of Adam, preceded by 'Notice sur une version géorgienne de la Caverne des Trésors':] *See* AVALISHVILI (Z. D.)

ADAMIA (Ilia). ქართული ხალხური ხუროთ‑მოძღვრება : აჭარა. [K'art'uli khalkhuri khurot'modzghvreba: Atchara. Georgian national architecture: Atchara province. Georgian text with summary in Russian. Illustrated.] (Грузинское народное зодчество: Аджара.) pp. 99,3. 52 *plates.* თბილისი [*Tiflis,*] 1956. 4⁰.   **17080. g. 3**

ADYGHE LANGUAGES. [For material on the Adyghe or Adigey languages:] *See* Circassian and Related Languages.

ADYSH GOSPELS. [For various editions and publications relating to the Adysh manuscript of the Georgian Gospels:] *See* Bible.—New Testament.—*Gospels.*

ADZHARIYA. *See* Atchara.

AESCHYLUS. მიჯაჭული პრომეთე. [Mijatchuli Promet'e. The Prometheus Bound of Aeschylus, trans. by G. Gvazava.] pp. 56. პარიზი [*Paris,*] 1935. 8⁰.   **17075. d. 21. (2.)**

AGABABIANI (Ruben Yakovlevich). [Edit. 'Gamok'vabuli nagebobani Sak'art'veloshi'.] *See* Mshvenieradze (D.M.)

AGATHANGELUS, *Historian.* [For 'Sur un fragment géorgien d'Agathange':] *See* Garitte (G.)

—— [For Грузинская версія Агаѳангелія, *etc.*':] *See* Melik'set'-Begi (L. M.)

AGATHANGELUS, *Saint and Martyr, of Damascus.* Житіе Агаѳангела, католикоса дамасскаго. [Edit. with Russian trans. by K. S. Kekelidze.] pp. 246–83. *Петроградъ,* 1916. 4⁰. [*Христіанскій Востокъ.* томъ 4. вып. 3.]   **Ac. 1125/105**

AGHNIASHVILI (Lado). ხალხური ზღაპრები. [Khalkhuri zghaprebi. A collection of Georgian folk tales.] bk. 1. pp. 142, 2. თბილისი [*Tiflis,*] N. D. [1891.] 8⁰. *No more published.*   **17075. c. 3**

—— სპარსეთი და იკაური ქართველები. [Sparset'i da ik'auri k'art'velebi. An account of a

visit to the Georgian community in Persia.] no. 2. pp. 29–65; no. 4. pp. 1–40. ტფილისი [*Tiflis,*] 1896. 8⁰. [*Moambe.* tom. 3. no. 2, 4.] *Wanting pt. 2, and all after pt. 3.*   **17089. b. 1**

'AINĪ (Ṣadr al-Dīn). ბუხარა : მოგონებანი. [Bukhara: mogonebani. Bukhara: Reminiscences. Translated from the Russian by K'. Nadiradze and V. Dzidziguri.] pp. 383. თბილისი [*Tiflis,*] 1956. 8⁰.   **17075. e. 37**

AISKHANOV (Shamsutdin). *See* Shams al-Din Aiskhanov.

AJARIA. *See* Atchara.

AKHVLEDIANI (Giorgi Saridanis-dze). [Edit. 'K'art'uli dialek'tebis k'restomat'ia lek'sikonit'urt'.] *See* Dzidziguri (Sh. V.)

—— Фонетический сборник. том I. [Being a Festschrift in honour of the 70th birthday of G. S. Akhvlediani. With a portrait.] *See* Tiflis.—*Tiflis State University.* Труды кафедры общего языковедения. no. 3. 1959. 8⁰.   **17076. f. 33**

—— *and others.* [Compilers and editors of 'Rusulk'art'uli lek'sikoni'.] *See* Tiflis.—*Academy of Sciences of the Georgian S. S. R.*

AKKERMAN (Georgy). [Joint trans. of novel 'Лело'.] *See* Tcheishvili (A. N.)

AKKERMAN (Nikolai Georgievich). [Joint trans. of 'Кровью героев'.] *See* Bak'radze (D.)

AKOBIA (Shot'a) *and others.* Грузинская весна. Стихи молодых поэтов Грузии, 1940–1957. [Trans. into Russian by various hands, with an introduction by G. Khukhashvili.] pp. 174. *Москва,* 1958. 8⁰.   **17075. c. 29**

ALADASHVILI (Nat'ela Alek'sandres-asuli). ნიკორწმინდის რელიეფები. ფასადების სკულპტურის შესახებ შუა საუკუნეების საქართველოში. [Nikordsmindis reliep'ebi. P'asadebis skulpturis shesakheb shua saukuneebis Sak'art'veloshi. The bas-reliefs of Nikordsminda. Concerning the sculpture of façades in mediaeval Georgia.] (Рельефы Никорцминда.) [With summaries in Russian and German.] pp. 113, 5. 43 *plates.* თბილისი [*Tiflis,*] 1957. 4⁰.   **17080. f. 13**

ALANIA (NODAR VASILIS-DZE). [For a biography in pictures of the Georgian writer Ilia Tchavtchavadze, compiled by N. Alania and others:] *See* TCHAVTCHAVADZE (I. G.) *Prince.*

ALBANIA, *in Transcaucasia.* [For 'Очерки по истории и культуре кавказской Албании':) *See* TREVER (K. V.)

ALBANIAN ALPHABET. [For 'The newly discovered alphabet of the Caucasian Albanians':] *See* KURDIAN (H.)

ALBANIAN LANGUAGE. [For 'Une chrétienté disparue: les Albaniens du Caucase':] *See* DUMÉZIL (G.)

—— [For 'Албанская надпись':] *See* MARR (N. Y.)

ALEKSANDROV (GEORGY FEDOROVICH) *and others.* იოსებ ბესარიონის-ძე სტალინი : მოკლე ბიოგრაფია. [Ioseb Besarionis-dze Stalini: mokle biograp'ia. Short biography of Stalin. Trans. from the second Russian edition of 1949.] Иосиф Виссарионович Сталин: краткая биография. [Second edition.] pp. 241. 14 *plates.* თბილისი [*Tiflis,*] 1952. 8⁰.   **17076. g. 7**

ALEXANDER, *the Great, King of Macedon.* [For 'Грузинская повѣсть объ Александрѣ Македонскомъ и сербская Александрія':] *See* KHAKHANOV (A. S.)

ALEXIS, *Saint, of Rome.* ალექსიანი. ბერძნულიდამ ნათარგმნი მეჩვიდმეტე საუკუნეში. [Alek'siani. Berdznulidam nat'argmni mechvidmete saukuneshi. The life of Alexis, Man of God, translated and adapted anonymously from the mediaeval Greek version in the 17th century. 12th edition.] pp. 16. ტფილისი [*Tiflis,*] 1892. 8⁰.   **17075. d. 2. (4)**

ALIBEGASHVILI (GAIANE VLADIMERIS-ASULI). Четыре портрета царицы Тамары. К истории портрета в грузинской монументальной живописи. (Vier Bildnisse der Königin Tamar, *etc.*) [With reproductions.] pp. 107. Тбилиси, 1957. 8⁰.   **7872. ddd. 1**

ALLEN (WILLIAM EDWARD DAVID). [Joint edit. of 'Georgica'.] *See* LONDON.—*Georgian Historical Society.*

—— A history of the Georgian people from the beginning down to the Russian conquest in the nineteenth century, *etc.* [With plates and a bibliography.] pp. xxiv. 429. *London,* 1932. 8⁰.   **09455. h. 36**

ALLENBY (EDMUND HENRY HYNMAN), *Viscount Allenby.* [For Georgian text of General Allenby's proclamation at Jerusalem:] *See* EUROPEAN WAR, 1914–1919.

ALPHABETUM IBERICUM. *See* IBERIAN ALPHABET.

AMIRAN. [For 'Eine georgische Ballade von Amiran':] *See* BLEICHSTEINER (R.)

—— [For 'Mijatchvuli Amirani':] *See* CHIK'OVANI (M. I.)

AMIRAN-DAREJANIANI. [For 'Analyse du Roman géorgien "Amiran Daredjaniani"':] *See* BROSSET (M.-F.)

—— [For 'Грузинская повѣсть объ Амиранѣ, сынѣ Дареджана':] *See* GREN (A. N.)

—— [For 'Изъ книги царевича Баграта о ... героической повѣсти "Дареджаніани"':] *See* MARR (N. Y.)

—— [For 'Персидская національная тенденція въ грузинскомъ романѣ "Амирандареджаніани"':) *See* MARR (N. Y.)

AMIRANASHVILI (SHALVA IASONIS-DZE). Бэка Опизари. [An account of the twelfth century Georgian goldsmith.] pp. 44. 44 *plates.* Тбилиси, 1939. fol.   **L. R. 261. c. 20**

AMIRANASHVILI *(cont.)*

—— История грузинского искусства. [History of Georgian art. With plates.] том I — *Москва*, 1950. 4⁰. *In progress.*   **W. P. 3943**

—— История грузинской монументальной живописи. (ქართული კედლის მხატვრობის ისტორია. [Kʻartʻuli kedlis mkhatvrobis istoria. History of Georgian mural painting.]) том I. pp. 181,3. 160 *plates. Тбилиси*, 1957. 4⁰.   **17080. f. 12**

ANANIASHVILI (Elizbar Giorgis-dze). [Trans. ʻДавид Строитель. Трилогия'.] *See* Gamsakhurdia (K. S.)

—— [Trans. ʻЧеловек гор'.] *See* Kʻiacheli (L.) *pseud.*

—— [Joint trans. of stories by K. Lortʻkʻipʻanidze. *See* Lortʻkʻipʻanidze (K. A.)

—— [Trans. drama ʻПотопленные камни'.] *See* Mosashvili (I. O.)

ANCHIN, *pseud.* [i. e. Akaki Chkhenkeli.] სახელმწიფო და ერი. [Sakhelmdsipʻo da eri. State and People. Essays on politics and sociology.] pp. 67. პარიზი [*Paris,*] 1939. 8⁰.   **17075. f. 19 (4)**

ANDREW, *Saint and Apostle.* [For ʻПроповѣдническая дѣятельность ап. Андрея и св. Нины въ Грузіи':] *See* Javakhishvili (I. A.).

ANTIOCHUS, *Laurae S. Sabae Monachus.* Плѣненіе Іерусалима персами въ 614 г. Грузинскій текстъ изслѣдовалъ, издалъ, перевелъ и арабское извлеченіе приложилъ Н. Марръ. pp. vi. 82. 66. 66. 10. *С.-Петербургъ, Тифлисъ*, 1907–9. 8⁰. [*Тексты и разысканія по армяно-грузинской филологіи.* кн. 9.]   **14005. f. 5**

ANTONI I, *Catholicos-Patriarch of Georgia.* [For ʻNotice... de la Grammaire géorgienne du patriarche Antoni I':] *See* Brosset (M.-F.)

ANTONOVSKAYA (Anna Arnol'dovna). Великий Моурави. [A biographical novel on the life of the 17th century Georgian military leader

Giorgi Saakadze]. Стихи и комментарии Б. К. Черного. кн. 1–3, 6 & 7. *Москва*, 1949–1953. 8⁰.   **012593. i. 18**

ANTONY, *Saint, the Monk.* [For ʻLes lettres de Saint Antoine en géorgien':] *See* Garitte (G.)

—— Lettres de S. Antoine. Version géorgienne et fragments coptes édités (traduits [into Latin]) par Gérard Garitte. 2 tom. *Louvain*, 1955. 8⁰. [*Corpus Scriptorum Christianorum Orientalium.* vol. 148–49. Scriptores Iberici. tom. 5–6.]   **14005. a**

ANTONY, *Saint, called* THE NEO-MARTYR. *See* Antony, *Saint and Martyr, called* Rawaḥ.

ANTONY, *Saint and Martyr, called* Rawaḥ. Житіе и мученичество св. Антонія-Раваха. [Edit. with Russian trans. by I. A. Qipʻshidze.] pp. 54–104. *С.-Петербургъ*, 1913. 4⁰. [*Христіанскій Востокъ.* томъ 2. вып. I.]   **Ac. 1125/105**

APʻAKʻIDZE (Andria Melitonis-dze). [Edit. of description of archaeological materials acquired by the Museum of Georgia in 1904–20.] *See* Tiflis. —*Museum of Georgia.* Muzeumshi 1904–1920 dslebshi shemosuli, Sakʻartʻveloshi aghmochenili arkʻeologiuri masalebis aghdseriloba. 1955. 4⁰.   **17080. f. 5**

—— მცხეთა. ქართლის სამეფოს ძველი დედაქალაქი. [Mtskhetʻa. Kʻartʻlis samepʻos dzveli dedakʻalakʻi. Mtskhetʻa. The ancient capital of the kingdom of Kʻartʻli.] pp. 125. თბილისი [*Tiflis,*] 1959. 8⁰.   **17075. e. 46**

—— *and others.* Мцхета. Итоги археологических исследований. том I. Археологические памятники Армазис-Хеви по раскопкам 1937–1946 гг. (Редактор Г. Н. Чубинашвили.) [With plates, some in colour, and diagrams and illustrations in the text.] *Тбилиси*, 1958, *etc.* fol. *In progress.*   **17080. g. 7**

—— *and others.* საქართველოს არქეოლოგია. [Sakʻartʻvelos arkʻeologia. A manual of Georgian archaeology.] pp. 395. 37 *plates.* თბილისი [*Tiflis,*] 1959. 8⁰.   **17080. b. 14**

APAZHEV (Magamed L.) *and others.* Кабардинско-русский словарь. Составили М. Л. Апажев, Н. А. Багов, П. М. Багов, *etc.* под общей редакцией Б. М. Карданова. (Къэбэрдей-урыс словарь.) [Followed by a grammatical outline of the Kabardian language by B. M. Kardanov.] pp. 576. *Москва,* 1957. 8⁰.

17076. f. 16

—— [Another copy.]   **012977. e. 68**

ARISTIDES, *Saint and Philosopher.* [For 'The Apology of Aristides — A Re-examination':] *See* Wolff (R. L.)

AP'KHAIDZE (Shalva Nikolozis-dze). [Joint edit. of 'K'art'vel dramaturgt'a piesebi'.] *See* Berdzenishvili (G. A.) *and others.*

—— [Edit. biography of Vaso Abashidze.] *See* P'aghava (A.)

—— ლექსები. [Lek'sebi. Poems. Edited by G. Leonidze.] pp. 322. თბილისი [*Tiflis,*] 1954. 8⁰.

17075. c. 11

ARABIC ALPHABET. [For 'Арабская азбука с древнегрузинской транскрипцией':] *See* Megrelidze (I. B.)

ARAGVISPIRELI (Shio) *pseud.* [i. e. Shio De-dabrishvili.] გაბზარული გული. [Gabzaruli guli. The broken heart. A novel.] pp. 214, 2. თბილისი [*Tiflis,*] 1959. 8⁰.   **17076. c. 12**

—— Избранное. Перевод с грузинского. [Trans. by M. Kakhidze and others.] pp. xiv. 324. *Тбилиси,* 1950. 8⁰.   **12594. aa. 34**

——Разбитое сердце. Старинное сказание. Перевод с грузинского М. Кахидзе. pp. 264. *Тбилиси,* 1937. 8⁰.

12592. h. 32

ARAK'EL, *Davrēžaçi.* [For extracts from the Book of Histories by Arak'el, relating to Georgia, translated from the Armenian:] *See* Brosset (M.-F.). Histoire de la Géorgie. pt. 2. livr. 1. 1856. 4⁰.

17075. e. 1

ARCHIL, *King of Imeret'i.* [For 'Notice sur une lettre géorgienne du roi Artchil, *etc*':] *See* Brosset (M.-F.)

—— [For 'Nouvelles recherches sur ... le roi Artchil, *etc.*':] *See* Brosset (M.-F.)

—— არჩილიანი: ტხზულებათა სრული კრებული. [Archiliani: t'khzulebat'a sruli krebuli. Collected works of King Archil. First part contains introduction by A. Baramidze and shorter poems; second part contains biography of Archil and 'Disputation between T'eimuraz and Rust'aveli'. Edit. by A. Baramidze and N. Berdzenishvili. With a plate.] 2 tom. თბილისი [*Tiflis,*] 1936–37. 8⁰.

17075. d. 3

ARMENIA. [For 'Кавказскій культурный міръ и Арменія':] *See* Marr (N. Y.)

—— *Laws,* etc. [For 'Détails sur le droit public arménien, extraits du code géorgien du roi Wakhtang, *etc.*':] *See* Vakhtang VI, *King of Georgia.*

ARMENIAN CHRONICLE. [For a French trans. of the Armenian version of the early Georgian annals, incorporated in 'Histoire de la Géorgie':] *See* Brosset (M.-F.)

ARMENIAN LANGUAGE. [For a vocabulary, with phrases, in the Georgian, Armenian and Azerbaijan Turkish languages:] *See* Russia. — *Министерство Народнаго Просвѣщенія.*

ARSENA, *of Marabda.* [For historical novel based on the life of Arsena Odzelashvili, or Arsena of Marabda:] *See* Javakhishvili (M. S.)

ARSENIUS, *Saint,* called the Great. Une "Lettre de S. Arsène" en géorgien. [Edit., with Latin trans., by] G. Garitte. pp. 259–78. *Louvain,* 1955. 8⁰. [*Le Muséon.* tom. 68.]   **P. P. 4453**

AS'AD (Fakhr al-Dīn) called Fakhrī, *Gurgānī.* [For 'Из грузино-персидских литературных связей', containing a study of the Georgian version of Vīs u Rāmīn:] *See* Marr (N. Y.)

AS'AD (cont.)

—— [For Georgian adaptation of the romance of Vīs and Rāmīn:] See SARGIS, of T'mogvi.

ASAT'IANI (ALEK'SANDRE). ქართული პოლიტი-კის ძველი და ახალი გზები. [K'art'uli politikis dzveli da akhali gzebi. Old and new paths of Georgian politics.] pp. 47. პარიზი [Paris,] 1934. 8⁰.
17075. f. 6

ASAT'IANI (LEVAN NIKIP'ORES-DZE). ქართველი ხალხის ლიტერატურული ურთიერთობანი მოძმე ხალხებთან. [K'art'veli khalkhis literaturuli urt'iert'obani modzme khalkhebt'an. The literary relationships of the Georgian people with fraternal peoples. Essays on Georgian literary contacts with other nations of the Soviet Union.] pp. 257. თბილისი [Tiflis,] 1955. 8⁰.
17075. f. 21

ASHKHAMAF (DAUD ALIEVICH). See YAKOVLEV (N. F.) and ASHKHAMAF (D. A.). Грамматика адыгей-ского литературного языка. 1941. 8⁰.
12977. d. 5

ASLANISHVILI (T'.) and others. შრომა. სამუშაო წიგნი. [Shroma. Samushao dsigni. Labour. A manual issued by the Georgian People's Commissariat of Education as a practical and theoretical guide for agricultural and industrial trainees. Illustrated.] pp. 264. ტფილისი [Tiflis,] 1931. 8⁰.
17075. ee. 9

ASSFALG (JULIUS). [For 'Lettres géorgiennes chrétiennes', being a summary of the book 'Geschichte der kirchlichen georgischen Literatur' by M. T'arkhnishvili and J. Assfalg:] See BRIÈRE (M.)

—— [For 'Geschichte der kirchlichen georgischen Literatur... bearbeitet ... in Verbindung mit Dr. Julius Assfalg':] See T'ARKHNISHVILI (M.)

ATAZHUKIN (KAVI). qабардеj аләфбе. Кабардин-ская азбука, составленная К. Атажукинымъ. pp. 86. Тифлисъ, 1865. 4⁰. Bound together with alphabets of the Avar and Lak languages.
12907. c. 23. (1.)

ATCHARA. [For 'K'art'uli khalkhuri khurot'-modzghvreba: Atchara':] See ADAMIA (I.)

—— [For 'Археологическое путешествіе по ... Адчарѣ':] See BAK'RADZE (D. Z.)

—— [For 'Rapport sur l'ouvrage manuscrit de M. Bakradzé, contenant l'exposé des recherches archéologiques faites par l'auteur, dans l'Adchara, etc.':] See BROSSET (M.-F.)

—— [For 'Atcharis A. S. S. R.':] See NIZHARADZE (N. I.) and JIBUTI (N. M.)

—— [For 'Советский Аджаристан', being a description of the Western Georgian A. S. S. R. of Atchara:] See SURMANIDZE (M.)

—— Soyuz Sovetskikh Pisatelei.—Adzharskoe Otdelenie. Литературная Аджария. Сборник произве-дений писателей Аджарии. [A collection of poems, stories and one play by Soviet writers of the Western Georgian A. S. S. R. of Atchara edit. by P. Loria and others, and translated into Russian by various hands.] pp. 210, 4. Батуми, 1954. 8⁰.
17075. c. 14

AT'ENI. [For inscriptions from ancient church at At'eni:] See JAVAKHISHVILI (I. A.)

ATHOS, Mount. [For 'The Athos Codex of the Georgian Old Testament':] See BLAKE (R. P.)

—— [For 'Explication de quelques inscriptions, photographiées ...au mont Athos':] See BROSSET (M.-F.)

—— [For the Metropolitan Timothy's travels to Mount Athos and other Holy Places:] See GABASH-VILI (T.), Metropolitan of K'ut'aisi.

—— [For 'Notice sur le couvent ibérien du Mont Athos':] See LANGLOIS (V.)

—— [For 'Le Synaxaire géorgien... d'après le manuscrit du couvent Iviron du Mont Athos, etc.':] See LITURGIES.—Greek Rite.—Synaxarion.

—— [For 'Агіографическіе матеріалы по грузин-скимъ рукописямъ Ивера':] See MARR (N. Y.)

ATHOS *(cont.)*

—— [For 'Изъ поѣздки на Афонъ':] *See* MARR (N. Y.)

—— [For 'L'activité littéraire des moines géorgiens au monastère d'Iviron, au Mont Athos':] *See* P'ERADZE (G.)

—— [For catalogue of the library of the Georgian monastery on Mt. Athos:] *See* TSAGARELI (A. A.). Свѣдѣнія о памятникахъ грузинской письменности. вып. I. 1886. 8⁰.   **7708. d. 3**

—— Catalogue des manuscrits géorgiens de la Bibliothèque de la Laure d'Iviron au mont Athos, par R. P. Blake. 3 pt. *Paris*, 1931–4. 8⁰. [*Revue de l'Orient Chrétien*. tom. 8 (28)—9 (29).]   **P.P. 37. ck**

AUCHER (PASQUALE). [Edit. 'Preces Sancti Nersetis Clajensis'.] *See* NERSES IV, *Klayeçi, Catholicos of Armenia*, called ŠNORHALI.

AVALISHVILI (IOSEB). მათემატიკური ტერმინები. [Mat'ematikuri terminebi. A Georgian-Russian and Russo-Georgian glossary of mathematical terms.] pp. 62, I. თბილისი [*Tiflis*,] 1917. 12⁰.   **17076. h. 11**

AVALISHVILI (ZURAB DAVIT'IS-DZE). A fifteenth-century Georgian Needle Painting in the Metropolitan Museum, New York. pp. 67–74. 2 *plates. London*, 1935. 8⁰. [*Georgica*. vol. I. no. I.]   **Ac. 8821. e**

—— Géographie et légende dans un écrit apocryphe de Saint Basile. pp. 279–304. *Paris*, 1927–28. 8⁰. [*Revue de l'Orient Chrétien*. tom. 6 (26).]   **P.P. 37. ck**

—— Notice sur une version géorgienne de la Caverne des Trésors, apocryphe syriaque attribué à saint Éphrem. [Followed by an edition and trans. of the Georgian version of the Testament of Adam.] pp. 381–405. *Paris*, 1927–28. 8⁰. [*Revue de l'Orient Chrétien*. tom. 6 (26).]   **P.P. 37. ck**

—— T'eimuraz I and his Poem "The Martyrdom of Queen K'et'evan". pp. 17–42. I *plate. London*, 1937. 8⁰. [*Georgica*. vol. I. nos. 4–5.]   **Ac. 8821. e**

AVAR LANGUAGE. [For 'Синтаксис аварского языка':] *See* BOKAREV (A. A.)

—— [For 'Awarische Texte':] *See* BOUDA (K.)

—— [For 'Subjekt- und Objektkasus beim awarischen Verbum':] *See* BOUDA (K.)

—— [For 'Textes avar':] *See* DUMÉZIL (G.)

—— [For 'The Avar Language':] *See* GRAHAM (C. C.)

—— [For 'Ausführlicher Bericht über Baron P. v. Uslar's Awarische Studien':] *See* SCHIEFNER (F. A. von).

—— [For 'Awarische Texte':] *See* SCHIEFNER (F. A. von).

—— [For 'Versuch über das Awarische':] *See* SCHIEFNER (F. A. von).

—— [For 'Стихотворения и поэмы', trans. from the Avar:] *See* TSADASA (G.)

—— [For 'Tschetschenzisches und Awarisches':] *See* USLAR (P. K.) *Baron.*

—— [For 'Аварско-русскій словарь':] *See* ZHIRKOV (L. I.)

BABYLON.—*Three Children of.* L'invention géorgienne des Trois Enfants de Babylone. [Georgian text published, with Latin trans., by G. Garitte.] pp. 69–100. *Louvain*, 1959. 8⁰. [*Le Muséon*. tom. 72.]   **P. P. 4453**

BACHANA, *pseud. See* RAZIKASHVILI (N.)

BADRIASHVILI (MERI MALKHAZIS-ASULI). [Joint compiler of description of archaeological materials acquired by the Museum of Georgia in 1904–20.] *See* TIFLIS.—*Museum of Georgia.* Muzeumshi 1904–1920 dslebshi shemosuli, Sak'art'veloshi aghmochenili ark'eologiuri masalebis aghdseriloba. 1955. 4⁰.   **17080. f. 5**

BAGHINANT'I (Grigol) *of Akhaltsikhe*. [Edit. revised version of 'Dottrina Cristiana per uso delle Missione della Giorgia'.] *See* TLUKAANT'I (D.)

BAGRAT, *Bishop of Tauromeni. See* PANCRAS, *Saint and Martyr, Bishop of Taormina.*

BAGRAT IV, *King of Georgia.* [For 'Paleograp'iuli albomi', containing facsimile of charter of Bagrat IV:] *See* T'AQAISHVILI (E. S.)

—— [For 'Сигель грузинскаго царя Баграта IV, 1027–1072':] *See* T'AQAISHVILI (E. S.)

BAGRAT, *Prince of Georgia.* [For 'Изъ книги царевича Баграта о грузинскихъ переводахъ духовныхъ сочиненій':] *See* MARR (N. Y.)

BAGRATID DYNASTY. [For 'Histoire des Bagratides géorgiens, d'après les auteurs arméniens et grecs':] *See* BROSSET (M.-F.)

—— [For 'The Early Bagratids, *etc.*':] *See* TOUMANOFF (C. L.) *Prince.*

—— [For 'The Fifteenth-Century Bagratids and the Institution of Collegial Sovereignty in Georgia':] *See* TOUMANOFF (C. L.) *Prince.*

BAGRATIONI (DAVIT' GIORGIS-DZE). *See* DAVID, *Prince-Regent of Georgia.*

BAGRY (ALEKSANDR VASIL'EVICH). Народная словесность Кавказа. Материалы для библиографического указателя. pp. 203–330. *Баку,* 1926. 8⁰. [*Известия Восточного факультета Азербайджанского гос. Университета. Востоковедение.* том I.]
                                                                Ac. 1109. c

—— [Another copy, being an offprint.]
                                                                011904. i. 23

BAHAISM. ბაჰაი-ს სარწმუნოება, კაცობრიობის ერთობის მოძღვრება. [Bahai-s sardsmunoeba, katsobriobis ert'obis modzghvreba. The Bahai faith, a doctrine of the unity of mankind. Trans. from the English by A. Gugushvili.] pp. 8. პარიზი [*Paris,*] 1955. 8⁰.
                                                                17071. a. 7

BAIADZE (VASO). [Foreword to 'Moranboni'.] *See* URJUMELASHVILI (I.)

BAILEY (*Sir* HAROLD WALTER). Caucasica. [A study, with bibliography, of epigraphical material from Transcaucasia.] pp. 1–5. *London,* 1943. 8⁰. [*Journal of the Royal Asiatic Society,* 1943.]
                                                                R. Ac. 8820/3

BAK'AR, *King of Georgia.* [For the first printed Georgian Bible of 1743, with a preface by the Georgian ex-king Bak'ar:] *See* BIBLE.

BAKLANOV (NIKOLAI BORISOVICH). Художественная культура Дагестана. [Illustrated.] pp. 255–65. *Москва,* 1924. 8⁰. [*Новый Восток.* кн. 5.]
                                                                Ac. 1096. b/5

BAK'RADZE (DAVIT'). Кровью героев. [By the Blood of Heroes. A war novel. Translated into Russian by N. G. Akkerman and P. P. Vershigora.] часть I. pp. 343. 4 *plates. Тбилиси,* 1953. 8⁰.
                                                                17076. b. 5

—— Кровью героев. Перевод с грузинского. [The first part trans. by N. G. Akkerman and P. P. Vershigora, the second by N. G. Akkerman. New edition.] pp. 585,2. 9 *plates. Тбилиси,* 1956. 8⁰.
                                                                17076. b. 30

BAK'RADZE (DIMITRI ZAK'ARIAS-DZE). [For 'Rapport sur les recherches archéologiques faites par M. Bakradzé':] *See* BROSSET (M.-F.)

—— [For 'Rapport sur l'ouvrage manuscrit de M. Bakradzé':] *See* BROSSET (M.-F.)

—— [For 'Опись памятниковъ древности въ ... Грузіи ... Грузинскія надписи прочтены и истолкованы Д. Бакрадзе':] *See* KONDAKOV (N. P.)

—— Археологическое путешествіе по Гуріи и Адчарѣ. pp. xix. 370. *Санктпетербургъ,* 1878. 8⁰. **7705. c. 32**

—— Атласъ. 4⁰.   **7705. cc. 23**

—— Исторія Грузіи на основаніи новыхъ изысканій.

BAK'RADZE *(cont.).*
pp. 183–200. *Санктпетербургъ*, 1873. 8⁰. [*Записки Императорской Академіи Наукъ.* томъ 22.]
Ac. 1125/48

—— Краткій отчетъ объ археологической поѣздкѣ въ Гурію въ 1873 году. pp. 235–47. *Санктпетербургъ*, 1874. 8⁰. [*Записки Императорской Академіи Наукъ.* томъ 23.]
Ac. 1125/48

—— პროფესორი პატკანოვი და ქართული ისტორიის წყაროები. [Profesori Patkanovi da k'art'uli istoriis dsqaroebi. Professor Patkanov and the sources of Georgian history. A polemical essay, edit. by Z. Tchitchinadze.] pp. 35, ii. თბილისი [*Tiflis,*] 1884. 8⁰.
17075. e. 5. (1.)

—— Статьи по исторіи и древностямъ Грузіи. pp. 38. *Санктпетербургъ*, 1887. 8⁰. [*Записки Императорской Академіи Наукъ.* томъ 55. приложеніе 1.]
Ac. 1125/48

BAK'RADZE (GIORGI KONSTANTINES-DZE). Возникновение и развитие капиталистической промышленности в Грузии в XIX веке. pp. 297, 5. *Тбилиси*, 1958. 8⁰.
17075. b. 7

BAK'RADZE (VLADIMER ALEK'SANDRES-DZE). [Writer of introduction to 'Ghrublian dgheebshi'.] *See* GELAZANIA (G.)

BAKURIANI (GRIGOL). [For 'La destinée du Typikon de Grégoire Bakouriani':] *See* NIKOLAEV (V.)

—— Typicon Gregorii Pacuriani. — [Fasc. 1]: Textus... Edidit Michael Tarchnišvili. ([Fasc. 2]: Versio. ... Interpretatus est Michael Tarchnišvili.) [The Typicon or book of monastic rules drawn up for the Georgian monastery at Petritzos or Bachkovo in Bulgaria by its founder, Grigol Bakuriani. Georgian text, with Latin translation.] 2 pt. *Louvain,* 1954. 8⁰. [*Corpus Scriptorum Christianorum Orientalium.* vol. 143–44. *Scriptores Iberici.* tom. 3–4.]
14005. a

—— Typikon de Grégoire Pacourianos pour le monastère de Pétritzos (Bačkovo) en Bulgarie. Texte original publié par .... Louis Petit. [Greek text with introduction and notes in French.] pp. xxxii. 63. *Санктпетербургъ*, 1904. 8⁰. [*Византійскій Временникъ.* том. 11. Приложеніе No. 1.]
Ac. 1125/56

BALANCHIVADZE (ANDRIA MELITONIS-DZE). [Joint edit. of 'Грузинская музыкальная культура'.] *See* CHKHIKVADZE (G. Z.) *and others.*

BALKAROV (BORIS KHAZEKHEVICH). [Joint compiler of 'Грамматика кабардино-черкесского литературного языка'.] *See* NAL'CHIK. — *Кабардино-балкарский научно-исследовательский институт.*

—— Некоторые особенности бесленеевского диалекта кабардинского языка. pp. 218–30. *Москва*, 1952. 8⁰. [*Труды Института языкознания.* том 1.]
Ac. 1125. sf

BAL'MONT (KONSTANTIN DMITRIEVICH). [Trans. 'Витязь в тигровой шкуре'.] *See* RUST'AVELI (SHOT'A).

BANDZELADZE (ALEK'SANDRE MAT'ES-DZE). [Illustrator of 'Robinson Crusoe'.] *See* DEFOE (D.)

—— [Illustrator of 'Robin Hood'.] *See* HOOD (R.)

BARAMIDZE (ALEK'SANDRE GIORGIS-DZE). [Joint edit. of 'Archiliani'.] *See* ARCHIL, *King of Imeret'i.*

—— [Joint edit. of 'Davit'iani'.] *See* GURAMISHVILI (D.)

—— [Joint edit. of Georgian version of the Shāhnāmeh.] *See* ḤASAN (ABU'L-ḲĀSIM), called FIRDAUSĪ, *Ṭūsī.*

—— [Joint edit. of 'K'art'uli enisa da mdserlobis istoriis sakit'khebi'.] *See* JAVAKHISHVILI (I. A.)

—— [Joint edit. of Festschrift in honour of K. S. Kekelidze.] *See* KEKELIDZE (K. S.)

—— [Joint author of 'Dzveli k'art'uli literatura: V–XVIII ss.'] *See* KEKELIDZE (K. S.) and BARAMIDZE (A. G.)

BARAMIDZE *(cont.)*.

—— [Joint edit. of 'Vep'khis tqaosani'.] *See* RUS-T'AVELI (SHOT'A).

—— [Joint compiler of 'Dzveli k'art'uli literatura'.] *See* SHANIDZE (A. G.) *and others.*

—— [Joint edit. of Catalogue of Georgian manuscripts in the Georgian State Museum.] *See* TIFLIS. —*Museum of Georgia.*

—— სულხან-საბა ორბელიანი. ცხოვრება და ლიტერატურული მოღვაწეობა. ნარკვევი. [Sulkhan-Saba Orbeliani. Tskhovreba da literaturuli moghvadseoba. Narkvevi. Sulkhan-Saba Orbeliani. His life and literary career. A critical study.] pp. 185. *2 plates.* თბილისი [*Tiflis,*] 1959. 8⁰.
17075. e. 41

—— *and others.* История грузинской литературы. Краткий очерк. [By] А. Барамидзе, Ш. Радиани, В. Жгенти. pp. 336. *Москва,* 1952. 8⁰.   **15007. h. 15**

—— [Another copy.]   **17080. d. 8**

BARAMIDZE (GRIGOL REJEBIS-DZE) and **JAKOBIA** (GIORGI PAVLES-DZE). ქართული ლიტერატურა. IX კლასის სახელმძღვანელო. [K'art'uli literatura. IX klasis sakhelmdzghvanelo. Georgian literature. Manual for the 9th Form of Georgian State Schools. 12th revised edition. Illustrated.] pp. 277. თბილისი [*Tiflis,*] 1955. 8⁰.   **17076. f. 12**

BARAMIDZE (REVAZ GRIGOLIS-DZE). [Joint edit. of collected works of Sulkhan-Saba Orbeliani.] *See* SAVVA, *the Monk* [*Prince* SULKHAN ORBELIANI].

BARATAEV (MIKHAIL PETROVICH) *Prince.* Нумизматическіе факты грузинскаго царства. (Documents numismatiques du Royaume de Géorgie.) [With plates, facsimiles and tables.] pp. xxii. vi. 112. 182. 18. 90. 54. 20,3. *Russ., Fr. & Georg. Санктпетербургъ,* 1844. 8⁰.   **813. h. 27**

BARAT'ASHVILI FAMILY. [For 'Еще одинъ изъ источниковъ исторіи Грузіи царевича Вахушта: Гуджаръ Баратовыхъ изъ Бетаніи':] *See* T'AQAISHVILI (E. S.)

BARAT'ASHVILI (B.). [Joint trans. 'Samok'alak'o omis istoria S. S. R. Kavshirshi'.] *See* GOR'KY (M.) *pseud.*

BARAT'ASHVILI (MARIKA). Стрекоза. [The Dragon-fly. Comedy in four acts, translated into Russian by M. Shtain.] pp. 107. *Москва,* 1953. 8⁰. *Note: pp. 99–106 are duplicated.*   **17075. d. 29**

BARAT'ASHVILI (NIKOLOZ MELITONIS-DZE), *Prince.* [For selected poems, in Russian translation:] *See* GOL'TSEV (V. V.) and CHIK'OVANI (S. I.). Поэзия Грузии. 1949. 4⁰.   **17075. dd. 1**

—— ლექსები. [Lek'sebi. Poems, together with eight letters of Barat'ashvili. Edit. by Z. Tchitchinadze. Fourth edition.] pp. iii. 66. ტფილისი [*Tiflis,*] 1890. 8⁰. *Imperfect: wants pp. 31, 32 and 37, 38.*   **17075. d. 2. (2)**

—— Стихи. Перевод с грузинского Бориса Пастернака. [With notes by V. V. Gol'tsev.] pp. 86. *Москва,* 1957. 12⁰.   **11589. a. 44**

—— Стихотворения. Перевод… Бориса Пастернака. Редакция В. В. Гольцева. pp. 78. *Москва,* 1948. 8⁰.
011586. df. 91

—— თხზულებანი. [T'khzulebani. Literary works, comprising poems and letters, and prefaced by a memorial address by Ilia Tchavtchavadze. Edited by G. Leonidze.] pp. 154. თბილისი [*Tiflis,*] 1954. 8⁰.
17076. d. 10

BARDAS, *Skleros.* [For 'Die Anfänge der schriftstellerischen Tätigkeit des hl. Euthymius und der Aufstand von Bardas Skleros':] *See* T'ARKHNISHVILI (M.)

BARDAVELIDZE (VERA VARDENIS-ASULI). Земельные владения древнегрузинских святилищ. pp. 92–109. *Москва, Ленинград,* 1949. 8⁰. [*Советская Этнография.* no. 1.]   **Ac. 1125. nd**

—— and **CHITAIA** (GIORGI SPIRIDONIS-DZE). ქართული ხალხური ორნამენტი. I : ხევსურული. [K'art'uli khalkhuri ornamenti. I: Khevsuruli.] Ornement populaire géorgien. I: Ornement khevsourien. [Georgian, Russian and French texts. Edit. by S. Janashia.] pp. 129. 34 *plates*; 1 *map*. თბილისი [*Tiflis*,] 1939. 8⁰.   **17080. e. 3**

BARLAAM, *Saint, of Antioch. See* BARLAAM, *Saint, of Asia Minor.*

BARLAAM, *Saint, of Asia Minor.* [For 'Изъ поѣздки на Афонъ... О св. Варлаамѣ':] *See* MARR (N. Y.)

—— [*Life.*] *See* MARR (N. Y.). Агіографическіе матеріалы по грузинскимъ рукописямъ Ивера. 1901. 8⁰.   **Ac. 5584**

—— [For 'S. Barlaam du Mont Casius':] *See* PEETERS (P.)

BARLAAM, *Saint, of India.* [THE LEGEND OF BARLAAM AND JOSAPHAT.—*Georgian*]. [For 'Les origines du "Barlaam et Joasaph" grec. À propos de la thèse nouvelle de M. Nucubidze':] *See* DEVOS (P.)

—— [For 'Le témoignage de Georges l'Hagiorite sur l'origine du "Barlaam" grec':] *See* GARITTE (G.)

—— [For *'The life of the Blessed Iodasaph:* a new Oriental Christian version of the Barlaam and Ioasaph romance':] *See* LANG (D. M.)

—— [For a translation of the Old Georgian version of the Legend of Barlaam and Josaphat, as contained in MS. 36 of the Greek Patriarchal Library at Jerusalem:] *See* LANG (D. M.). The Wisdom of Balahvar, *etc.* 1957. 8⁰.   **W.P. 5206/20**

—— [For 'St. Euthymius the Georgian and the Barlaam and Ioasaph Romance':] *See* LANG (D. M.)

—— [For 'Изъ поѣздки на Афонъ... О св. Варлаамѣ':] *See* MARR (N. Y.)

—— [For 'Житіе св. Варлаама Сирокавказскаго. Къ вопросу о "Варлаамѣ и Іоасафѣ"':] *See* MARR (N. Y.) Агіографическіе матеріалы по грузинскимъ рукописямъ Ивера. 1901. 8⁰.   **Ac. 5584**

—— [For 'Les deux recensions du "Barlaam" géorgien':] *See* TʻARKHNISHVILI (M.)

—— [For 'Le roman de Balahvar et sa traduction anglaise':] *See* TʻARKHNISHVILI (M.)

—— [For 'The Apology of Aristides—A Re-examination', being a study of one of the sources of the Greek Barlaam and Ioasaph romance:] *See* WOLFF (R. L.)

—— [For 'Barlaam and Ioasaph':] *See* WOLFF (R. L.)

—— Армянско-грузинскіе матеріалы для исторіи Душеполезной Повѣсти о Варлаамѣ и Іоасафѣ. [By N. Y. Marr]. pp. 49–78. С.-Петербургъ, 1899. 8⁰. [*Записки Восточнаго Отдѣленія Имп. Русскаго Археологическаго Общества.* томъ II.].   **Ac. 5584**

—— ბალავარიანის ქართული რედაქციები. [Balavarianis kʻartʻuli redakʻtsiebi. The ancient Georgian redactions of the story of Barlaam and Josaphat. Edit. by Ilia Abuladze, under the direction of A. G. Shanidze.] (Грузинскіе редакции повести "Варлаам и Иоасаф".) pp. 048. 216, 3. თბილისი [*Tiflis*,] 1957. 8⁰. [*Dzveli kʻartʻuli enis dzeglebi.* no. 10.].   **17071. c. 2**

—— Балнваръ и Іодасафъ. Грузинскій текстъ по рукописямъ XI–XII вв. [Georgian text, edited with Russian translation and introduction by A. S. Khakhanov.] pp. xv. 32. 2 *plates*. Москва, 1902. 8⁰. [*Лазаревскій институтъ. Труды по Востоковѣдѣнію.* вып. 9.]   **17068. g. 1**

—— Мудрость Балавара. [Trans. by I. A. Javakhishvili from the Georgian text published by E. S. Tʻaqaishvili.]. pp. 1–48. С.–Петербургъ, 1899. 8⁰. [*Записки Восточнаго Отдѣленія Имп. Русскаго Археологическаго Общества.* томъ II.].   **Ac. 5584**

—— "Мудрость Балавара", грузинская версія "Душеполезной исторіи о Варлаамѣ и Іоасафѣ". [A critical study by N. Y. Marr of the Georgian version, citing parallel passages from the Greek and Arabic versions.] pp. 223–60. С.-Петербургъ, 1889.

8⁰. [*Записки Восточнаго Отдѣленія Имп. Русскаго Археологическаго Общества.* томъ 3.]   **Ac. 5584**

BARNAVELI (SARA). [Joint edit. of 'K'art'uli khelovneba' ('Ars Georgica').] *See* TIFLIS.—*Academy of Sciences of the Georgian S. S. R.*—*Institute of the History of Georgian Art.*   **17080. g. 1**

BARTHOLOMAEI (IVAN ALEKSEEVICH) *Lt.-General.* [For 'Inscriptions et antiquités géorgiennes et autres recueillies par M. le colonel Bartholomaei':] *See* BROSSET (M.-F.)

—— [For 'Lettres de M. Bartholomaei, relatives aux antiquités géorgiennes, *etc.*':] *See* BROSSET (M.-F.)

—— [For 'Réponse à M. de Bartholomaei':] *See* BROSSET (M.-F.)

—— Апсща анбан. Абхазскій букварь, *etc.* pp. 188. *Тифлисъ*, 1865. 8⁰.   **12907. ee. 2**

—— [Another copy.]   **12907. ee. 13**

—— [Чеченскій букварь.] [An alphabet compiled by B. with Chechen assistants, containing original and other folktales.] *Russ. & Chechen.* pp. 154. [*Тифлисъ*, 1866.] 8⁰. *Imperfect; wanting the titlepage.*   **12910. e. 40**

—— Краткая священная исторія переведена на абхазскій языкъ, *etc. Russ. & Abkhazian.* pp. 242. *Тифлисъ*, 1866. 8⁰.   **3127. dd. 17**

—— Lettres numismatiques et archéologiques, relatives à la Transcaucasie, *etc.* pp. ix. 116. 4 *plates. St.-Pétersbourg,* 1859. 4⁰.   **7756. g. 11**

—— Lettres sur la numismatique géorgienne. pp. 82–106. *St.-Pétersbourg,* 1857. 8⁰. [*Mélanges Asiatiques de l'Académie des Sciences.* tom. 3.]   **Ac. 1125/11**

BARTOLOMEI (IVAN ALEKSEEVICH). *See* BARTHOLOMAEI (I. A.) *Lt.-General.*

BASIL, *Laurae S. Sabae Presbyter.* La Passion de S. Michel le Sabaïte. [Latin translation of the Georgian version, with introduction and commentary, by P. Peeters.] pp. 65–98. *Bruxelles,* 1930. 8⁰. [*Analecta Bollandiana.* tom. 48.]   **2002. f**

BASIL, *Saint,* surnamed *the Great, Archbishop of Caesarea in Cappadocia.* [For 'Géographie et légende dans un écrit apocryphe de Saint Basile':] *See* AVALISHVILI (Z. D.)

—— [For 'Histoire du texte des Ascétiques de S. Basile', with a chapter on the Georgian versions of the 'Regulae monasticae':] *See* GRIBOMONT (J.)

BASIL, *Saint, Bishop of Epiphania.* La Passion de S. Basile d'Épiphanie. [Trans. into Latin, with introduction, by P. Peeters.] pp. 302–323. *Bruxelles,* 1930. 8⁰. [*Analecta Bollandiana.* tom. 48.]   **2002. f**

BATONI, *pseud. See* TSERET'ELI (M. G.)

BATS LANGUAGE. *See* TUSH LANGUAGE

BAUMSTARK (ANTON). [Edit. 'Die Weihnachtsfeier Jerusalems im siebten Jahrhundert. Übersetzung nach Kekelidze ... von Dr. Gregor Peradze'.] *See* LITURGIES.—Greek Rite.—*Euchologion.*

—— [Edit. 'Oster- und Pfingstfeier Jerusalems im siebten Jahrhundert. Übersetzung nach Kekelidze ... von Dr. Theodor Kluge'.] *See* LITURGIES.—Greek Rite.—*Pentekostarion.*

—— [Edit. 'Quadragesima und Karwoche Jerusalems im siebten Jahrhundert. Übersetzung nach Kekelidze .... von Dr. Theodor Kluge'.] *See* LITURGIES.—Greek Rite.—*Triodion.*

—— [Edit. of 'Oriens Christianus'.] *See* ROME.—*Collegium des deutschen Campo Santo.*

—— Eine georgische Miniaturenfolge zum Markusevangelium. [Being a description of a set of illustrations to St. Mark's Gospel in a codex in the Gelat'i Monastery library.] pp. 152–61. *Leipzig,* 1916. 8⁰. [*Oriens Christianus.* Neue Folge. Bd. 6.]   **Ac. 2002. b**

—— Eine georgische Miniaturenfolge zum Matthäusevangelium. [Description of miniatures in

BAUMSTARK *(cont.)*.
the Jrutchi Gospel codex.] pp. 140–47. *Leipzig*, 1915. 8⁰. [*Oriens Christianus*. Neue Folge. Bd. 5.]

           Ac. 2002. b

—— Eine Wanderausstellung georgischer Kunst. pp. 239–42. *Leipzig*, 1930. 8⁰. [*Oriens Christianus*. Dritte Serie. Bd. 5.]   **Ac. 2002. b**

—— Zum georgischen Evangelientext. pp. 117–24. *Leipzig*, 1930. 8⁰. [*Oriens Christianus*. Dritte Serie. Bd. 3–4.]   **Ac. 2002. b**

BEKʻA, *Opizari*. [*Biography*.] *See* AMIRANASHVILI (S. I.)

BELIACHVILI (VLADIMIR). *See* BELIASHVILI (LADO).

BELIASHVILI (AKAKI IONAS-DZE). Бесики. Роман. [A historical novel based on the life of the poet B. Gabashvili. Trans. into Russian by A. Zardiashvili and others.] pp. 584, 2. 1 *plate*. *Тбилиси*, 1955. 8⁰.   **17075. e. 26**

—— ერთტომეული. [Ertʻtomeuli. Collected tales, in one volume.] pp. 729. თბილისი [*Tiflis*,] 1954. 8⁰.   **17077. a. 13**

—— უღელტეხილი, რომანი. [Ugheltekhili, romani. The mountain peak, a novel.] pp. 344, 1. თბილისი [*Tiflis*,] 1956. 8⁰. **17076. b. 23**

BELIASHVILI (LADO). რუსთველის და დანტეს იდუმალი. [Rustʻvelis da Dantes idumali.] Les secrets de Rousthaveli et de Dante Aliguiery. Premier discours. pp. 77. პარიზი [*Paris*,] 1956. 8⁰.   **17076. h. 10**

BELINSKY (VISSARION GRIGORʼEVICH). *See* BYELINSKY.

BELLARMINO (ROBERTO FRANCESCO ROMOLO). *See* ROBERT [Bellarmino] *Saint, Cardinal, Archbishop of Capua*.

BENASHVILI (DIMITRI). [Joint edit. of works of Niko Lortʻkʻipʻanidze.] *See* LORTʻKʻIPʻANIDZE (N. M.)

—— სახისა და ხასიათის პრობლემა "ვეფხისტყაოსანში". [Sakhisa da khasiatʻis problema 'Vepʻkhistqaosanshi'. The problem of image and character in 'The Man in the Panther's Skin', the epic poem by Shotʻa Rustʻaveli.] pp. 311. თბილისი [*Tiflis*,] 1954. 8⁰.   **17076. b. 9**

BENESHEVICH (VLADIMIR NIKOLAEVICH). [Editor of the old Georgian version of the Gospels.] *See* BIBLE.—New Testament.—*Gospels*.

—— [Edit. and trans. extracts from the Nomocanon of the Georgian Church.] *See* GEORGIAN ORTHODOX CHURCH.—*Nomocanon*.

—— Изображеніе грузинскаго царя Давида Строителя на иконѣ Синайскаго монастыря. pp. 62–64. *С.-Петербургъ*, 1912. 4⁰. [*Христіанскій Востокъ*. томъ I. вып. I.]   **Ac. 1125/105**

—— О древнемъ іерусалимскомъ спискѣ грузинской минеи-четьей. pp. 65–68. *С.-Петербургъ*, 1912. 4⁰. [*Христіанскій Востокъ*. томъ I. вып. I.]

          Ac. 1125/105

BERDZENISHVILI (GRIGOL ALEKʻSIS-DZE) *and others*. ქართველ დრამატურგთა პიესები. [Kʻartʻvel dramaturgtʻa piesebi. Plays by Georgian dramatists. Edited by Sh. N. Apʻkhaidze and B. Nanitashvili.] pp. 588, 4. თბილისი [*Tiflis*,] 1959. 8⁰.

          17076. c. 19

BERDZENISHVILI (NIKOLOZ ALEKʻSANDRES-DZE). [Joint edit. of 'Archiliani'.] *See* ARCHIL, *King of Imeretʻi*.

—— [Edit. 'Тбилиси в XIX столетии, 1865–1869'.] *See* CHKHETIA (SH. Q.)

—— [Edit. 'Mtskhetʻis udzvelesi arkʻeologiuri dzeglebi'.] *See* CHUBINISHVILI (T. N.)

—— [Edit. 'Akhali Kʻartʻlis tskhovreba'.] *See* GRIGOLIA (K. G.)

BERIA (LAVRENTI PAVLES-DZE). *See* BERIYA.

BERIDZE (SHALVA). Bibliographie française de la Géorgie du XIIIème au XXème siècle. pp. 193–

BERIDZE *(cont.)*.
229. *Paris*, 1932. 8⁰. [*Extracted from the 'Revue des Bibliothèques'. With a typewritten supplement.*] **11912. aaa. 10**

—— Ch. Rousthawéli: sa vie, son poème, ses maximes, sa philosophie. Conférence, *etc.* [With a portrait.] pp. 26. *Paris*, [1928.] 8⁰. **10607. i. 11**

—— La Géorgie et les lettres françaises. pp. 144–50. *Paris*, 1930. 8⁰. [*Journal Asiatique.* sér. 12. tom. 16.] **R. Ac. 8808**

—— La Vie et l'oeuvre de M.-F. Brosset, *etc.* pp. 11. *Paris*, 1922. 8⁰. **10657. h. 19**

BERIDZE (VAKHTANG VUKOLIS-DZE). სამცხის ხუროთმოძღვრება, XIII–XVI საუკუნეები. [Samtskhis khurot'modzghvreba, XIII–XVI saukuneebi. Architecture of Samtskhe in the 13th to 16th centuries.] (Архитектура Самцхе, XIII–XVI вв.) [With summaries in Russian & German, and plans and diagrams in the text.] pp. 264, 3. 118 *plates*. თბილისი [*Tiflis*,] 1955. 4⁰. **17080. f. 9**

BERIDZE (VUKOL MIKHEILIS-DZE). სიტყვის-კონა იმერულ და რაჭულ თქმათა. [Sitqvis-kona Imerul da Ratchul t'k'mat'a. Glossary of the dialects of Imeret'i and Ratcha.] (Грузинскій (к̔арт̔скій) глоссарій по имерскому и рач̔инскому говорамъ.) pp. viii. 76. *С.-Петербургъ*, 1912. 8⁰. [*Матеріалы по яфетическому языкознанію.* кн. 6.] **17073. a. 3**

—— *and others.* ტექნიკური ტერმინოლოგია. რუსულ-ქართული ნაწილი. [Tek'nikuri terminologia. Rusul-k'art'uli nadsili. A Russo-Georgian technical dictionary, compiled by a committee of scholars, and edited by V. M. Beridze and others.] (Техническая терминология. Русско-грузинская часть.) pp. 08.433. თბილისი [*Tiflis*,] 1957. 8⁰. **17076. h. 17**

BERITASHVILI (IVANE SOLOMONIS-DZE). [For 'Transactions of the J. Beritashvili Physiological Institute, edited by Prof. J. S. Beritoff':] *See* TIFLIS.—*Tiflis State University.*

BERITOFF (J. S.). *See* BERITASHVILI (IVANE).

BERIYA (LAVRENTY PAVLOVICH). სიტყვა საკავშირო კ. პ. (ბ) XIX ყრილობაზე, 7 ოქტომბერი, 1952 წ. [Sitqva sakavshiro k. p. (b) XIX qrilobaze, 7 ok'tomberi, 1952 ds. Speech at the 19th Congress of the Communist Party of the Soviet Union, October 7th, 1952.] pp. 30. [თბილისი. *Tiflis*,] 1953. 8⁰. **17075. f. 8 (4)**

BERKOV (PAVEL NAUMOVICH). Шота Руставели в русской литературе. pp. 49–80. *Москва, Ленинград*, 1938. 8⁰. [*Известия Академии Наук СССР. Classe des Sciences Sociales.* no. 3.] **Ac. 1125/44 (9)**

BERLIN. — *Koenigliche Preussische Akademie der Wissenschaften. — Kirchenvaeter-Commission. See* GEBHARDT (O. von) and HARNACK (C. G. A. von). Texte und Untersuchungen zur Geschichte der altchristlichen Literatur... herausgegeben von O. von Gebhardt und A. von Harnack. 1882– 8⁰. **3628. d. 1/1-**

BERNARDO MARIA, *da Napoli. See* GIOFFI (B. M.)

BERZHE (ADOL'F PETROVICH). [Edit. 'Die Sagen und Lieder des Tscherkessen-Volks'.] *See* SHORA-BEKMURZIN-NOGMOV.

—— [Edit. 'Акты собранные Кавказскою Археографическою Коммиссіею'.] *See* TIFLIS. — *Кавказская Археографическая Коммиссія.*

BESIKI. [Pseudonym for B. Gabashvili.] *See* GABASHVILI (B. I.)

BESTIARY. *See* PHYSIOLOGUS.

BGHAZHBA (KHUKHUTI SOLOMONIS-DZE). [Edit. 'D. Gulias sakhelobis Ap'khazet'is enis, literaturis da istoriis institutis shromebi'.] *See* SUKHUMI.—*Abkhazian Linguistic, Literary and Historical Institute.*

BIBLE. — COMPLETE BIBLE. ႡႨႡႪႨႠ. Ⴀⴃⴑ ⴀⴞⴀⴊⴈ ⴃⴀⴁⴄⴜⴃⴓⴊⴈ ⴕⴀⴐⴇⴓⴊⴑ ⴄⴌⴀⴑⴀ ⴆⴄⴃⴀ. [Biblia. Ads akhali dabetchduli k'art'uls enasa zeda. The Bible. Now newly printed in the Georg-

BIBLE *(cont.)*
ian tongue. The first printed Georgian Bible, with the Apocrypha. Followed by a list of Saints' Days, *etc.*, and a treatise on chronology. With a preface by the Georgian ex-king Bak'ar, and a concluding discourse by the editor, Prince Vakhushti.] pp. xiv. 995. 96. x. **ⴋⴍⴑⴉⴍⴡⴑ, ႹႶႫႢ.** [*Moscow,* 1743.] fol. *A note in Georgian on the verso of p. 995 records that this copy was the property of Archimandrite Cyril in the year 1768.* **Or. 72. d. 2**

—— *Appendix.* [For 'Notice sur la Bible géorgienne imprimée à Moscou en 1742':] *See* BROSSET (M.-F.)

—— [For 'Catalogue des manuscrits géorgiens littéraires du Mont Sinaï', including description of a number of Biblical Mss.:] *See* CATHARINE, *Saint, of Alexandria.* — CONVENT OF, ON MOUNT SINAI.

—— [For 'Die georgische Bibelübersetzung. A) Alte kirchliche Abhängigkeit Georgiens von Armenien':] *See* GOUSSEN (H.)

—— [For 'О кавказской версии Библии в грузинских палимпсестных фрагментах':] *See* MARR (N. Y.)

—— [For 'Замѣтки по текстамъ св. Писанія у древнихъ армянъ и грузинъ':] *See* MARR (N. Y.)

—— [For 'Altgeorgisches Glossar zu ausgewählten Bibeltexten:'] *See* MOLITOR (J.)

—— [For 'Die georgische Bibelübersetzung':] *See* MOLITOR (J.)

—— [For 'Monumenta Iberica Antiquiora. Textus Chanmeti et Haemeti ex Inscriptionibus, S. Bibliis et Patribus':] *See* MOLITOR (J.)

—— OLD TESTAMENT.—*Jeremiah.* [For 'Khanmeti palimpsest fragments of the old Georgian version of Jeremiah', edited and translated by Robert P. Blake:] *See* BLAKE (R.P.)

—— [For 'Оксфордский фрагмент древне-грузинской версии Иеремии':] *See* GENKO (A. N.)

—— *Pentateuch.—Appendix.* [For 'Hippolyte de Rome. Sur les bénédictions d'Isaac, de Jacob et de Moïse'. Greek, Armenian and Georgian texts, with French translation:] *See* HIPPOLYTUS, *Saint, of Rome.*

—— *Psalms.* ფსალმუნი დავითისი. [P'salmuni Davit'isi. Psalms of David. Published by the British and Foreign Bible Society.] pp. 121. ტფილისი [*Tiflis,*] 1879. 8⁰. **17071. a. 2 (2)**

—— *Song of Solomon.—Appendix.* [For the Georgian version of St. Hippolytus's Commentary on the Song of Solomon:] *See* HIPPOLYTUS, *Saint, of Rome.*

—— *Apocrypha.* The Georgian text of Fourth Esdras from the Athos manuscript. [Containing only divergent readings from the Jerusalem text previously published. Edit. with Latin trans. and an introduction by] Robert P. Blake. pp. 57–105. *Cambridge, Mass.,* 1929. 8⁰. [*Harvard Theological Review.* vol. 22.] **R. Ac. 2692/13**

—— The Georgian version of Fourth Esdras from the Jerusalem manuscript. [Edit., with Latin trans. and an introduction by] Robert P. Blake. pp. 299–375. *Cambridge, Mass.,* 1926. 8⁰. [*Harvard Theological Review.* vol. 19.] **R. Ac. 2692/13**

—— *Appendix.* [For 'Ancient Georgian versions of the Old Testament':] *See* BLAKE (R. P.)

—— [For 'The Athos Codex of the Georgian Old Testament':] *See* BLAKE (R. P.)

—— NEW TESTAMENT. **ⴜⴂⴌⴢ ⴀⴞⴊⴈⴑⴀⴢ ⴀⴖⴇⴕⴋⴈⴑⴀⴢ** [**ⴀⴖⴇⴕⴋⴈⴑⴀⴢ**]. [Dsigni akhlisay aght'k'misa. Book of the New Testament. Printed in the ecclesiastical character by the Moscow Bible Society. With sketches of the lives of the Evangelists by St. Sophronius and by Dorotheus, Bishop of Tyre.] pp. ii. 400. **ⴋⴍⴑⴉⴍⴡ** [*Moscow,*] 1816. 4⁰. **4. b. 13**

—— [Another copy.] **17071. b. 1**

—— [Another copy.] **17071. b. 2**

—— [Another copy.] **17071. b. 3**

BIBLE *(cont.)*

—— [Another copy.]　　　　　　　**17071. b. 5**

—— [Another copy.]　　　　　　　**17071. b. 6**

—— წიგნი ახლისა აღთქმისა. [Dsigni akhlisa aght'k'misa. Book of the New Testament. Printed in the civil character by the St. Petersburg Bible Society. With sketches of the lives of the Evangelists by St. Sophronius and by Dorotheus, Bishop of Tyre.] pp. ii. 614. სანკტპეტერბურღ [*St. Petersburg,*] 1818. 4⁰.　　　　　　　**17071. b. 4**

—— უფლისა ჩუჱნისა იესო ქრისტესი წმიდა სახარება, *etc.* [Up'lisa chûeynisa Ieso K'ristesi dsmida sakhareba. The Holy Gospel of Our Lord Jesus Christ. Published by the British and Foreign Bible Society]. pp. ii. 492. ტფილისი [*Tiflis,*] 1879. 8⁰.　　　　　　　**17071. a. 2 (1)**

—— *Appendix.* [For 'Recent work on the Georgian New Testament':] *See* LANG (D. M.)

—— [For 'Chanmetifragmente. Ein Beitrag zur Textgeschichte der altgeorgischen Bibelübersetzung':] *See* MOLITOR (J.)

—— [For 'Early Versions of the New Testament: Manuscript Studies', with a chapter on the Old Georgian version:] *See* VÖÖBUS (A.)

—— *Gospels.* Das Adysh-Tetraevangelium. Neu übersetzt und mit altgeorgischen Paralleltexten verglichen, von Joseph Molitor. pt. 1, *etc.* Wiesbaden, 1953, *etc.* 8⁰. [*Oriens Christianus.* Bd. 37 – (Vierte Serie. Bd. 1 –).] *In progress.* **Ac. 2002. b**

—— სᲦᲮᲐᲠᲔᲑᲐჲ ᲝᲗᲮᲗᲐᲕᲘ. [Sakharebay ot'kht'avi.] Quattuor Evangeliorum versio Georgiana vetus. E duobus codicibus, aa. p. Ch. n. 913 et 995, edidit Vladimir Benešević. Fasc. 1. Evangelium secundum Matthaeum. (Fasc. 2. Evangelium secundum Marcum.) [Printed in the ecclesiastical character.] pp. iii. 303. С.-Петербургъ, 1909,11. 4⁰. *No more published.*　**17071. c. 1**

—— *Appendix.* [For 'Zum georgischen Evangelientext':] *See* BAUMSTARK (A.)

—— [For 'Notes on the text of the Georgian and Armenian Gospels':] *See* BLAKE (R. P.)

—— [For 'The Gospels of Bert'ay, *etc.*':] *See* BLAKE (R. P.) and DER NERSESSIAN (S.)

—— [For a Concordance to the Georgian Gospels:] *See* IMNAISHVILI (I. B.)

—— [For 'Сванетскія рукописныя евангелія':] *See* KHAKHANOV (A. S.)

—— [For 'Les origines de la version arménienne et le diatessaron':] *See* LYONNET (S.)

—— [For 'Evangelienzitate in einem altgeorgischen Väterfragment':] *See* MOLITOR (J.)

—— [For 'Zur Geschichte des altgeorgischen Evangelientextes':] *See* VÖÖBUS (A.)

—— Описаніе персидскаго рукописнаго Четвероевангелія. [Description, with extracts, by N. Y. Marr of a manuscript copy of the Gospels in the Persian language but written in Georgian transcription.] pp. 377–81. С.-Петербургъ, 1889. 8⁰. [*Записки Восточнаго Отдѣленія Имп. Русскаго Археологическаго Общества.* томъ 3.]　**Ac. 5584**

—— *Matthew.* The Old Georgian Version of the Gospel of Matthew from the Adysh Gospels, with the variants of the Opiza and Tbet' Gospels. Edited with a Latin translation by Robert P. Blake. pp. 168. *Paris,* 1933. 4⁰. [*Patrologia Orientalis.* tom. 24. fasc. 1.]　　　　　　　**14005. c**

—— [Another copy.]　　　　　　　**2002. d**

—— *Appendix.* [For 'Eine georgische Miniaturenfolge zum Matthäusevangelium':] *See* BAUMSTARK (A.)

—— *Mark.* The Old Georgian Version of the Gospel of Mark from the Adysh Gospels, with the variants of the Opiza and Tbet' Gospels. Edited with a Latin translation by Robert P. Blake. pp. 140. *Paris,* 1928. 4⁰. [*Patrologia Orientalis.* tom. 20. fasc. 3.]　　　　　　　**14005. c**

BIBLE *(cont.)*
—— [Another copy.]   **2002. d**

—— *Appendix.* [For 'Eine georgische Miniaturen-folge zum Markusevangelium':] *See* BAUMSTARK (A.)

—— *Luke.* La version géorgienne ancienne de l'Évangile de Luc, d'après les Évangiles d'Adich avec les variantes des Évangiles d'Opiza et de Tbet'. Éditée avec une traduction latine par Maurice Brière. pp. 183. *Paris,* 1955. 4⁰. [*Patrologia Orientalis.* tom. 27. fasc. 3.]   **14005. c**

—— [Another copy.]   **2002. d**

—— *John.* ახალი აღთქმა უფლისა ჩჳენისა იესო ქრისტესი. სახარება იოანესი. [Akhali aght'k'ma Up'lisa Chûeynisa Ieso K'ristesi. Sakhareba Ioanesi. New Testament of Our Lord Jesus Christ. Gospel of John.] pp. 96. ტფილისი [*Tiflis,*] 1900. 8⁰.
17071. a. 4

—— The Gospel according to S. John, translated from the eleven oldest versions [including the Georgian] except the Latin, and compared with the English Bible; with notes on every one of the alterations proposed by The Five Clergymen in their Revised Version of this Gospel ... By ... S. C. Malan. 2 pt. *London,* 1862. 4⁰.   **3051. e. 4**

—— The Old Georgian Version of the Gospel of John from the Adysh Gospels, with the variants of the Opiza and Tbet' Gospels. Edited with a Latin translation by Robert P. Blake and Maurice Brière. pp. 149. *Paris,* 1950. 4⁰. [*Patrologia Orientalis.* tom. 26. fasc. 4.]   **14005. c**

—— [Another copy.]   **2002. d**

—— *Acts.* L'ancienne version géorgienne des Actes des Apôtres. [Edited,] d'après deux manuscrits du Sinaï, [together with a Latin translation,] par Gérard Garitte. pp. 183, 1. 2 *plates. Louvain,* 1955. 8⁰. [*Bibliothèque du Muséon.* vol. 38.]   **P.P. 1927. d**

——*Acts.—Appendix.* [For 'À propos de la plus

ancienne version géorgienne des Actes des Apôtres':] *See* T'ARKHNISHVILI (M.)

—— *Epistles.* კათოლიკე ეპისტოლეთა ქართული ვერსიები X–XIV საუკუნეთა ხელნაწერების მიხედვით. [Kat'olike epistolet'a k'art'uli versiebi X–XIV saukunet'a khelnadserebis mikhedvit'. The Georgian versions of the Catholic Epistles, according to manuscripts of the 10th to 14th centuries. Edited by K'. I. Lort'k'ip'anidze under the supervision of A. G. Shanidze.] (Грузинские версии Соборных Посланий по рукописям X–XIV веков.) pp. 037. 142. 2 *plates.* თბილისი [*Tiflis,*] 1956. 8⁰. [*Dzveli k'art'uli enis dzeglebi.* no. 9.]   **17071. c. 2**

—— *Apocrypha.* [For the Georgian version of the apocryphal legend of Joseph of Arimathea:] *See* JOSEPH, *of Arimathea.*

—— [For 'Eine Benutzung des Testamentum Domini nostri Jesu Christi':] *See* SCHMIDT (C.)

—— Le fragment géorgien de l'Évangile de Thomas. [Trans. into Latin from the edition of A. G. Shanidze, with introduction, by] G. Garitte. pp. 513–20. *Louvain,* 1956. 8⁰. [*Revue d'Histoire Ecclésiastique.* vol. 51. no. 2–3.]   **Ac. 2646/3**

—— ქართული ვერსიები აპოკრიფების მოციქულთა შესახებ, IX–XI სს. ხელნაწერთა მიხედვით. [K'art'uli versiebi apokrip'ebisa motsik'ult'a shesakheb, IX–XI ss. khelnadsert'a mikhedvit'. Georgian versions of apocryphal writings on the Apostles, according to Manuscripts of the 9th–11th centuries. Edit. by Ts. I. K'urtsikidze.] (Грузинские версии апокрифических деяний апостолов.) pp. 077. 113. თბილისი [*Tiflis,*] 1959. 8⁰.   **17071. c. 3**

—— Le "protévangile de Jacques" en géorgien. [Edit. with Latin trans. by G. Garitte.] pp. 233-65. *Louvain,* 1957. 8⁰. [*Le Muséon.* tom. 70.]   **P.P. 4453**

BICHOEV (ASLAN T.). [Joint compiler of Russian-Kabardo-Circassian dictionary.] *See* KARDANOV (B. M.) and BICHOEV (A. T.)

BLAKE (ROBERT PIERPONT). [Compiler of 'Catalogue des manuscrits géorgiens de la Bibliothèque

BLAKE *(cont.)*
de la Laure d'Iviron au mont Athos'.] *See* ATHOS, *Mount*.

—— [Edit., with Latin trans., of Georgian version of Fourth Esdras from the Jerusalem manuscript.] *See* BIBLE.—Old Testament.—*Apocrypha*.

—— [Edit., with Latin trans., of the variants of the Georgian text of Fourth Esdras from the Athos manuscript.] *See* BIBLE.—Old Testament.—*Apocrypha*.

—— [Edit. of Old Georgian version of the Gospel of Matthew with Latin translation.] *See* BIBLE.—New Testament.—*Matthew*.

—— [Edit. of Old Georgian version of the Gospel of Mark with Latin translation.] *See* BIBLE.—New Testament.—*Mark*.

—— [Joint edit. of Old Georgian version of the Gospel of John with Latin translation.] *See* BIBLE.—New Testament.—*John*.

—— [Joint edit. and translator of 'Epiphanius de gemmis'.] *See* EPIPHANIUS, *Saint, Bishop of Constantia in Cyprus*.

—— [For 'Une page de saint Hippolyte retrouvée', being an edition and trans. by R. P. Blake of a fragment of the Benedictions of Moses:] *See* HIPPOLYTUS, *Saint, of Rome*.

—— [Compiler of 'Catalogue des manuscrits géorgiens de la Bibliothèque Patriarcale Grecque à Jérusalem'.] *See* JERUSALEM.— *Greek Patriarchal Library*.

—— [Joint editor and translator of the Georgian Passion of Saints Theodore, Julian, *etc.*] *See* THEODORE, *Saint and Martyr, of Pella*.

—— Ancient Georgian versions of the Old Testament. pp. 271–97. *Cambridge, Mass.*, 1926. 8⁰. [*Harvard Theological Review*. vol. 19.]   **R. Ac. 2692/13**

—— The Athos Codex of the Georgian Old Testa-
ment. pp. 33–56. 1 *plate.Cambridge, Mass.*, 1929. 8⁰. [*Harvard Theological Review*. vol. 22.]
R. Ac. 2692/13

—— Deux lacunes comblées dans la "Passio XX monachorum Sabaitarum". [Containing Georgian version of two passages missing in the Greek text, edit. with introduction by R. P. Blake.] pp. 27–43. *Bruxelles*, 1950. 8⁰. [*Analecta Bollandiana*. tom. 68.]
2002. g

—— Catalogue of the Georgian manuscripts in the Cambridge University Library [compiled by R. P. Blake].—Khanmeti palimpsest fragments of the old Georgian version of Jeremiah [edited and translated by] Robert P. Blake. pp. 207–76. 8 *plates*. *Cambridge, Mass.*, 1932. 8⁰. [*Harvard Theological Review*. vol. 25.]   **R. Ac. 2692/13**

—— [Another copy, being an offprint.] **17071. a. 3**

—— Georgian secular literature, epic, romantic and lyric. pp. 25–48. *Cambridge, Mass.*, 1933. 8⁰. [*Harvard Studies and Notes in Philology and Literature*. vol. 15.]   **Ac. 2692. b**

—— Georgian theological literature. pp. 50–64. *London*, 1924. 8⁰. [*Journal of Theological Studies*. vol. 26.]   **P.P. 296. ca**

—— Greek script and Georgian scribes on Mt. Sinai. [With a palaeographical table.] pp. 273–76. *Cambridge, Mass*, 1932. 8⁰. [*Harvard Theological Review*. vol. 25.]   **R. Ac. 2692/13**

—— Note supplémentaire sur Fou-lin. pp. 83–88. *Paris*, 1923. 8⁰. [*Journal Asiatique*. sér. 12. tom. 1.]
R. Ac. 8808

—— Notes on the text of the Georgian and Armenian Gospels. pp. 355–63. *London*; *Baltimore* printed, [1937.] 8⁰. [*Quantulacumque. Studies presented to Kirsopp Lake*.]   **12354. 1. 27**

—— Some Byzantine accounting practices illustrated from Georgian sources. pp. 11–33. *Cambridge, Mass.*, 1940. 8⁰. [*Harvard Studies in Classical Philology*. vol. 51.]   **Ac. 2692/9**

BLAKE *(cont.)*

—— and **DER NERSESSIAN** (Sirarpie). The Gospels of Bert'ay: An Old-Georgian MS. of the tenth century. pp. 226–85. 8 *plates. Boston,* 1944. 8⁰. [*Byzantion.* vol. 16.] **P.P. 4748. pc**

BLEICHSTEINER (Robert). [For 'Gesänge russischer Kriegsgefangener... Transkription und Übersetzung der Texte von Robert Bleichsteiner':] *See* Lach (R.)

—— Beiträge zur Sprach- und Volkskunde des georgischen Stammes der Gurier. fasc. 7. pp. 87–110; fasc. 9. pp. 64–87. *Leipzig,* 1931. 8⁰.[*Caucasica.* fasc. 7, 9.] **P.P. 3803. eba**

—— Eine georgische Ballade von Amiran. pp. 148–72. *Wien,* 1918. 8⁰. [*Berichte des Forschungsinstituts für Osten und Orient.* Bd. 2.] **Ac. 8817. d**

—— Kaukasische Forschungen .... Erster Teil. Georgische und Mingrelische Texte. pp. clx. 308. *Wien,* 1919. 8⁰. [*Osten und Orient.* Reihe 1. Tl. 1.] *No more published.* **17076. b. 4**

—— [Another copy.] **Ac. 8817. d/2**

——Kaukasische Forschungen im k. u. k. Kriegsgefangenen Lager Eger. pp. 86–103. *Wien,* 1917. 8⁰. [*Berichte des Forschungsinstituts für Osten und Orient.* Bd. 1.] **Ac. 8817. d**

—— Die kaukasischen Sprachproben in Evliya Çelebi's Seyahetname. pp. 84–126. *Leipzig,* 1934. 8⁰. [*Caucasica.* fasc. 11.] **P.P. 3803. eba**

—— Überblick über kaukasische Völker und Sprachen. pp. 66–85. *Wien,* 1918. 8⁰. [*Berichte des Forschungsinstituts für Osten und Orient.* Bd. 2.] **Ac. 8817. d**

BOBOKHIDZE (Kale Piranis-dze). [Edit., with biographical postscript, selections of writings by D. I. Gulia.] *See* Gulia (D. I.)

BOKAREV (Anatoly Alekseevich). Аварское соответствие русскому творительному предикативному падежу. pp. 15–47. *Москва, Ленинград,* 1940. 8⁰. [*Язык и мышление.* вып. 10.] **Ac. 1125. t/2**

—— О классных показателях в аваро-андоцезских языках. pp. 48–63. *Москва, Ленинград,* 1940. 8⁰. [*Язык и мышление.* вып. 10.] **Ac. 1125. t/2**

—— Очерк грамматики чамалинского языка. [An outline of the Chamalal language of Daghestan.] pp. 175. *Москва, Ленинград,* 1949. 8⁰. **12977. c. 14**

—— Синтаксис аварского языка. pp. 277. *Москва, Ленинград,* 1949. 8⁰. **12977. d. 18**

BOKAREV (Evgeny Alekseevich). [Edit. 'Грамматика хиналугского языка'.] *See* Desheriev (Yu. D.)

—— [Edit. 'Лакский язык'.] *See* Zhirkov (L. I.)

—— Гинухский язык. Предварительное сообщение. pp. 193–204. *Москва,* 1952. 8⁰. [*Труды Института Языкознания.* том 1.] **Ac. 1125. sf**

—— Локативные и нелокативные значения местных падежей в дагестанских языках. pp. 56–68. *Москва, Ленинград,* 1948. 8⁰. [*Язык и мышление.* вып. 11.] **Ac. 1125. t/2**

—— Цезские (дидойские) языки Дагестана. pp. 290. *Москва,* 1959. 8⁰. **17076. f. 35**

—— Выражение субъектно-объектных отношений в дагестанских языках. pp. 35–44. *Москва, Ленинград,* 1948. 8⁰. [*Известия Академии Наук СССР. Отделение литературы и языка.* tom. 7. no. 1.] **Ac. 1125/44 (11)**

BONWETSCH (Gottlieb Nathanael). [For 'Die unter Hippolyts Namen überlieferte Schrift Ueber den Glauben', trans. from the Georgian version and edit. by G. N. Bonwetsch:] *See* Hippolytus, *Saint, of Rome.*

—— [Trans. and edit. Georgian version of three writings by St. Hippolytus: 'Der Segen Jakobs', 'Der Segen Moses', 'Die Erzählung von David und Goliath':] *See* Hippolytus, *Saint, of Rome.*

—— [Trans. St. Hippolytus's Commentary on the Song of Solomon, on the basis of the edition of the Georgian text by N. Y. Marr.] *See* Hippolytus, *Saint, of Rome.*

BOPP (FRANZ). [For 'Lettre à M. Bopp, *etc.*':] *See* BROSSET (M.-F.)

BORIN (ACHAS). [Adaptor of epic poem 'Vep'khis tqaosani'.] *See* RUST'AVELI (SHOT'A).

—— Contes orientaux: Daniel; La Peau de Léopard; L'Hospitalité. pp. 174. *Paris*, 1886. 8⁰. *The second of these tales is a prose paraphrase of Shot'a Rust'aveli's epic poem, 'Vep'khis tqaosani'.*

17076. a. 3

BOROZDIN (IL'YA NIKOLAEVICH). В горной Ингушетии. pp. 309–23. *Москва*, 1928. 8⁰. [*Новый Восток.* кн. 20–21.] **Ac. 1096. b/5**

BOTARRO (GUSTAVO DE LA TORRE). [Preface to 'Vep'khistqaosanis mzis metqveleba'.] *See* NOZADZE (V.)

—— [Preface to 'Vep'khistqaosanis sazogadoebat'-metqveleba'.] *See* NOZADZE (V.)

BOTCHORIDZE (GIORGI). The Monument of Juarisa. pp. 50–52. 3 *plates*. *London*, 1936. 8⁰. [*Georgica.* vol. I. nos. 2–3.] **Ac. 8821. e**

BOTCHORISHVILI (LUBA ILIAS-ASULI). ეთნო-გრაფიული ნაწერები. [Et'nograp'iuli nadserebi. Writings on ethnography.] (Статьи по этнографии. Ethnographische Beiträge.) pp. 228. 20 *plates*. 1956. 8⁰. *See* TIFLIS.—*Academy of Sciences of the Georgian S. S. R.—I. A. Javakhishvili Historical Institute.* მასალები საქართველოს ეთნოგრაფიი-სათვის. [Masalebi Sak'art'velos et'nograp'iisat'vis.] tom. 8, *etc.* **17080. d. 22**

—— ქართული კერამიკა, I: კახური. [K'art'uli keramika, I: Kakhuri. Georgian ceramics, I: Kakhet'ian.] (Грузинская керамика, I: Кахетинская.) pp. iv, 257. 64 *plates*. თბილისი [*Tiflis*,] 1949. 8⁰. **17080. d. 12**

BOTSVADZE (NINO IOSEBIS-ASULI) and **BUR-JANADZE** (EKATERINE IOSEBIS-ASULI). დედა ენა. პირველი ნაწილი : ანბანი. [Deda ena. Pirveli nadsili: anbani. Mother tongue. First part: Alphabet. An elementary manual for children, based on the work by I. S. Gogebashvili. Illustrated. Thirteenth edition.] pp. 112. თბილისი [*Tiflis*,] 1956. 8⁰.

17076. i. 12

—— დედა ენა. მეორე ნაწილი : ანბანის შემდეგ საკითხავი წიგნი. [Deda ena. Meore nadsili: anbanis shemdeg sakit'khavi dsigni. Mother tongue. Second part: Reading book for use after the Alphabet. A manual for children, based on the work by I. S. Gogebashvili. Illustrated. Fourteenth edition.] pp. 106. თბილისი [*Tiflis*,] 1957. 8⁰. **17076. i. 12**

BOUDA (KARL). Awarische Texte. [Edit. with German trans. and notes.] pp. 43–66. [*Caucasica.* fasc. 10.] **P.P. 3803. eba**

—— Beiträge zur kaukasischen und sibirischen Sprachwissenschaft. No. 1: Die darginische Schrift-sprache; No. 2: Das kottische Verbum; No. 3: Das Tabassaranische; No. 4: Das Tschuktschische. 3 fasc. *Leipzig*, 1937–1941. 8⁰. [*Abhandlungen für die Kunde des Morgenlandes.* Bd. 22, Hft. 4; Bd. 24, Hft. 1; and Bd. 26, Hft. 1.] **753. f. 30/4**
753. f. 32/1   **753. f. 34/1**

—— Lakkische Studien. pp. 90. *Heidelberg*, 1949. 8⁰. [*Bibliothek der allgemeinen Sprachwissenschaft.* Reihe 3.] **W. P. 1958/1**

—— Subjekt- und Objektkasus beim awarischen Verbum. pp. 41–63. *Leipzig*, 1931. 8⁰. [*Caucasica.* fasc. 9.] **P.P. 3803. eba**

BRAUN (THEODOR ALEKSANDROVICH). [Trans. 'Der japhetitische Kaukasus, *etc.*'] *See* MARR (N. Y.)

BREGADZE (T'AMAR MIKHEILIS-ASULI). [Edit. 'Discourse on the conversion of the Georgians, *etc.*'] *See* EPHRAIM, *Mtsire.*

BRIÈRE (MAURICE). [Edit., with Latin translation, of Old Georgian version of the Gospel of St. Luke.] *See* BIBLE.—New Testament.—*Luke.*

—— [Joint edit. of Old Georgian version of the Gospel of John, with Latin translation.] *See* BIBLE.—New Testament.—*John.*

BRIÈRE *(cont.)*

—— [Joint edit. of 'Hippolyte de Rome. Sur les bénédictions d'Isaac, de Jacob et de Moïse'.] *See* HIPPOLYTUS, *Saint, of Rome.*

—— *See* MARR (N. Y.) and BRIÈRE (M.). La langue géorgienne. 1931. 8⁰.   **2272. g. 26**

—— Lettres géorgiennes chrétiennes. [Being a summary of the book 'Geschichte der kirchlichen georgischen Literatur' by M. T'arkhnishvili and J. Assfalg.] pp. 75–98. *Paris*, 1957. 8⁰. [*Journal Asiatique.* tom. 245.]   **R. Ac. 8808**

BRIK (BORIS). *See* GOL'TSEV (V. V.). Поэты советской Грузии в переводах Бориса Брика, *etc.* 1936. 8⁰.   **11587. a. 4**

—— [Joint trans. of three poems by Titsian Tabidze.] *See* TABIDZE (T. I.)

BRILLIANTOV (ALEKSANDR IVANOVICH). О мѣстѣ кончины и погребенія св. Максима Исповѣдника. pp. 1–62. *Петроградъ*, 1917. 4⁰. [*Христіанскій Востокъ.* томъ 6. вып. 1.]   **Ac. 1125/105**

BROSSET (LAURENT). Bibliographie analytique des ouvrages de Monsieur Marie-Félicité Brosset … 1824–1879. [With a portrait.] pp. lxii. col. 704. *Saint-Pétersbourg*, 1887. 8⁰.   **11904. aa. 26**

BROSSET (MARIE-FÉLICITÉ). [Trans., with introduction, of Georgian treatise on chronology.] *See* ABUSERIDZE, *of Tbet'i.*

—— [*Life.*] *See* BERIDZE (SH.)

—— [Bibliography of works by.] *See* BROSSET (L.)

—— [Edit. Грузинско-русско-французскій словарь'.] *See* CHUBINOV (D. I.)

—— [Edit. and trans. extracts of the Georgian nomocanon.] *See* EUTHYMIUS, *of Mt'a-dsminda, Saint.*

—— [For 'К столѣтію дня рожденія М. И. Броссе':] *See* MARR (N. Y.)

—— [For 'Inscriptions recueillies par M. Dimitri Méghwineth-Khoutzésis-Chwili', trans. with introduction by M.-F. Brosset:] *See* MEGHVINET'-UKHUTSESI (D.)

—— [Trans. 'Le Miriani, ou histoire du roi Miri'.] *See* MIRI, *King of Egypt.*

—— [For 'Première Histoire de Rostévan, roi d'Arabie', being an extract from the poem 'Vep'khistqaosani' by Shot'a Rust'aveli, trans. into French by M.-F. Brosset:] *See* RUST'AVELI (SHOT'A).

—— [Trans., with commentary, of 'Dissertation sur les monnaies géorgiennes'.] *See* T'EIMURAZ GIORGIS-DZE, *Prince of Georgia.*

—— [Edit. and trans. 'Description géographique de la Géorgie'.] *See* VAKHUSHTI, *Prince of Georgia.*

—— À propos du livre intitulé: "Essai de classification des suites monétaires de la Géorgie", par M. Victor Langlois. pp. 153–203. *St.-Pétersbourg*, 1861. 8⁰. [*Mélanges Asiatiques de l'Académie des Sciences.* tom. 4. livr. 2.]   **Ac. 1125/11**

—— Acquisition de livres géorgiens par le Musée asiatique. pp. 26–32. *St.-Pétersbourg*, 1839. 4⁰. [*Bulletin Scientifique de l'Académie des Sciences.* tom. 5.]   **Ac. 1125/6**

—— Activité littéraire des Géorgiens et des Arméniens, en Russie, en Transcaucasie et en Crimée. 4 pt. *St.-Pétersbourg*, 1863–68. 8⁰. [*Mélanges Asiatiques de l'Académie des Sciences.* tom. 4, 5.]   **Ac. 1125/11**

—— Additions au 'Mémoire sur les documens originaux concernant la Géorgie'. [Including reproductions of Georgian royal arms, seals, *etc.*] pp. 168–90. 2 *plates. Paris*, 1832. 8⁰. [*Nouveau Journal Asiatique.* tom. 10.]   **R. Ac. 8808**

—— Analyse du Roman géorgien 'Amiran Daredjaniani'. pp. 7–16. *St.-Pétersbourg*, 1838. 4⁰. [*Bulletin Scientifique de l'Académie des Sciences.* tom. 3.]   **Ac. 1125/6**

BROSSET *(cont.)*

—— Aperçu général de la langue géorgienne. pp. 369–405. *Paris*, 1834. 8⁰. [*Nouveau Journal Asiatique*. tom. 14.]   **R. Ac. 8808**

—— Aperçu général du voyage de M. Brosset dans la Transcaucasie. pp. 169–92. *St.-Pétersbourg*, 1850. 8⁰. [*Mélanges Asiatiques de l'Académie des Sciences*. tom. 1. livr. 2.]   **Ac. 1125/11**

—— Archéographie géorgienne. 2 pt. tom. 3, pp. 378–81; tom. 4, pp. 266–72. *St.-Pétersbourg*, 1838. 4⁰. [*Bulletin Scientifique de l'Académie des Sciences*. tom. 3, 4.]   **Ac. 1125/6**

—— L'Art Libéral, ou Grammaire Géorgienne. pp. xv. 291. 2 *plates*. *Paris*, 1834. 8⁰. *Lithographed*.   **17073. a. 2**

—— Autographie géorgienne. 1⁰. Sentences morales; 2⁰. Almanach lunaire; 3⁰. Sur Mme. Catalani; 4⁰. Lettre de St. Cyrille. *Georg. and Fr.* pp. 32. [*Paris*, 1829.] 8⁰. *Lithographed*.   **17076. c. 1**

—— Chronique géorgienne, *etc. See infra* Tskhovreba Sak'art'veloisa, *etc.* 1829–31. 8⁰.   **17075. e. 10**

—— Copie figurée de quelques cachets géorgiens. pp. 165–69. 1 *plate*. *St.-Pétersbourg*, 1840. 4⁰. [*Bulletin Scientifique de l'Académie des Sciences*. tom. 7.]   **Ac. 1125/6**

—— Correspondance en grec des rois géorgiens du Cakheth avec la Russie, pendant le XVIIe siècle. 2 pt. tom. 9. pp. 349–80; tom. 10. pp. 112–28. 1 *plate*. *St.-Pétersbourg*, 1842. 4⁰. [*Bulletin Scientifique de l'Académie des Sciences*. tom. 9, 10.]   **Ac. 1125/6**

—— De la chronologie technique géorgienne. pp. 41–87. *St.-Pétersbourg*, 1877. 8⁰. [*Mélanges Asiatiques de l'Académie des Sciences*. tom. 8. livr. 1, 2.]   **Ac. 1125/11**

—— De la littérature romanesque géorgienne. pp. 417–42. *St.-Pétersbourg*, 1877. 8⁰. [*Mélanges Asiatiques de l'Académie des Sciences*. tom. 8. livr. 1, 2.]   **Ac. 1125/11**

—— De l'état religieux et politique de la Géorgie jusqu'au XVIIe siècle. pp. 225–56. *St.-Pétersbourg*, 1839. 4⁰. [*Bulletin Scientifique de l'Académie des Sciences*. tom. 5.]   **Ac. 1125/6**

—— Description de quelques antiquités géorgiennes. pp. 153–56. 1 *plate*. *St.-Pétersbourg*, 1842. 4⁰. [*Bulletin Scientifique de l'Académie des Sciences*. tom. 9.]   **Ac. 1125/6**

—— Documens originaux sur les relations diplomatiques de la Géorgie avec la France vers la fin du règne de Louis XIV. 3 pt. pp. 193–221; 339–66; 437–56. 1 *plate*. *Paris*, 1832. 8⁰. [*Nouveau Journal Asiatique*. tom. 9.]   **R. Ac. 8808**

—— Éléments de la langue géorgienne. [Incorporating an unfinished grammar by H. J. von Klaproth.] pp. lvi. 366. *Paris*, 1837. 8⁰.   **825. h. 26**

—— Essai chronologique sur la série des catholicos d'Aphkhazeth. pp. 305–24. *St.-Pétersbourg*, 1844. 4⁰. [*Bulletin Historico-Philologique de l'Académie des Sciences*. tom. 1.]   **Ac. 1125/7**

—— Essai de déchiffrement des inscriptions de l'église de Manglis. pp. 252–60. *St.-Pétersbourg*, 1850. 8⁰. [*Mélanges Asiatiques de l'Académie des Sciences*. tom. 1. livr. 2.]   **Ac. 1125/11**

—— État actuel de la littérature géorgienne. pp. 434–54. *Paris*, 1828. 8⁰. [*Nouveau Journal Asiatique*. tom. 1.]   **R. Ac. 8808**

—— Études de chronologie technique. [Including text, with translation, of three Georgian treatises on the Calendar.] 2 pt. pp. li. 178. *St.-Pétersbourg*, 1868. 4⁰. [*Mémoires de l'Académie Impériale des Sciences*. sér. 7. tom. 11. no. 13, 18.] *No more published*.   **Ac. 1125/3**

—— Études sur les monuments géorgiens photographiés par M. Iermakof. pp. 447–523. *St.-Pétersbourg*, 1872. 8⁰. [*Mélanges Asiatiques de l'Académie des Sciences*. tom. 6. livr. 3, 4.]   **Ac. 1125/11**

—— Examen critique des annales géorgiennes, pour les temps modernes, au moyen des documents

BROSSET *(cont.)*

russes. 4 pt. *St.-Pétersbourg*, 1845–47. 4⁰. [*Bulletin Historico-Philologique de l'Académie des Sciences.* tom. 2, 3.]   **Ac. 1125/7**

—— Explication de diverses inscriptions géorgiennes, arméniennes et grecques. pp. 315–446. II *plates. St.-Pétersbourg*, 1840. 4⁰. [*Mémoires de l'Académie Impériale des Sciences.* sér. 6. Sciences politiques, histoire et philologie. tom. 4.] *The plates are bound, through an error, in tom. 5.*   **Ac. 1125/2**

—— Explication de quelques inscriptions géorgiennes. pp. 372–77. *St.-Pétersbourg*, 1837. 4⁰. [*Bulletin Scientifique de l'Académie des Sciences.* tom. 2.]   **Ac. 1125/6**

—— Explication de quelques inscriptions, photographiées par M. Sévastianof, au mont Athos. pp. 369–91. *St.-Pétersbourg*, 1861. 8⁰. [*Mélanges Asiatiques de l'Académie des Sciences.* tom. 4. livr. 3.]   **Ac. 1125/11**

—— Histoire de la Géorgie depuis l'Antiquité jusqu'au XIXe siècle, traduite du géorgien par M. Brosset. Iʳᵉ partie. Histoire Ancienne, jusqu'en 1469 de J.-C., [with a supplement containing] Additions et Eclaircissements. (IIᵉ partie. Histoire Moderne, livr. 1, 2.) (Introduction et tables des matières.) 5 tom. *St.-Pétersbourg*, 1849–58. 4⁰. *Note: For an edition of the original texts of the Georgian chronicles, published by M.-F. Brosset and D. Chubinov, see infra.*   **17075. e. 1**

—— Histoire des Bagratides géorgiens, d'après les auteurs arméniens et grecs, jusqu'au commencement du XIᵉ siècle. pp. 145–74; 177–208. I *plate. St.-Pétersbourg*, 1844. 4⁰. [*Bulletin Historico-Philologique de l'Académie des Sciences.* tom. I.]   **Ac. 1125/7**

—— Histoire et littérature de la Géorgie. pp. 67–178. *St.-Pétersbourg*, 1838. 4⁰. [*Recueil des Actes de l'Académie Impériale des Sciences*, 1837.] **Ac. 1125/5**

—— Inscriptions et antiquités géorgiennes et autres recueillies par M. le colonel Bartholomaei. pp. 90–116. 3 *plates. St.-Pétersbourg*, 1852. 8⁰.

[*Mélanges Asiatiques de l'Académie des Sciences.* tom. 2. livr. I.]   **Ac. 1125/11**

—— Inscriptions géorgiennes et autres, recueillies par le Père Nersès Sargisian, et expliquées par M. Brosset. pp. 24. 4 *plates. St.-Pétersbourg*, 1864. 4⁰. [*Mémoires de l'Académie Impériale des Sciences.* sér. 7. tom. 8. no. 10.]   **Ac. 1125/3**

—— Inscriptions tumulaires géorgiennes de Moscou et de Saint-Pétersbourg. pp. 461–521. *St.-Pétersbourg*, 1840. 4⁰. [*Mémoires de l'Académie des Sciences.* Sér. 6.—*Sciences Politiques.* tom. 4.]   **Ac. 1125/2**

—— Instruction et itinéraire pour le voyage archéologique de M. Dimitri Méghwineth-Khoutzésof. pp. 155–63. *St.-Pétersbourg*, 1849. 8⁰. [*Mélanges Asiatiques de l'Académie des Sciences.* tom. I. livr. I.]   **Ac. 1125/11**

—— ქართლის ცხოვრება.... ნაწილი პირველი. ძველი მოთხრობა, 1469 წლამდის ქრისტეს აქეთ. [K'art'lis tskhovreba ... Nadsili pirveli. Dzveli mot'khroba, 1469 dslamdis K'ristes aket'.] Histoire de la Géorgie depuis l'antiquité jusqu'au XIXᵉ siècle, publiée en géorgien par M. Brosset. Iʳᵉ Partie. Histoire ancienne, jusqu'en 1469 de J.-C. Iʳᵉ livraison, en partie. Réédition faite par N. Marr. pp. viii. 200. პეტროგრადს [Petrograd,] 1923. 4⁰. *No more published.*   **Ac. 1124/61**

—— ქართული თვით-წერილება. [K'art'uli t'vit'-dserileba.] Autographie géorgienne. 1⁰. Sentences morales; 2⁰. Almanach lunaire; 3⁰. Sur Mme. Catalani; 4⁰. Lettre de St. Cyrille. *Georg. and Fr.* pp. 32, *lith.* [*Paris*, 1829.] 8⁰.   **17076. c. 1**

—— ჯელოვნება აზნაურებითი, გინა ქართულის ენისა თვით მასწავლებელი. [Khelovneba aznaurebit'i, gina k'art'ulis enisa t'vit' masdsavlebeli.] L'Art Libéral, ou Grammaire Géorgienne. pp. xv. 291. 2 *plates. Paris*, 1834. 8⁰. *Lithographed.*   **17073. a. 2**

—— Lettre à M. Bopp sur son Rapport relatif aux recherches philologiques de M. le docteur Rosen. [Concerning the supposed affinities between Georg-

BROSSET *(cont.)*

ian and Sanskrit.] pp. 129–42. *St.-Pétersbourg*, 1845.
4⁰. [*Bulletin Historico-Philologique de l'Académie des
Sciences*. tom. 2.]   **Ac. 1125/7**

—— Lettre au Prince Alexandré Eristhwis-Chwili.
[Describing antiquities of the region of Gori.]. 3 pt.
pp. 55–94; 97–124; 140–48. *St.-Pétersbourg*, 1849. 4⁰.
[*Bulletin Historico-Philologique de l'Académie des
Sciences*. tom. 6.]   **Ac. 1125/7**

—— Lettre .... sur l'emploi des chiffres arabes
dans une inscription géorgienne du XIᵉ siècle. pp.
465–72. *Paris*, 1837. 8⁰. [*Journal Asiatique*. sér. 3.
tom. 3.]   **R. Ac. 8808**

—— Lettres de M. Bartholomaei, relatives aux
antiquités géorgiennes; envoi de M. le colonel
Khodzko; inscriptions d'Akhal-Kalak, par M. Pérévalenko. pp. 264–344. 5 *plates*. *St.-Pétersbourg*, 1854.
8⁰. [*Mélanges Asiatiques de l'Académie des Sciences*.
tom. 2.]   **Ac. 1125/11**

—— Liste des travaux de M. Brosset, † le 22 août/
3 septembre 1880. pp. 19. *St.-Pétersbourg*, 1881. 4⁰.
[*Bulletin de l'Académie des Sciences*. tom. 27.
Supplément.]   **Ac. 1125/44**

—— Matériaux pour l'histoire de Géorgie depuis
le XIIIᵉ siècle. pp. 100–104. *St.-Pétersbourg*, 1839.
4⁰. [*Bulletin Scientifique de l'Académie des Sciences*.
tom. 5.]   **Ac. 1125/6**

—— Matériaux pour servir à l'histoire de la Géorgie depuis l'an 1201 jusqu'en 1755. pp. 165–315.
1 *map*. *St.-Pétersbourg*, 1845. 4⁰. [*Mémoires de
l'Académie des Sciences*. Sér. 6.–*Sciences Politiques*.
tom. 5.]   **Ac. 1125/2**

—— Mémoires inédits, relatifs à l'histoire et à la
langue géorgiennes, *etc. Georg. & Fr.* pp. 222, xi.
[*Paris*,] 1833. 8⁰. *Lithographed*.   **17075. b. 1**

—— Monographie géorgienne de Moscou. 2 pt.
pp. 279–302; 328–36. *St.-Pétersbourg*, 1838. 4⁰.
[*Bulletin Scientifique de l'Académie des Sciences*.
tom. 4.]   **Ac. 1125/6**

—— Note sur le manuscrit géorgien No. 23, de la
Bibliothèque Impériale de Paris. pp. 233–52. *St.-
Pétersbourg*, 1870. 8⁰. [*Mélanges Asiatiques de l'Aca-
démie des Sciences*. tom. 6. livr. 2.]   **Ac. 1125/11**

—— Note sur quelques monnaies géorgiennes du
Musée Asiatique. pp. 381–83. *St.-Pétersbourg*, 1837.
4⁰. [*Bulletin Scientifique de l'Académie des Sciences*.
tom. 2.]   **Ac. 1125/6**

—— Note sur un manuscrit grec des quatre Évangiles, rapporté du Souaneth-Libre. pp. 269–86.
St.-Pétersbourg, 1872. 8⁰. [*Mélanges Asiatiques de
l'Académie des Sciences*. tom. 6. livr. 3, 4.]
                                              Ac. 1125/11

—— Notice concernant les inscriptions géorgiennes
recueillies par le P. Nersès Sargisian. pp. 49–58.
St.-Pétersbourg, 1864. 8⁰. [*Mélanges Asiatiques de
l'Académie des Sciences*. tom. 5. livr. 1.] **Ac. 1125/11**

—— Notice des manuscrits géorgiens envoyés en
France par le prince Théimouraz, *etc.* pp. 155–62.
Paris, 1833. 8⁰. [*Nouveau Journal Asiatique*. tom.
12.]   **R. Ac. 8808**

—— Notice des manuscrits géorgiens récemment
acquis par l'Académie. pp. 305–20. *St.-Pétersbourg*,
1841. 4⁰. [*Bulletin Scientifique de l'Académie des
Sciences*. tom. 8.]   **Ac. 1125/6**

—— Notice détaillée sur les églises de Sawané et
de Manglis. pp. 36–46. 2 *plates*. *St.-Pétersbourg*,
1856. 8⁰. [*Mélanges Asiatiques de l'Académie des
Sciences*. tom. 3.]   **Ac. 1125/11**

—— Notice du Code géorgien, manuscrit de la
Bibliothèque Royale. (Errata pour la notice du
Code géorgien.) pp. 177–201; 384. *Paris*, 1829. 8⁰.
Nouveau Journal Asiatique. tom. 3.]   **R. Ac. 8808**

—— Notice du roman géorgien intitulé Rousoudaniani. pp. 53–62. *St.-Pétersbourg*, 1838. 4⁰. [*Bulletin Scientifique de l'Académie des Sciences*. tom. 4.]
                                              Ac. 1125/6

—— Notice et analyse raisonnée du commencement de la Grammaire géorgienne du patriarche

BROSSET *(cont.)*

Antoni I, intitulé L'art libéral, ou Préceptes grammaticaux. pp. 385–414. *Paris*, 1833. 8⁰. [*Nouveau Journal Asiatique*. tom. 11.]   **R. Ac. 8808**

—— Notice historique sur les trois dernières années du règne de Wakhtang VI et sur son arrivée en Russie. 2 pt. pp. 321–45; 353–76. *St.-Pétersbourg*, 1847. 4⁰. [*Bulletin Historico-Philologique de l'Académie des Sciences*. tom. 3.]   **Ac. 1125/7**

—— Notice sur deux fragments relatifs à l'histoire de la Géorgie, au XIIIme siècle, sous le règne de Thamar. pp. 563–84. *St.-Pétersbourg*, 1852. 8⁰. [*Mélanges Asiatiques de l'Académie des Sciences*. tom. 1. livr. 5.]   **Ac. 1125/11**

—— Notice sur la Bible géorgienne imprimée à Moscou en 1742, *etc*. pp. 42–50. *Paris*, 1828. 8⁰. [*Nouveau Journal Asiatique*. tom. 2.]   **R. Ac. 8808**

—— Notice sur la Langue Géorgienne. pp. 351–64. *Paris*, 1827. 8⁰. [*Journal Asiatique*. tom. 10.]   **R. Ac. 8808**

—— Notice sur le dictionnaire géorgien de Soulkhan Saba Orbéliani, récemment acquis par la Bibliothèque royale de Paris. pp. 171–87. *Paris*, 1834. 8⁰. [*Nouveau Journal Asiatique*. tom. 13.]   **R. Ac. 8808**

—— Notice sur le mari russe de Thamar. pp. 209–29. *St.-Pétersbourg*, 1844. 4⁰. [*Bulletin Historico-Philologique de l'Académie des Sciences*. tom. 1.]   **Ac. 1125/7**

—— Notice sur quelques auteurs géorgiens. 2 pt. pp. 143–64; 232–50. *Paris*, 1834. 8⁰. [*Nouveau Journal Asiatique*. tom. 14.]   **R. Ac. 8808**

—— Notice sur un document géorgien du XVIIe siècle. [Being the marriage contract of Queen Mariam.] pp. 17–35. *St.-Pétersbourg*, 1856. 8⁰. [*Mélanges Asiatiques de l'Académie des Sciences*. tom. 3.]   **Ac. 1125/11**

—— Notice sur un manuscrit géorgien [containing a collection of hymns, treatise on chronology, etc.]

pp. 229–34. *St.-Pétersbourg*, 1844. 4⁰. [*Bulletin Historico-Philologique de l'Académie des Sciences*. tom. 1.]   **Ac. 1125/7**

—— Notice sur un manuscrit géorgien de la Bibliothèque Impériale publique, provenant de M. Tischendorf. pp. 264–80. *St.-Pétersbourg*, 1858. 8⁰. [*Mélanges Asiatiques de l'Académie des Sciences*. tom. 3.]   **Ac. 1125/11**

—— Notice sur un manuscrit géorgien palimpseste, appartenant à M. Sreznevski. pp. 665–75. *St.-Pétersbourg*, 1859. 8⁰. [*Mélanges Asiatiques de l'Académie des Sciences*. tom. 3.]   **Ac. 1125/11**

—— Notice sur une lettre géorgienne, du roi Artchil à Charles XII, 2 février 1706, et sur les divers séjours du roi Artchil en Russie. pp. 211–48. *St.-Pétersbourg*, 1853. 8⁰. [*Mélanges Asiatiques de l'Académie des Sciences*. tom. 2.]   **Ac. 1125/11**

—— Notice sur une médaille de l'an 1790, se rapportant à l'histoire de la Géorgie. pp. 430–434. 1 *plate*. *St.-Pétersbourg*, 1851. 8⁰. [*Mélanges Asiatiques de l'Académie des Sciences*. tom. 1. livr. 4.]   **Ac. 1125/11**

—— Nouvelles recherches sur l'historien Wakhoucht, sur le roi Artchil et sa famille, et sur divers personnages géorgiens enterrés à Moscou. pp. 533–75. *St.-Pétersbourg*, 1859. 8⁰. [*Mélanges Asiatiques de l'Académie des Sciences*. tom. 3.]   **Ac. 1125/11**

—— Pièces diverses relatives à la Géorgie, traduites par M. Brosset. [Comprising description of Prince Vakhushti's map of Georgia; an inscription from the church of Kasara; and fragments of Georgian verse. Georgian texts with French translation.] pp. 305–20. *Paris*, 1830. 8⁰. [*Nouveau Journal Asiatique*. tom. 6.]   **R. Ac. 8808**

—— Projet d'un voyage littéraire à exécuter en Géorgie. pp. 305–16. *St.-Pétersbourg*, 1848. 4⁰. [*Bulletin Historico-Philologique de l'Académie des Sciences*. tom. 4.]   **Ac. 1125/7**

—— Quelques remarques sur un livre intitulé: *Reise durch Russland nach dem kaukasischen Isth-*

BROSSET *(cont.)*

mus, in den Jahren 1836, 1837, 1838, von K. Koch.
pp. 49–80. *St.-Pétersbourg*, 1848. 4⁰. [*Bulletin Historico-Philologique de l'Académie des Sciences.* tom. 4.]
                               Ac. 1125/7

—— Rapport à S. E. le Prince Vorontzof, sur les chartes géorgiennes. 3 pt. pp. 234–54; 257–64; 273–88. *St.-Pétersbourg*, 1848. 4⁰. [*Bulletin Historico-Philologique de l'Académie des Sciences.* tom. 5.]
                               Ac. 1125/7

—— Rapport à Son Excellence M. le Comte Ouvarof, Ministre de l'Instruction Publique. pp. 369–78. *St.-Pétersbourg*, 1848. 4⁰. [*Bulletin Historico-Philologique de l'Académie des Sciences.* tom. 4.]
                               Ac. 1125/7

—— Rapport à S. E. M. le Ministre, Président de l'Académie, sur ses recherches dans les archives de Moscou. pp. 145–60. *St.-Pétersbourg*, 1845. 4⁰. [*Bulletin Historico-Philologique de l'Académie des Sciences.* tom. 2.]
                               Ac. 1125/7

—— Rapport général sur les résultats d'un voyage littéraire en Géorgie. pp. 48–86. *Paris*, 1850. 8⁰. [*Journal Asiatique.* sér. 4. tom. 15.]   **R. Ac. 8808**

—— Rapport sur différents documents géorgiens envoyés à l'Académie par Mgr. Eugène, Exarque de Géorgie. pp. 347–49. *St.-Pétersbourg*, 1844. 4⁰. [*Bulletin Historico-Philologique de l'Académie des Sciences.* tom. 1.]
                               Ac. 1125/7

—— Rapport sur la publication de la Géographie de la Géorgie par Wakhoucht. pp. 141–60. *St.-Pétersbourg*, 1840. 4⁰. [*Bulletin Scientifique de l'Académie des Sciences.* tom. 6.]
                               Ac. 1125/6

—— Rapport sur le dictionnaire manuscrit géorgien-russe-latin de M. D. Tchoubinof. pp. 41–48. *St.-Pétersbourg*, 1838. 4⁰. [*Bulletin Scientifique de l'Académie des Sciences.* tom. 3.]   **Ac. 1125/6**

—— Rapport sur le voyage de M. Dimitri Méghwineth-Khoutzésis-Chwili. pp. 28–69. *St.-Pétersbourg*, 1849. 8⁰. [*Mélanges Asiatiques de l'Académie des Sciences.* tom. 1. livr. 1.]   **Ac. 1125/11**

—— Rapport sur les recherches archéologiques faites par M. Bakradzé dans le Gouria, en 1873. pp. 167–72. *St.-Pétersbourg*, 1874. 8⁰. [*Mélanges Asiatiques de l'Académie des Sciences.* tom. 7. livr. 2, 3.]   **Ac. 1125/11**

—— Rapport sur les voyages exécutés sous les auspices du prince Vorontsov, par M. Dimitri Méghwineth-Khoutsésov. pp. 69–89. *St.-Pétersbourg*, 1852. 8⁰. [*Mélanges Asiatiques de l'Académie des Sciences.* tom. 2. livr. 1.]   **Ac. 1125/11**

—— Rapport sur l'ouvrage manuscrit de M. Bakradzé, contenant l'exposé des recherches archéologiques faites par l'auteur, dans l'Adchara et dans le Gouria, en 1873. pp. 1–20. *St.-Pétersbourg*, 1877. 8⁰. [*Mélanges Asiatiques de l'Académie des Sciences.* tom. 8. livr. 1, 2.]   **Ac. 1125/11**

—— Rapport sur un recueil de documents historiques publié par la Commission archéographique du Caucase. pp. 651–67. *St.-Pétersbourg*, 1868. 8⁰. [*Mélanges Asiatiques de l'Académie des Sciences.* tom. 5. livr. 6.]   **Ac. 1125/11**

—— Rapports sur un voyage archéologique dans la Géorgie et dans l'Arménie, exécuté en 1847–1848 … Avec un atlas, *etc.* 6 livr. *St.-Pétersbourg*, 1851 [1849–51]. 8⁰ & *obl.* fol.   **1294. f. 2, 3**

—— Recherches sur la poésie géorgienne; notice de deux manuscrits et extraits du roman de Tariel. 3 pt. tom. 5. pp. 257–84; tom. 6. pp. 373–94; tom. 7. pp. 321–72. *Paris*, 1830–31. 8⁰. [*Nouveau Journal Asiatique.* tom. 5–7.]   **R. Ac. 8808**

—— Registre des cartes géorgiennes manuscrites, acquises par le Musée Asiatique. pp. 317–20. *St.-Pétersbourg*, 1838. 4⁰. [*Bulletin Scientifique de l'Académie des Sciences.* tom. 3.]   **Ac. 1125/6**

—— Réponse à M. de Bartholomaei [relating to questions of Georgian numismatics]. pp. 340–45. *St.-Pétersbourg*, 1848. 4⁰. [*Bulletin Historico-Philologique de l'Académie des Sciences.* tom. 4.]
                               Ac. 1125/7

—— Revue des antiquités géorgiennes. pp. 35–48

BROSSET *(cont.)*

St.-Pétersbourg, 1839. 4⁰. [*Bulletin Scientifique de l'Académie des Sciences*. tom. 5.]   **Ac. 1125/6**

—— Second rapport, adressé à la Conférence de l'Académie Impériale des Sciences. pp. 4–8. *St.-Pétersbourg*, 1848. 4⁰, [*Bulletin Historico-Philologique de l'Académie des Sciences*. tom. 5.]   **Ac. 1125/7**

—— Sur la langue géorgienne. pp. 321–44. *Paris*, 1827. 8⁰. [*Journal Asiatique*. tom. 11.]   **R. Ac. 8808**

—— Sur un projet d'étude des chartes géorgiennes. pp. 545–57. *St.-Pétersbourg*, 1879. 8⁰. [*Mélanges Asiatiques de l'Académie des Sciences*. tom. 8. livr. 3, 4.]   **Ac. 1125/11**

—— Sur une inscription géorgienne de l'église patriarchale de Mtzkhétha. pp. 251–67. *St.-Pétersbourg*, 1877. 8⁰. [*Mélanges Asiatiques de l'Académie des Sciences*. tom. 8. livr. 1, 2.]   **Ac. 1125/11**

—— Troisième rapport, adressé à Son Excellence le Prince-Lieutenant du Caucase. 2 pt. pp. 8–16; 21–30. *St.-Pétersbourg*, 1848. 4⁰. [*Bulletin Historico-Philologique de l'Académie des Sciences*. tom. 5.]   **Ac. 1125/7**

—— ᲚᲘᲤᲔ ᲝᲤ ᲒᲔᲝᲠᲒᲘᲐ [Tskhovreba Sak'art'veloisa. The life of Georgia.] Chronique géorgienne, traduite par M. Brosset Jeune. [An anonymous chronicle, relating to the history of Georgia during the sixteenth and seventeenth centuries. French trans. by Brosset, accompanied by essays on Georgian chronology, palaeography, *etc.*, and followed by lithographed Georgian text.] 2 pt. *Paris*, 1829–31. 8⁰.   **17075. e. 10**

—— [Another copy.]   **14003. b. 1**

—— [Another copy.]   **15007. h. 14**

—— [Another copy.] *Dept. of Oriental Printed Books & MSS. Reference Library.*

—— Variétés géorgiennes: 1) Calendriers lunaires; 2) Sur une плащаница géorgienne, du XVIᵉ s.; 3) Tombeau et épitaphe du roi Solomon II, d'Imé-reth, à Trébisonde. pp. 721–41. *St.-Pétersbourg*, 1868. 8⁰. [*Mélanges Asiatiques de l'Académie des Sciences*. tom. 5. livr. 6.]   **Ac. 1125/11**

—— and **CHUBINOV** (DAVID IESSEEVICH). ქართლის ცხოვრება. [K'art'lis tskhovreba. The Life of Georgia.] Histoire de la Géorgie depuis l'Antiquité jusqu'au XIXᵉ siècle. Iʳᵉ Partie.-Histoire ancienne, jusqu'en 1469 de J.-C., publiée an géorgien par M. Brosset. (IIᵐᵉ Partie.-Histoire moderne, depuis 1469, jusqu'en 1800 de J.-C. publiée en géorgien par M. Tchoubinof.) 2 tom სანკტპეტერბურგს [*St. Petersburg*,] 1849–1854 4⁰. *Note: For a French translation of the Georgian chronicles, by M.-F. Brosset, see supra.*   **17075. e. 1**

BRUSSELS.—*Société des Bollandistes. Analecta Bollandiana.* [Edited by C. de Smedt and others.] *Paris; Bruxelles* [printed], 1882—. 8⁰. *In progress.*

2002. e — 2003. a

—— Indices in tomos I–XX [*etc.*] 1882–1901 [*etc.*] *Bruxelles*, 1904—. 8⁰. *In progress.*

2002. e — 2003. a

BUDDHA. [For the history of the early life of Buddha, as contained in the Georgian version of the legend of Barlaam and Josaphat:] *See* BARLAAM, *Saint, of India.*

BUKHNIKASHVILI (GRIGOL VARDENIS-DZE). Грузинский театр за сто лет. Краткий обзор. pp. 101. *Тбилиси*, 1950. 8⁰.   **11798. a. 40**

BURJANADZE (EKATERINE IOSEBIS-ASULI). [Joint author of new version of 'Deda ena'.] *See* BOTSVADZE (N. I.) and BURJANADZE (E. I.).

BURJANADZE (SHOT'A VIK'TORIS-DZE). ისტორიული დოკუმენტები იმერეთის სამეფოსა და გურია-ოდიშის სამთავროებისა, 1466–1770 წწ. [Istoriuli dokumentebi Imeret'is samep'osa da Guria-Odishis samt'avroebisa, 1466–1770 dsds. Historical documents on the kingdom of Imeret'i and the principalities of Guria and Mingrelia, 1466–1770. Edited by Sh. V. Burjanadze.] bk. 1, *etc.* თბილისი [*Tiflis*,] 1958—. 8⁰. *In progress.*

17075. ee. 10

BYELINSKY (Vissarion Grigor'evich). რჩეული თხზულებანი. [Rcheuli t'khzulebani. Selected works. Trans. by V. K. Mgaloblishvili and others, and edit. with an introduction by G. Jibladze. With plates.] 2 tom. თბილისი [*Tiflis,*] 1952–57. 8⁰.

17076. d. 7

BYKHOVSKAYA (Sofiya L'vovna). Имена существительные в даргинском литературном языке. pp. 64—101. *Москва, Ленинград,* 1940. 8⁰. [*Язык и мышление.* вып. 10.]

Ac. 1125. t/2

—— Пережитки inclusiv'а и exclusiv'а в даргинских диалектах. pp. 85—90. *Москва, Ленинград,* 1940. 8⁰. [*Язык и мышление.* вып. 9.]　　**Ac. 1125. t/2**

CALLISTHENES, *pseud.* [For 'Грузинская повѣсть объ Александрѣ Македонскомъ и сербская Александрія':] *See* Khakhanov (A. S.)

CAMBRIDGE.—*University Library.* [For Catalogue of the Georgian manuscripts in the Cambridge University Library, compiled by R. P. Blake:] *See* Blake (R. P.)

CAMBRIDGE, Mass.—*Harvard University.* The Harvard Theological Review. vol. 1— *New York, Cambridge, Mass.,* 1908, *etc.* 8⁰.　　**R. Ac. 2692/13**

CATECHISM. [Georgian version.] *See* Robert [Bellarmino] *Saint*; Tlukaant'ı (D.)

CATHARINE, *Saint, of Alexandria.*—Convent of, on Mount Sinai. [For 'Изображеніе грузинскаго царя Давида Строителя на иконѣ Синайскаго монастыря':] *See* Beneshevich (V. N.)

—— [For 'Greek script and Georgian scribes on Mt. Sinai':] *See* Blake (R. P.)

—— [For 'Le calendrier palestino-géorgien du Sinaiticus 34':] *See* Liturgies.—Greek Rite.—*Calendar.*

—— [For 'Памятники грузинской старины .... на Синаѣ':] *See* Tsagareli (A. A.)

—— Catalogue des manuscrits géorgiens littéraires du Mont Sinaï, par Gérard Garitte. pp. xiii. 322.

Louvain, 1956. 8⁰. [*Corpus Scriptorum Christianorum Orientalium.* vol. 165 = Subsidia. tom. 9.]

14005. a

—— Описаніе грузинскихъ рукописей синайскаго монастыря. [Description of the Georgian Mss. of the Sinai Monastery. By N. Y. Marr. Edited and published posthumously by I. B. Megrelidze. Includes extracts from the Mss.] pp. xii. 276. 25 *plates. Москва, Ленинград,* 1940. 8⁰. *Contains description of one portion of the Mss. only. The other Mss. were catalogued separately by I. A. Javakhishvili.*

11916. k. 16

CAUCASUS. [For 'Матеріалы по исторіи Грузіи и Кавказа':] *See* Tiflis.—*Academy of Sciences of the U. S. S. R., Georgian Filial.*

CHABOT (Jean-Baptiste). Corpus Scriptorum Christianorum Orientalium. Curantibus I.-B. Chabot, *etc.* 1903, *etc.* 8⁰. *See* Louvain.—*Academia Lovaniensis.*　　**14005. a**

CHACHIBAIA (Archil). [Joint compiler of chrestomathy of 19th century Georgian literature.] *See* Kiknadze (G.) and Chachibaia (A.)

CHACHKHALIA (Kirshal). Сердце говорит. [Poems, translated from the Abkhazian by various hands.] pp. 115. *Москва,* 1959. 12⁰.　**17075. c. 39**

CHAKHRUKHADZE. [For 'Древнегрузинскіе одописцы', including Chakhrukhadze's eulogy of Queen T'amar':] *See* Marr (N. Y.)

CHAMALAL LANGUAGE. [For a grammar of the Chamalal language of Daghestan:] *See* Bokarev (A. A.)

CHARAYA (Petre Giorgis-dze). მეგრული დიალექტის ნათესაობრივი დამოკიდებულება ქართულთან. [Megruli dialek'tis nat'esaobrivi damokidebuleba k'art'ult'an. The generic dependence of the Mingrelian dialect on Georgian.] 4 pt. ტფილისი [*Tiflis,*] 1895–96. 8⁰. [*Moambe.* tom. 2. no. 10, 12; tom. 3. no. 1, 2.]　　**17089. b. 1**

—— Объ отношеніи абхазскаго языка къ яфетическимъ. [Edit. and revised by N. Y. Marr.] pp. viii.

82. *С.-Петербургъ*, 1912. 8⁰. [*Матеріалы по яфе-тическому языкознанію*. no. 4.]   **17073. a. 3**

CHARLES XII, *King of Sweden*. [For 'Notice sur une lettre géorgienne, du roi Artchil à Charles XII, etc.':] *See* Brosset (M.-F.)

CHAUDOIR (Stanislas de) *Baron*. Aperçu sur les monnaies russes, et sur les monnaies étrangères, qui ont eu cours en Russie, depuis les temps les plus reculés jusqu'à nos jours. [Containing a description of Georgian coinage struck under Russian suzerainty. With plates.] 3 pt. *St.-Pétersbourg*, 1836–37. 8⁰.   **603. g. 26**

CHAVCHAVADZE. [For the surname of this form:] *See* Tchavtchavadze.

CHECHEN LANGUAGE. [For 'Чеченскій букварь':] *See* Bartholomaei (I. A.)

—— [For 'Поэзия Чечено-Ингушетии':] *See* Mamakaev (M.) *and others.*

—— [For 'Говорит Селим. Сказание о Чечне':] *See* Muzaev (N.)

—— [For 'Tschetschenzische Studien':] *See* Schiefner (F. A. von).

—— [For 'Tschetschenzisches und Awarisches':] *See* Uslar (P. K.) *Baron.*

CHEISHVILI (Aleksandr Nikolaevich). *See* Tcheishvili (A. N.)

CHELIDZE (Vakhtang). *See* Tchelidze (V.)

CHĒQONIA (Ilia Mirianis-dze). *See* Tchqonia (I. M.)

CHERKESI (Eca). *See* Cherkezi.

CHERKESSK.—*Adygeisky Nauchno-Issledovatel'-sky Institut Kul'turnogo Stroitel'stva. See* Yakovlev (N. F.) and Ashkhamaf (D. A.). Грамматика адыгейского литературного языка. 1941. 8⁰.   **12977. d. 5**

—— *Cherkessky Nauchno-Issledovatel'sky Institut.* Русско-абазинский словарь. [Russian-Abaza Dictionary. Compiled by S. Kh. Gonov and others, and edit. by Kh. D. Zhirov and N. B. Ekba. With a study of the Abaza language by G. P. Serdyuchenko.] (Урышв-Абаза словарь.) pp. 646. *Москва*, 1956. 8⁰.   **17076. h. 3**

CHERKEZI (Eca). Georgian-English Dictionary. pp. i. 275. *Oxford* [*Hertford* printed,] 1950. 8⁰. [*Printed for the Trustees of the Marjory Wardrop Fund.*]   **15007. h. 12**

CHERK'EZISHVILI (Ekaterine). *See* Cherkezi (E.)

CHERNY (Boris Konstantinovich). [For 'Великий Моурави. Стихи и комментарии Б. К. Черного':] *See* Antonovskaya (A. A.)

CHERNYAVSKY (Kollau). [Joint trans. of three poems by Titsian Tabidze.] *See* Tabidze (T. I.)

—— [Contributor to symposium 'Niko P'irosmanishvili'.] *See* Tabidze (T. I.) *and others.*

CHIK'OBAVA (Arnold Step'anes-dze). [Edit. 'Ashkharuli dialek'ti'.] *See* Lomt'at'idze (K'. V.)

—— ენათმეცნიერების შესავალი. [Enat'metsnierebis shesavali. Introduction to linguistics.] (Введение в языкознание.) pp. xvi. 401. თბილისი [*Tiflis*,] 1952. 8⁰.   **17076. f. 9**

—— Историческое взаимоотношение номинативной и эргативной конструкций по данным древне-грузинского языка. pp. 221–34. *Москва, Ленинград*, 1948. 8⁰. [*Известия Академии Наук СССР. Отделение литературы и языка.* том 7. no. 3.]   **Ac. 1125/44. (11.)**

—— О лингвистических чертах картвельских языков. pp. 25–33. *Москва, Ленинград*, 1948. 8⁰. [*Известия Академии Наук СССР. Отделение литературы и языка.* том 7. no. 1.]   **Ac. 1125/44. (11.)**

—— სახელის ფუძის უძველესი აგებულება ქართველურ ენებში. [Sakhelis p'udzis udzvelesi

CHIK'OBAVA *(cont.)*
agebuleba k'art'velur enebshi. The oldest structure of noun bases in K'art'velian languages. Georgian text, with summaries in Russian and English.] pp. xxxvi. 343. თბილისი [*Tiflis*,] 1942. 8⁰.

                           17076. f. 2

—— ჭანური ტექსტები. [Tchanuri tek'stebi. Laz texts.] pt. 1. pp. x. 168. ტფილისი [*Tiflis*,] 1929. 8⁰.   **17076. f. 5**

—— ჭანურ-მეგრულ-ქართული შედარებითი ლექსიკონი. [Tchanur-megrul-k'art'uli shedarebit'i lek'sikoni. Edit. by S. N. Janashia.] (Dictionnaire comparé tchane-mégrélien-géorgien.) pp. xix. 509. ტფილისი [*Tiflis*,] 1938. 8⁰.   **17076. f. 1**

—— *and others.* ქართული ენის განმარტებითი ლექსიკონი.[K'art'uli enis ganmartebit'i lek'sikoni. Explanatory dictionary of the Georgian language, the definitions being given in Georgian.] Толковый словарь грузинского языка. [Compiled by a committee of Georgian scholars, under the general editorship of A. S. Chik'obava.] tom. 1–6, *etc.* თბილისი [*Tiflis*], 1950—. 4⁰. *In progress.* **17076. i. 1**

CHIK'OBAVA (Benedik'te Ek'vt'imes-dze). [Edit. poetic works of Galaktion Tabidze.] *See* Tabidze (G. B.)

CHIK'OVANI (Mikheil Iasonis-dze). Грузинские народные сказки. Сто сказок. Перевод Н. К. Долидзе. Под редакцией ... М. Я. Чиковани. [With illustrations by S. S. K'obuladze.] pp. 430. *Тбилиси*, 1954. 8⁰.   **12589. t. 53**

—— ქართული ეპოსი. [K'art'uli eposi. The Georgian epic.] (Грузинский эпос.) bk. 1. [Containing 'მიჯაჭვული ამირანი', 'Mijatchvuli Amirani', a study of the Amiran legend. With a map.] თბილისი [*Tiflis*,] 1959, *etc.* 8⁰. *In progress.* **17076. b. 49**

CHIK'OVANI (Simon Ivanes-dze). [Joint edit. of 'Тамарджвеба'.] *See* Abasheli (A. B.) *and others.*

—— [Joint edit. of 'Поэзия Грузии'.] *See* Gol'tsev (V. V.) and Chik'ovani (S. I.)

—— [Joint edit. of selected writings of Pushkin.] *See* Pushkin (A. S.)

—— [Edit. of works of A. M. Qazbegi.] *See* Qazbegi (A. M.)

—— [Joint edit. of selected works of Akaki Tseret'eli in Russian translation.] *See* Tseret'eli (A. R.) *Prince.*

—— [Edit. poems by Vazha-P'shavela in Russian trans.] *See* Vazha-P'shavela, *pseud.*

—— [Joint edit. of poems by Vazha-P'shavela in Russian trans.] *See* Vazha-P'shavela, *pseud.*

—— Избранное. Перевод с грузинского. [Poems, trans. by various hands.] pp. 223. *Тбилиси*, 1950. 8⁰.   **11588. bb. 57**

—— Новые стихи. [Trans. by various hands.] pp. 142. *Тбилиси*, 1954. 8⁰.   **11588. i. 63**

—— Песнь о Давиде Гурамишвили. [A poem based on the life of the poet Davit' Guramishvili. Trans. into Russian by V. Derzhavin, and edit. with a preface by V. V. Gol'tsev.] pp. 88, 4. *Советский Писатель*: [*Leningrad* printed,] 1946. 12⁰.   **17075. d. 28**

—— Тбилиси в поэзии. [An anthology of poems and verses about Tiflis by Georgian, Russian and other authors, translated into Russian by various hands, and edited by S. I. Chik'ovani.] pp. 436. *Тбилиси*, 1958. 8⁰.   **17075. d. 45**

CHITAIA (Giorgi Spiridonis-dze). [Joint author of 'K'art'uli khalkhuri ornamenti'.] *See* Bardavelidze (V. V.) and Chitaia (G. S.)

—— [Edit. Dictionary of Georgian figurative and metaphorical expressions.] *See* Sakhokia (T'. T.)

CHKHAIDZE (Mikheil Pavles-dze). Кахетинские революционные песни. [With trans., introduction and notes in Russian.] pp. 112–21. *Москва, Ленинград*, 1939. 8⁰. [*Советский фольклор.* no. 6.]   **Ac. 1125. nba**

CHKHEIDZE (BORIS). მოთხრობები. [Mot'khrobebi. Short stories.] pp. 214, 2. თბილისი [*Tiflis,*] 1954. 8⁰.   **17076. b. 22**

CHKHEIDZE (NATA). [Trans. works of D. S. Kldiashvili.] *See* KLDIASHVILI (D. S.)

—— [Trans. 'Грузинские новеллы'.] *See* KLDIASHVILI (S. D.)

—— [Trans. novel 'Ketskhoveli'.] *See* LISASHVILI (I.)

CHKHEIDZE (SEKHNIA). [For a French trans. of the chronicle of Sekhnia Chkheidze, incorporated in 'Histoire de la Géorgie':] *See* BROSSET (M.-F.)

—— [For chronicle of, incorporated as a continuation to 'K'art'lis tskhovreba':] *See* BROSSET (M.-F.) and CHUBINOV (D. I.)

CHKHENKELI (AKAKI). *See* ANCHIN, *pseud.*

CHKHENKELI (KITA). Einführung in die georgische Sprache. Band 1. Theoretischer Teil. (Band 2. Praktischer Teil.) 2 Bd. *Zürich,* 1958. 8⁰.   **17076. h. 14**

—— [Another copy.]   **12900. c. 17**

CHKHETIA (SHALVA QARAMANIS-DZE). Тбилиси в XIX столетии, 1865—69. (Ответств. редактор Н. Бердзенишвили.) pp. iv. 520. 13 plates. *Тбилиси,* 1942. 8⁰.   **Ac. 1128. db/3**

—— ტფილისის ისტორიისათვის. [Tp'ilisis istoriisat'vis. Contribution to the history of Tiflis, with reference to the state of the city in 1865, with an introduction covering earlier periods.] (К истории Тбилиси.) pp. 221. 1 *map.* ტფილისი [*Tiflis,*] 1938. 8⁰. [*Masalebi Sak'art'velos da Kavkasiis istoriisat'vis.* fasc. I.]   **17075. e. 12**

CHKHIKVADZE (GRIGOL ZAK'ARIAS-DZE). [Edit. 'K'art'uli khalkhuri simgheris ostatebi'.] *See* GEGETCHKORI (L.)

—— Гурийские революционные песни. Из записей экспедиции 1933 г. [With musical notations, and Russian translation.] pp. 93–100. *Москва, Ленинград,* 1936. 8⁰. [*Советский фольклор.* no.2–3.] **Ac. 1125. nba**

—— *and others.* Грузинская музыкальная культура. Сборник статей. (ქართული მუსიკალური კულტურა. წერილების კრებული. [K'art'uli musikaluri kultura. Dserilebis krebuli. Georgian musical culture. A collection of articles by various hands, edited by A. Balanchivadze and others. With musical illustrations in the text.]) pp. 444, 2. *Москва,* 1957. 4⁰.   **17080. b. 9**

CHKHIKVISHVILI (IVANE DIMITRIS-DZE). საქართველოს ხერხემლიანთა ნომენკლატურა. [Sak'art'velos kherkhemliant'a nomenklatura. Nomenclature of Georgian vertebrate animals. With glossary in Georgian, Russian and Latin.] Nomenclature des animaux vertébrés de Géorgie. pp. iv. 80. ტფილისი [*Tiflis,*] 1926. 8⁰. [*Sak'art'velos Muzeumis shromebi.* no. 5.]   **17080. b. 1**

CHKONIYA (IL'YA). *See* TCHQONIA (I. M.)

CHOLAQASHVILI (DAVIT') *Prince.* [Trans. tragedy 'Iphigénie' by Racine.] *See* TSAGARELI (A. A.). Свѣдѣнія о памятникахъ грузинской письменности. вып. 3. 1894. 8⁰.   **7708. d. 3**

CHOLAQASHVILI (NICEPHORUS). *See* IRBAK'I-CHOLAQASHVILI (N.)

CHOTA ROUSTAVÉLI. *See* RUST'AVELI (SHOT'A).

CHQONIA. [For this surname:] *See* TCHQONIA.

CHRISTIAN DOCTRINE. [For 'Dottrina Christiana breve, *etc.*':] *See* ROBERT [Bellarmino] *Saint, Cardinal, Archbishop of Capua.*

—— [For 'Dottrina Cristiana per uso delle missioni della Giorgia':] *See* TLUKAANT'I (D.)

CHUBINASHVILI (DAVIT'). *See* CHUBINOV (D. I.)

CHUBINASHVILI (GIORGI NIKOLOZIS-DZE). [Edit. 'Мцхета. Итоги археологических исследований'.] *See* AP'AK'IDZE (A. M.) *and others.*

CHUBINASHVILI *(cont.)*

—— [Edit. Грузинская художественная керамика XI–XII вв.'] *See* MAISURADZE (Z. P.)

—— [Edit. 'Kʻartʻul khelnadsertʻa mortulobis nimushebi'.] *See* SCHMERLING (R. O.)

—— [Joint author of 'Кумурдо и Никорцминда'.] *See* SEVEROV (N. P.) and CHUBINASHVILI (G. N.)

—— [For a volume of essays on Georgian art and archaeology in honour of the 70th birthday of G. N. Chubinashvili:] *See* TIFLIS.—*Academy of Sciences of the Georgian S. S. R.—Institute of the History of Georgian Art.* ქართული ხელოვნება. [Kʻartʻuli khelovneba.] (Ars Georgica.) tom. 4. 1955. 4⁰.　　**17080. g. 1**

—— Архитектура Кахетии. Исследование развития архитектуры в восточной провинции Грузии в IV–XVIII вв. (კახეთის ხუროთმოძღვრება. [Kakhetʻis khurotʻmodzghvreba.]) [Tom. 1 comprising Russian text, with numerous illustrations, sketches, diagrams and plans; tom. 2 containing 473 plates.] 2 tom. *Тбилиси*, 1956–59. 4⁰.　　**17080. g. 11**

—— ქართული ოქრომჭედლობა VIII–XVIII საუკუნეებისა. ალბომი, ისტორიული მიმოხილვა და ანოტაციები. [Kʻartʻuli okʻromtchedloba VIII–XVIII saukuneebisa. Albomi, istoriuli mimokhilva da anotatsiebi. Georgian gold repoussé work of the 8th to 18th centuries. An album with historical survey and notes. With five brochures, containing explanatory text in Georgian, Russian, English, French andGerman.] (Грузинское чеканное искусство с VIII по XVIII век.) pp. 28. 20. 20. 20. 20. 200 *plates.* თბილისი [*Tiflis*,] 1957. fol.　　**14999. h. 9**

—— [Another copy.]　　**1899. a. 10**

—— Памятники типа Джвари. Исследования по истории грузинского искусства. (Monuments architectoniques du type de Djouari. Recherches historiques sur l'histoire de l'art géorgien.—Résumé.) [With illustrations.] 2 vol. pp. xxiv. 217. VII. 85 *plates. Тбилиси*, 1948. 4⁰ & fol.　　**07705. t. 3**

—— Пещерные монастыри Давид-Гареджи. Очерк по истории искусства Грузии. Иллюстрации по акварелям и рисункам... Е. Е. Лансере, *etc.* pp. xv. 117. 130 *plates. Тбилиси*, 1948. fol.　　**07708. p. 5**

—— Саорбисская церковь. pp. 180—90. 7 *plates. Петроградъ*, 1915. 4⁰. [*Христіанскій Востокъ.* томъ 4. вып. 2.]　　**Ac. 1125/105**

—— Церковь близъ селенія Болнис-Капанакчи. pp. 217—20. 2 *plates. Петроградъ*, 1917. 4⁰. [*Христіанскій Востокъ.* томъ 5. вып. 3.]　　**Ac. 1125/105**

CHUBINASHVILI (NIKOLOZ). Грузинская средневековая художественная резьба по дереву, перелома X–XI вв. (შუასაუკუნეთა ქართული ხის ჩუქურთმა, X–XI საუკუნეები. [Shuasaukunetʻa kʻartʻuli khis chukʻurtʻma, X–XI saukuneebi. Mediaeval Georgian wood-carving of the 10th–11th centuries.]) pp. 119. 99 *plates. Тбилиси*, 1958. 4⁰.　　**17080. g. 5**

—— [Another copy.]　　**L. R. 403. e. 28**

CHUBINIDZE (VALIKO). მოგონება. [Mogoneba.] Mémoires. [Illustrated.] bk. 2. pp. ii. 447. პარიზი [*Paris*,] 1953. 8⁰.　　**17075. b. 5**

CHUBINISHVILI (TARIEL NIKOLOZIS-DZE). მცხეთის უძველესი არქეოლოგიური ძეგლები. [Mtskhetʻis udzvelesi arkʻeologiuri dzeglebi. The most ancient archaeological monuments of Mtskhetʻa. Edit. by N. A. Berdzenishvili. Illustrated.] (Древнейшие археологические памятники Мцхета.) pp. 143. 19 *plates.* თბილისი [*Tiflis*,] 1957. 4⁰.　　**17080. b. 11**

CHUBINOV (DAVID IESSEEVICH). [For 'Rapport sur le dictionnaire ... de M. D. Tchoubinof':] *See* BROSSET (M.-F.)

—— [Joint edit. of 'Kʻartʻlis tskhovreba'.] *See* BROSSET (M.-F.) and CHUBINOV (D. I.)

—— [For a supplement to Chubinov's Georgian lexicons:] *See* TCHQONIA (I. M.)

—— Грузинская грамматика, вновь составленная Д. Ч. (Грузино-русскій словарь, вновь составленный

CHUBINOV *(cont.)*
Д. Ч.) pp. xl. vi. coll. 1780. *Санктпетербургъ*, 1887
[1887–90]. 4⁰.   **2059. b**

—— ქართულ-რუსულ-ფრანცუზული ლექსიკონი.
[K'art'ul-rusul-frantsitsuli lek'sikoni.] .... Грузинско-русско-французскій словарь .... Dictionnaire
géorgien-russe-français. [Edit., with a preface, by
M.-F. Brosset.] pp. xvi. 734,2. 6 *tables*. *въ Санкт-
петербургѣ*, 1840. 4⁰. *Imperfect; wanting table 3.*
              2059. b

—— ქართული კრისტომათია. [K'art'uli k'ristomatia. Chrestomathy of Georgian literature. Pt. 1:
Prose, from Bible, historical chronicles and charters, romances, etc.; pt. 2: Verse, epic, lyric, drama,
proverbs.] 2 pt. pp. 236, 180. სანკტ-პეტერბურგს
[*St.Petersburg*,] 1863. 8⁰.   **17075. c. 1**

—— Краткая грузинская грамматика. pp. 76. *Санктпетербургъ*, 1855. 8⁰.   **12907. e. 26. (3.)**

—— Русско-грузинскій словарь, *etc.* 2 част. pp. ii.
xxiv. 1187. *Санктпетербургъ*, 1846. 4⁰. *The first
seven leaves of част. 1 are mutilated.*   **12976. t. 9**

—— Русско-грузинскій словарь. [A revised and ex-
panded version of Chubinov's Russo-Georgian
dictionary, first pubd. in 1846.] pp. xii. coll. 815.
Санктпетербургъ, 1886. 4⁰.   **12976. m. 14**

CHUKOVSKY (Nikolai Korneevich). [Edit. collected works of E. Ninoshvili.] *See* Ninoshvili (E.)
pseud.

CIRCASSIAN AND RELATED LANGUAGES.
See Abaza Language.

—— [For 'Инкорпорация в кабардино-черкесском
языке':] *See* Abitov (M. L.)

—— [For 'Кабардинско-русский словарь':] *See* Ara-
zhev (M. L.) *and others.*

—— [For 'Кабардинская азбука':] *See* Atazhukin
(K.)

—— [For 'Некоторые особенности бесленеевского

диалекта кабардинского языка':] *See* Balkarov (B.
Kh.)

—— [For 'Elementare tscherkessische Texte':]
See Deeters (G.)

—— [For 'Eine tscherkessische Grammatik':] *See*
Deeters (G.)

—— [For 'Études comparatives sur les langues
caucasiennes du nord-ouest':] *See* Dumézil (G.)

—— [For 'Къэбэрдей литературэ', a chrestomathy
of Kabardian literature:] *See* Kambiev (Kh. P.)

—— [For 'Русско-кабардинско-черкесский словарь':]
See Kardanov (B. M.) and Bichoev (A. T.)

—— [For 'Стихи, перевод с кабардинского':] *See*
Keshokov (A. P.)

—— [For 'Phoneme and Morpheme in Kabardian':] *See* Kuipers (A. H.)

—— [For 'Кабардинское сказание "Красавица Елена
и Богатырь-женщина"':] *See* Lopatinsky (L. G.)

—— [For 'Грамматика кабардино-черкесского литературного языка':] *See* Nal'chik.— *Кабардино-
балкарский Научно-исследовательский институт.*

—— [For 'Нарты. Кабардинский эпос':] *See* Narty.

—— [For 'Die Sagen und Lieder des Tscherkessen-
Volks':] *See* Shora-Bekmurzin-Nogmov.

—— [For 'Rapport sur un ouvrage manuscrit intitulé: "Словарь Русско-черкесскій"':] *See* Sjoegren
(A. J.)

—— [For 'Литература и писатели Кабарды':] *See*
Teunov (Kh. I.)

—— [For 'Erinnerungen an einen Aufenthalt bei
den Tscherkessen':] *See* Trubetskoi (N. S.) *Prince.*

—— [For 'О категории грамматических классов в
кабардинском':] *See* Turchaninov (G. F.)

CIRCASSIAN *(cont.)*

—— [For 'О категории вида в черкесских языках':] *See* TURCHANINOV (G. F.)

—— [For 'Рукописные материалы акад. Шёгрена по черкесским языкам':] *See* TURCHANINOV (G. F.)

—— [For 'Грамматика кабардинского языка':] *See* TURCHANINOV (G. F.) and TSAGOV (M. N.)

—— *See* UBYKH LANGUAGE.

—— [For 'Грамматика литературного кабардино-черкесского языка':] *See* YAKOVLEV (N. F.)

—— [For 'Kurze Übersicht über die tscherkessischen (adygheischen) Dialekte und Sprachen':] *See* YAKOVLEV (N. F.)

—— [For 'Грамматика адыгейского литературного языка':] *See* YAKOVLEV (N. F.) and ASHKHAMAF (D. A.)

CIRCASSIANS. [For 'Обычное семейное право черкес':] *See* LADYZHENSKY (A. M.)

CODRINGTON (HUMPHREY WILLIAM). *See* LITURGIES.—Greek Rite.—*Leitourgikon I*. The Liturgy of Saint Peter. By H. W. Codrington, *etc.* [With the text.] 1936. 8⁰.

CONSTANTINE, *Saint and Martyr, of Kakhetʿi*. De S. Constantino, martyre in Babylonia. [Georgian text of the Passion, edit. with Latin trans. and commentary by P. Peeters.] pp. 541–63. *Bruxellis*, 1925. fol. [*Acta Sanctorum*: *Novembris*. tom. 4.]
               Circ. 28. b

CONSTITUTIONS. [For Georgian text of the Soviet Constitution:] *See* RUSSIA. —*Laws, etc.*

CONYBEARE (FREDERICK CORNWALLIS). [Joint trans. of 'The Georgian Version of the Liturgy of St. James'.] *See* LITURGIES.—Greek Rite.—*Leitourgikon I*.

—— [Trans. 'Life of St. Nino, Armenian version'.] *See* NINO, *Saint, of Cappadocia*.

—— A Catalogue of the Armenian Manuscripts in the British Museum ... To which is appended a Catalogue of Georgian Manuscripts in the British Museum. By J. Oliver Wardrop. pp. viii. 410. *London*, 1913. 4⁰.   **Circ. 85. b**

—— [Another copy.] *Dept. of Oriental Printed Books & MSS. Reference Library.*

—— [Another copy.] *Oriental Students Room. Catalogue Desk.* B. 6.

CUST (ROBERT NEEDHAM). The Languages of the Caucasus. pp. 145–62. 1 *map*. London, 1885. 8⁰. [*Journal of the Royal Asiatic Society*. New ser. vol. 17.]   **R. Ac. 8820/3**

DADIANI (NIKOLOZ GIORGIS-DZE). დასტურ-ლამა. [Dastur-lama. Manual of administration, drawn up in 1818 under the direction of Levan Dadian, prince of Mingrelia. Edited by I. M. Meunargia.] pt. 1. pp. 41–61. ტფილისი [*Tiflis,*] 1896. 8⁰. [*Moambe.* tom. 3. no. 4.]   **17089. b. 1**

DADIANI (SHALVA NIKOLOZIS-DZE). [For 'Грузинская советская драматургия', including a tragedy by Sh. N. Dadiani:] *See* KAKABADZE (P. M.) *and others.*

—— რჩეული თხზულებანი ხუთ ტომად. [Rcheuli tʿkhzulebani khutʿ tomad. Selected writings in five volumes. Edited by B. Zhghenti, A. Mirtskhulava and V. Mgaloblishvili. With a portrait.] tom. 1— თბილისი [*Tiflis,*] 1958— 8⁰. *In progress.*
               17076. b. 38

—— Юрий Боголюбский. Исторический роман. [Translated into Russian by N. I. Dolidze and A. M. Drozdov.] pp. 370. 4 *plates*. Тбилиси, 1951. 8⁰.   **17076. c. 6**

DADISHKELIANI (TʿATʿARKHAN TʿENGIZIS-DZE) *Prince*. L'armée géorgienne au Moyen Âge. [Translated from the Georgian] par J. Mourier. pp. 28. *Tiflis*, 1886. 8⁰.   **17075. a. 1**

DAGHESTANIAN LANGUAGES. [For 'Даргала поэзияла антология':] *See* ABAKAROV (AHMAD-KHĀN).

DAGHESTANIAN *(cont.)*

—— [For 'Аварское соответствие русскому творительному предикативному падежу':] *See* BOKAREV (A. A.)

——[For 'О классных показателях в аваро-андоцезских языках':] *See* BOKAREV (A. A.)

—— [For 'Очерк грамматики чамалинского языка':] *See* BOKAREV (A. A.)

—— [For 'Синтаксис аварского языка':] *See* BOKAREV (A. A.)

—— [For 'Тинухский язык. Предварительное сообщение':] *See* BOKAREV (E. A.)

—— [For 'Локативные и нелокативные значения местных падежей в дагестанских языках':] *See* BOKAREV (E. A.)

—— [For 'Цезские (дидойские) языки Дагестана':] *See* BOKAREV (E. A.)

—— [For 'Выражение субъектно-объектных отношений в дагестанских языках':] *See* BOKAREV (E. A.)

—— [For 'Beiträge zur kaukasischen und sibirischen Sprachwissenschaft':] *See* BOUDA (K.)

—— [For 'Lakkische Studien':] *See* BOUDA (K.)

—— [For 'Имена существительные в даргинском литературном языке':] *See* BYKHOVSKAYA (S. L.)

—— [For 'Пережитки inclusiv'a и exclusiv'a в даргинских диалектах':] *See* BYKHOVSKAYA (S. L.)

—— *See* DARGWA LANGUAGE.

—— [For 'Бацбийский язык':] *See* DESHERIEV (YU. D.)

—— [For 'Грамматика хиналугского языка':] *See* DESHERIEV (YU. D.)

—— [For 'Арчинскій языкъ':] *See* DIRR (A.)

—— [For 'Грамматическій очеркъ табассаранскаго языка':] *See* DIRR (A.)

—— [For 'Краткій грамматическій очеркъ андійскаго языка':] *See* DIRR (A.)

—— [For 'Матеріалы для изученія языковъ и нарѣчій андо-дидойской группы':] *See* DIRR (A.)

—— [For 'Рутульскій языкъ':] *See* DIRR (A.)

—— [For 'Textes avar':] *See* DUMÉZIL (G.)

—— [For 'Материалы по лезгинской диалектологии':] *See* GENKO (A. N.)

—— [For 'Несколько образцов южно-дагестанского словесного творчества':] *See* GENKO (A. N.)

—— [For 'The Avâr Language':] *See* GRAHAM (C. C.)

—— [For 'Дагестанская народная лирика':] *See* GREBNEV (N.)

—— [For 'Балхарский диалект лакского языка':] *See* KHAIDAKOV (S. M.)

—— [For 'Рутульцы':] *See* LAVROV (L. I.)

—— [For 'Количественные числительные языков дидойской группы':] *See* MEGRELIDZE (I. B.)

—— [For 'Склонение в дидойском языке':] *See* MEGRELIDZE (I. B.)

—— [For 'Звуковой состав цезского (дидойского) языка:] *See* MEGRELIDZE (I. B.)

—— [For 'Функции эргативного падежа в лезгинском языке':] *See* MEILANOVA (U. A.)

—— [For 'Народы Дагестана':] *See* NIKOLSKAYA (Z. A.) *and others.*

—— [For 'Ausführlicher Bericht über Baron P. v. Uslar's Awarische Studien':] *See* SCHIEFNER (F. A. von).

—— For 'Ausführlicher Bericht über Baron P. v. Uslar's Hürkanische Studien':] *See* SCHIEFNER (F. A. von).

DAGHESTANIAN *(cont.)*

—— [For 'Ausführlicher Bericht über Baron P. v. Uslar's Kasikumükische Studien':] *See* SCHIEFNER (F. A. von).

—— [For 'Ausführlicher Bericht über Baron P. v. Uslar's Kürinische Studien':] *See* SCHIEFNER (F. A. von).

—— [For 'Awarische Texte':] *See* SCHIEFNER (F. A. von).

—— [For 'Языки Северного Кавказа и Дагестана':] *See* SERDYUCHENKO (G. P.)

—— [For 'Грамматический очерк агульского языка':] *See* SHAUMYAN (R. M.)

—— [For 'Предварительное сообщение об агульском языке':] *See* SHAUMYAN (R. M.)

—— [For 'Следы грамматических классов (родов) в агульском языке'] *See* SHAUMYAN (R. M.)

—— [For 'Яфетические языки "шах-дагской подгруппы"':] *See* SHAUMYAN (R. M.)

—— [For 'Избранные песни и стихи', trans. from the Lezghian by various hands:] *See* STAL'SKY (S.)

—— [For 'Lezgiuri zmnis dzirit'adi morp'ologiuri kategoriebi':] *See* T'OP'URIA (G. V.)

—— [For 'Studien auf dem Gebiete... der nordkaukasischen Sprachen':] *See* TRUBETSKOI (N. S.) *Prince.*

—— [For 'Die Konsonantensysteme der Ostkaukasischen Sprachen':] *See* TRUBETSKOI (N. S.) *Prince.*

—— [For 'Стихотворения и поэмы', trans. from the Avar:] *See* TSADASA (G.)

—— [For 'Аварско-русский словарь':] *See* ZHIRKOV (L. I.)

—— [For 'Лакский язык':] *See* ZHIRKOV (L. I.)

—— [For 'Законы лезгинского ударения':] *See* ZHIRKOV (L. I.)

DANIEL, *Saint, the Stylite*. [For 'Историко-агиографические отрывки', containing extracts from the life of Daniel the Stylite:] *See* KEKELIDZE (K. S.)

DANIYALOV (ABDURAKHMAN DANIELOVICH). [Introduction to 'Народы Дагестана'.] *See* NIKOLSKAYA (Z. A.) *and others.*

DANTE ALIGHIERI. [For 'Rust'velis da Dantes idumali':] *See* BELIASHVILI (L.)

DARGWA LANGUAGE. [For 'Даргала поэзияла антология':] *See* ABAKAROV (AHMAD-KHAN).

—— [For 'Die darginische Schriftsprache':] *See* BOUDA (K.). Beiträge zur kaukasischen und sibirischen Sprachwissenschaft, No. 1. 1937. 8⁰.
    753. f. 30/4

—— [For poems trans. from Dargwa:] *See* RASHIDOV (R.)

DAVID, *King of Israel*. [For 'Hippolyts Erklärung in betreff Davids und Goliaths':] *See* HIPPOLYTUS, *Saint, of Rome*. Drei georgisch erhaltene Schriften von H., herausgegeben von G. Nath. Bonwetsch. 1904. 8⁰.   **3628. d. 1/26**

DAVID II, *King of Georgia*, surnamed *the Builder*. [For 'Изображение грузинскаго царя Давида Строителя на иконе Синайскаго монастыря':] *See* BENESHEVICH (V. N.)

—— [For 'Давид Строитель. Трилогия':] *See* GAMSAKHURDIA (K. S.)

—— [For 'Davit' aghmashenebeli', a novel based on the life of King David II:] *See* GAMSAKHURDIA (K. S.)

—— [For 'Древнегрузинские одописцы', including Shavt'eli's ode to King David II, 'Abdulmesia':] *See* MARR (N. Y.)

—— [For 'Mep'e Davit' Aghmashenebeli', a his-

DAVID *(cont.)*

torical drama:] *See* ORBELIANI (A. V̆. JAMBAKU-RIAN-).

—— [*Life.*] *See* URBNELI (N.) *pseud.*

DAVID IV, *King of Georgia.* [For 'Paleograp'iuli albomi', containing facsimile of a charter of David IV:] *See* T'AQAISHVILI (E. S.)

DAVID, *Prince-Regent of Georgia.* საქართველოს სამართლისა და კანონთმცოდნეობის მიმოხილვა. [Sak'art'velos samart'lisa da kanont'mtsodneobis mimokhilva. Survey of the laws and jurisprudence of Georgia. Edited with a biographical and critical introduction by A. A. Rogava.] (Обозрение Грузии по части прав и законоведения.) pp. 419. 4 *plates.* თბილისი [*Tiflis,*] 1959. 8⁰.   **17078. e. 1**

DAVIT'ASHVILI (IOSEB SVIMONIS-DZE). [*Life.*] *See* TCHITCHINADZE (Z. E.)

—— ლექსები, ვარლამ ხუროძის რედაქციით. [Lek'sebi, Varlam Khurodzis redak'tsiit'. Poems, edited with an introduction by V. Khurodze, and a biographical sketch of the poet by N. Mt'vare-lishvili.] pp. 400, viii. 3 *plates.* ტფილისი [*Tiflis,*] 1927. 8⁰.   **17075. c. 32**

DEDABRISHVILI (SHIO). *See* ARAGVISPIRELI (SHIO) *pseud.*

DEETERS (GERHARD). [Edit. 'Studien zur georgischen Wortbildung'.] *See* NEISSER (F.)

—— Das Alter der georgischen Schrift. [With facsimiles and a paleographical table.] pp. 56–65. *Wiesbaden,* 1955. 8⁰. [*Oriens Christianus.* Bd. 39. (Vierte Serie. Bd. 3.)].   **Ac. 2002. b**

—— Armenisch und Südkaukasisch. Ein Beitrag zur Frage der Sprachmischung. 2 pt. fasc. 3. pp. 37–82; fasc. 4. pp. 1–64. *Leipzig,* 1926–27. 8⁰. [*Caucasica.* fasc. 3, 4.]   **P.P. 3803. eba**

—— Elementare tscherkessische Texte. pp. 68–83. *Leipzig,* 1934. 8⁰. [*Caucasica.* fasc. 11.]

P.P. 3803. eba

—— Das kharthwelische Verbum. Vergleichende Darstellung des Verbalbaus der südkaukasischen Sprachen. pp. x. 258. *Leipzig,* 1930. 8⁰.

12977. b. 40

—— Die Namen der Wochentage im Südkaukasi-schen. pp. 1–9. *Leipzig,* 1931. 8⁰ [*Caucasica.* fasc. 7.]

P.P. 3803. eba

—— Eine tscherkessische Grammatik. pp. 129–41. *Leipzig,* 1931. 8⁰. [*Caucasica.* fasc. 9.]

P.P. 3803. eba

DEFOE (DANIEL). რობინზონ კრუზო. [Robinzon Kruzo.] (Robinson Crusoe. Translated into Georgian by V. Chelidze.) [Illustrated by A. Bandzel-adze.] pp. ix. 491. 9 *plates.* თბილისი [*Tiflis,*] 1956. 8⁰.   **17076. c. 9**

DEFRÉMERY (CHARLES FRANÇOIS). არაბელ და სპარსელ მწერალთა გეოგრაფიული და ისტო-რიული ცნობები საქართველოს შესახებ. [Arabel da sparsel mdseralt'a geograp'iuli da istoriuli tsnobebi Sak'art'velos shesakheb. Geographical and historical data of Arabic and Persian writers concerning Georgia. Translated by I. N. Matcha-variani from the article by Defrémery in the *Journal Asiatique,* 1849.]. pt. 1. pp. 1–16. ტფილისი [*Tiflis,*] 1897. 8⁰. [*Moambe.* tom. 4. no. 12.]   **17089. b. 1**

DE HALLEUX (ANDRÉ). [For 'Le sermon géorgien du moine Martyrius', accompanied by the corresponding passages of the Syriac original in a Latin translation by A. de Halleux:] *See* SĀHDŌNĀ, *Bishop of Māhōzē dh-Arēwān in Bēth Garmai.*

DEKANOZISHVILI (DIMITRI). [Trans. 'Shent'an amkhanagebi arian'.] *See* PRILEZHAEVA (M.)

DENYS, *the Areopagite. See* DIONYSIUS, *Saint,* called *the Areopagite.*

DER NERSESSIAN (SIRARPIE). [For 'The Gospels of Bert'ay', by R. P. Blake and S. Der Nerses-sian:] *See* BLAKE (R. P.) and DER NERSESSIAN (S.)

DERZHAVIN (VLADIMIR). [Trans. 'Песнь о Да-виде Гурамишвили'.] *See* CHIK'OVANI (S. I.)

DESHERIEV (Yunus Desherievich). [Joint compiler of 'Грамматика кабардино-черкесского литературного языка'.] *See* Nal'chik.—*Кабардино-балкарский Научно-исследовательский институт.*

—— Бацбийский язык. Фонетика, морфология, синтаксис, лексика. [A study of the Batsbian or Tushian language, a Daghestanian language strongly influenced by Georgian.] pp. 384. *Москва,* 1953. 8⁰.

17076. i. 2

—— Грамматика хиналугского языка. (Ответственный редактор Е. А. Бокарев.) pp. 222. *Москва,* 1959. 8⁰.

17076. h. 16

—— Система грамматических классов в бацбийском языке. pp. 205–17. *Москва,* 1952. 8⁰. [*Труды Института языкознания.* том I.]

Ac. 1125. sf

DE VIS (Henri). *See* Vis (H. de).

DEVOS (Paul). Les origines du "Barlaam et Joasaph" grec. À propos de la thèse nouvelle de M. Nucubidze. pp. 83–104. *Bruxelles,* 1957. 8⁰. [*Analecta Bollandiana.* tom. 75.]

2003. a

DGEBUADZE (Mariya Davidovna). *See* Dgebuadze-P'ularia (P'.)

DGEBUADZE-P'ULARIA (P'utsu). მოღვაწე ქალები რევოლუციამდელ საქართველოში. [Moghvadse k'alebi revolutsiamdel Sak'art'veloshi. Prominent women of pre-revolutionary Georgia. Short biographies.] pp. 205. სოხუმი [*Sukhumi,*] 1957. 8⁰.

17075. b. 10

—— ოქროს ბეჭედი. რომანი წარსულიდან. [Ok'ros betchedi. Romani dsarsulidan. The golden ring. A novel from the past. A story of Western Georgia in feudal times. Second edition.] pp. 497. აფხაზეთის სახელგამო [*State Publishing House of Abkhazia:* *Sukhumi,*] 1954. 8⁰.

17076. c. 8

DIASAMIDZE (Mikheil). [Editor of newspaper 'Musha'.] *See* Periodical Publications.—*Tiflis.*

DICKENS (Charles). ნიკოლას ნიკლები. [Nikolas Niklbi.] (Nicholas Nickleby. Translated into Georgian by V. Chelidze.) bk. 1. pp. viii. 477. 1 *plate.* თბილისი [*Tiflis,*] 1954. 8⁰. *In progress.* **17076. c. 11**

—— სკრუჯი და მარლეი. საბავშვო მოთხრობა. [Skruji da Marlei. Sabavshvo mot'khroba. A Christmas Carol, trans. into Georgian by Nino Nakashidze. Illustrated.] pp. 108. ტფილისი [*Tiflis,*] [1910]. 8⁰. **17077. a. 6**

DIONYSIUS, *Saint,* called THE Areopagite. [For 'La version géorgienne de l'autobiographie de Denys l'Aréopagite':] *See* Peeters (P.)

—— List apokryficzny Dionizego Areopagity do Biskupa Efeskiego Tymoteusza o męczeńskiej śmierci Apostołów Piotra i Pawła. [An analysis of all the known versions of the text, by G. P'eradze, with a Polish trans. of the Georgian text and with a summary in French.] pp. 35. *Warszawa,* 1937. 8⁰.

3805. ee. 18

—— La version ibéro-arménienne de l'autobiographie de Denys l'Aréopagite. [Edit., with Latin trans. by] P. Peeters. pp. 277–313. *Bruxelles,* 1921. 8⁰. [*Analecta Bollandiana.* tom. 39.] **2002. f**

DIRR (Adolf). [Edit. and trans. 'Ein polyglottes Liebeslied'.] *See* Grishashvili (I. G.)

—— [For 'Gesänge russischer Kriegsgefangener... Transkription und Übersetzung der georgischen Texte von A. Dirr':] *See* Lach (R.)

—— [Edit. of 'Caucasica'.] *See* Periodical Publications.—*Leipsic.*

—— [Trans. 'Kurze Übersicht über die tscherkessischen (adygheischen) Dialekte und Sprachen'.] *See* Yakovlev (N. F.)

—— Арчинскій языкъ. Грамматическій очеркъ, тексты, сборникъ арчинскихъ словъ, *etc.* pp. vii. 227. *Тифлисъ,* 1908. 8⁰. **12976. w. 13**

—— Caucasian Folk-Tales. Selected and translated from the originals by Adolf Dirr. Translated into English by Lucy Menzies. pp. xiii. 306. *London, Toronto,* 1925. 8⁰. **012403. de. 22**

DIRR *(cont.)*

—— Einführung in das Studium der kaukasischen Sprachen. Mit einer Sprachenkarte. pp. x. 380. *Leipzig*, 1928. 8⁰.   **012904. g. 59**

—— Грамматическій очеркъ табассаранскаго языка съ текстами, сборникомъ табассаранскихъ словъ, *etc.* pp. ix. 247. *Тифлисъ*, 1905. 8⁰.   **12976. w. 12**

—— Грамматика удинскаго языка. pp. xi. 101. *Тифлисъ*, 1903. 8⁰.   **12976. w. 17**

—— Kaukasische Märchen. Ausgewählt und übersetzt von A. Dirr. pp. xi. 294. *Jena*, 1920. 8⁰. [*Die Märchen der Weltliteratur.*]   **12411. d. 5/12**

—— Краткій грамматическій очеркъ андійскаго языка съ текстами, сборникомъ андійскихъ словъ, *etc.* pp. vii. 200. *Тифлисъ*, 1906. 8⁰.   **12976. w. 15**

—— Матеріалы для изученія языковъ и нарѣчій андо-дидойской группы. 1. Грамматическія замѣтки съ фразами. 2. Слова. pp. vii. 114. *Тифлисъ*, 1909. 8⁰.   **12976. w. 14**

—— Рутульскій языкъ. Грамматическій очеркъ, тексты, сборникъ рутульскихъ словъ, *etc.* pp. v. 204. *Тифлисъ*, 1911. 8⁰.   **12976. w. 16**

—— Die Sprache der Ubychen. Grammatische Skizze, Texte, ubychisches Glossar nebst deutschem Index. 2 pt. fasc. 4. pp. 65–144; fasc. 5. pp. 1–54. *Leipzig*, 1927–28. 8⁰. [*Caucasica.* fasc. 4, 5.]   **P.P. 3803. eba**

—— Theoretisch-praktische Grammatik der modernen georgischen (grusinischen) Sprache, *etc.* pp. xiv. 170. *Leipzig*, [1904]. 8⁰. [*Die Kunst der Polyglottie.* Tl. 81.]   **2272. a. 84**

—— Udische Texte. [Text and German trans.] pp. 60–72. *Leipzig*, 1928. 8⁰. [*Caucasica.* fasc. 5.]   **P.P. 3803. eba**

DMANISI. [For 'Ангобированная керамика Дманиси':] *See* MAISURADZE (Z. P.)

—— [For 'Раскопки в Дманиси':] *See* MUSKHELISHVILI (L. V.)

DODASHVILI (SOLOMON). [*Life.*] *See* GOTSADZE (M. K.); TCHITCHINADZE (Z. E.)

DOLIDZE (NINO ISIDORES-ASULI). [Trans. 'Грузинские народные сказки'.] *See* CHIK'OVANI (M. I.)

—— [Joint trans. of historical novel 'Юрий Боголюбский'.] *See* DADIANI (SH. N.)

DOLIDZE (VAKHTANG ONISIMES-DZE). გარბანი. ქართული ხუროთმოძღვრების IX–X სს. ძეგლი ხევში. [Garbani. K'art'uli khurot'modzghvrebis IX–X ss. dzegli Khevshi. Garbani church. A monument of Georgian architecture of the 9th-10th centuries in Khevi.] (Гарбани. Памятник грузинской архитектуры IX–X вв. в Хеви.) [With a summary in Russian.] pp. 116. 51 *plates.* თბილისი [*Tiflis,*] 1958. 8⁰.   **17080. b. 13**

DONDUA (KARPEZ DARISPANIS-DZE). [Edit. 'Грамматический очерк агульского языка'.] *See* SHAUMYAN (R. M.)

—— Феминизирующий гласный в грузинском. pp. 245–57. *Москва, Ленинград*, 1935. 8⁰. [*Язык и мышление.* вып. 3–4.]   **Ac. 1125. t/2**

—— К генезису формы сравнительно-превосходной степени в картвельских языках. pp. 29–38. *Москва, Ленинград*, 1940. 8⁰. [*Язык и мышление.* вып. 9.]   **Ac. 1125. t/2**

—— К вопросу о родительном эмфатическом в древнелитературном грузинском языке. pp. 195–209. *Ленинград*, 1930. 8⁰. [*Известия Академии Наук СССР.* ser. 7. *Отделение гуманитарных наук.*]   **Ac. 1125/44. (2)**

—— Морфологическое выражение активного (эргативного) строя в адыгейской и картвельской группах кавказских языков. pp. 211–20. *Москва, Ленинград*, 1948. 8⁰. [*Известия Академии Наук СССР. Отделение литературы и языка.* tom. 7. no. 3.]   **Ac.1125/44. (11)**

—— Н. Я. Марр и грузиноведение. pp. 49–70. *Москва, Ленинград*, 1937. 8⁰. [*Язык и мышление.* вып. 8.]   **Ac. 1125. t/2**

—— Настоящее "обычности" в активной конструкции. pp. 53–59. *Москва, Ленинград*, 1949. 8⁰. [*Из-*

DONDUA *(cont.)*
вестия Академии Наук СССР. Отделение литературы
и языка. tom. 8. no. 1.]　　　　　　　**Ac. 1125/44. (11)**

—— О двух суффиксах множественности в грузинском. pp. 43–66. *Ленинград*, 1933. 8⁰. [*Язык и мышление*. вып. 1.]　　　　　　　　　　　　**Ac. 1125. t/2**

—— Об одной лингвистической кальке. Турецкое
выражение в армянском и грузинском. pp. 102–106.
Москва, Ленинград, 1940. 8⁰. [*Язык и мышление*. вып.
10.]　　　　　　　　　　　　　　　　　**Ac. 1125. t/2**

—— Шота Руставели и грузинская литература. pp.
11–28. *Москва, Ленинград*, 1938. 8⁰. [*Известия Академии Наук СССР. Classe des Sciences Sociales*. no.
3.]　　　　　　　　　　　　　　　　**Ac. 1125/44. (9)**

—— Творение Мерчула в латинском переводе бель-
гийского ориенталиста. [A critical study of the Latin
trans. by P. Peeters of the biography of Gregory
of Khandzt'a by Giorgi Merchule.] pp. 14–25.
Ленинград, 1925. 4⁰. [*Тексты и разыскания по кавказской филологии*. том 1.]　　　　　**Ac. 1125/228**

DONDUA (Varlam Darispanis-dze). [Edit. 'Giorgi Merchule'.] *See* Ingoroqva (P. I.)

—— [Trans. 'Калмасоба'.] *See* John, *Prince of
Georgia.*

DORÉ (Paul Gustave). [Illustrator of 'Paradise
Lost'.] *See* Milton (J.)

DORN (Bernhard). Beiträge zur Geschichte der
kaukasischen Länder und Völker. pt. 1–5. *St.-
Pétersbourg*, 1840–48. 4⁰. [*Mémoires de l'Académie
des Sciences*. sér. 6. *Sciences Politiques*. tom. 4–7.]
　　　　　　　　　　　　　　　　　　　Ac. 1125/2

—— Die jetzigen Kubätschi. pp. 717–40. *St.-Pé-
tersbourg*, 1873. 8⁰. [*Mélanges Asiatiques de l'Académie des Sciences*. tom. 6. livr. 6.]　　**Ac. 1125/11**

—— Versuch einer Erklärung von drei Münzen mit
Sasaniden-Gepräge. [A study of coins of Georgian
rulers of the Sassanian period.] pp. 33–43. 1 *plate*.

St.-Pétersbourg, 1844. 4⁰. [*Bulletin Historico-Philologique de l'Académie des Sciences*. tom. 1.]
　　　　　　　　　　　　　　　　　　　Ac. 1125/7

DOROTHEUS, *Bishop of Tyre*. [Author of sketches of lives of the Evangelists.] *See* Bible.—New
Testament.

DOSITHEOS, *Patriarch of Jerusalem*. [For 'Les
sources des notices du Patriarche de Jérusalem
Dosithée sur les rois d'Aphkhazie':] *See* T'aqaishvili (E. S.)

DROZDOV (Aleksandr Mikhailovich). [Joint
trans. of historical novel 'Юрий Боголюбский'.]
See Dadiani (Sh. N.)

—— [Joint trans. of selected works by D. I. Gulia.]
See Gulia (D. I.)

—— [Edit. works of D. S. Kldiashvili in Russian
trans.] *See* Kldiashvili (D. S.)

—— Абхазские рассказы. (Редактор А. Дроздов.)
pp. 305. *Москва*, 1950. 8⁰.　　　　　**12594. ee. 7**

DSCHAWACHISCHWILI (Iwane). *See* Javakhishvili (I. A.)

DSCHAWACHOFF. *See* Javakhishvili (I. A.)

DSERET'ELI. *See* Tseret'eli.

DSULUKIDZE (Petre Giorgis-dze) *Prince*. [Edit.
'Vep'khvis-tqaosani'.] *See* Rust'aveli (Shot'a).

DUDUCHAVA (Mamia Iosebis-dze). Гиго Габа-
швили. [A biography of the Georgian painter. Illustrated.] pp. 82. 5 *plates*. *Москва*, 1958. 8⁰.
　　　　　　　　　　　　　　　　　　　17075. b. 8

DUMÉZIL (Georges). [Trans. and edit. 'Textes
populaires Inguš'.] *See* Jabagi (M.)

—— [Joint trans. and edit. of fables of Tsey
Ibrāhīm.] *See* Tsey Ibrāhīm.

—— Une chrétienté disparue: les Albaniens du

DUMÉZIL *(cont.)*
Caucase. pp. 125–32. *Paris*, 1940. 8⁰. [*Journal Asiatique*. sér. 13. tom. 11.]   **R. Ac. 8808**

—— Contes et légendes des Oubykhs. [Text with French trans. and notes.] pp. xiii. 103, 6. *Paris*, 1957. 8⁰. [*Université de Paris.—Travaux et mémoires de l'Institut d'Ethnologie*. tom. 60.]   **Ac. 442. 1**

—— Contes lazes. [Text with French trans. and notes.] pp. xiii. 132, 2. *Paris*, 1937. 8⁰. [*Université de Paris.—Travaux et mémoires de l'Institut d'Ethnologie*. tom. 27.]   **Ac. 442. 1**

—— Études comparatives sur les langues caucasiennes du nord-ouest. Morphologie. pp. 262. *Paris*, 1932. 8⁰.   **12902. i. 39**

—— L'icone de l'église de Saint-Kviriké, Haute-Svanétie. pp. 241–244. *Bruxelles*, 1950. 8⁰. [*Analecta Bollandiana*. tom. 68.]   **2002. g̣**

—— Introduction à la grammaire comparée des langues caucasiennes du nord. pp. xvi. 132. *Paris*, 1933. 8⁰. [*Bibliothèque de l'Institut français de Léningrad*. tom. 14.]   **Ac. 1117**

—— La langue des Oubykhs. pp. xvi. 216. *Paris*, 1931. 8⁰. [*Collection linguistique*. no. 35.]   **R. Ac. 9810/3**

—— Recherches comparatives sur le verbe caucasien, *etc*. pp. 93. *Paris*, 1933. 8⁰. [*Bibliothèque de l'Institut français de Léningrad*. tom. 15.]   **Ac. 1117**

—— Textes avar. [With French translation.] pp. 265–302. *Paris*, 1933. 8⁰. [*Journal Asiatique*. sér. 13. tom. 1.]   **R. Ac. 8808**

—— and **NAMITOK** (AYTEK). Récits oubykh. [With French translation.] pp. 1–47. *Paris*, 1955. 8⁰. [*Journal Asiatique*. tom. 243=sér. 15. tom. 3.]   **R. Ac. 8808**

DZHALAGANIYA (IRINA LEVANOVNA). *See* JALAGHANIA (I. L.)

DZHANASHIA (SIMON NIKOLAEVICH). *See* JANASHIA (S. N.)

DZHANASHVILI (MOSE). *See* JANASHVILI (M.G.)

DZHAVAKHISHVILI (IVANO). *See* JAVAKHISHVILI (I. A.)

DZHAVAKHOV (IVAN ALEKSANDROVICH). *See* JAVAKHISHVILI (I. A.)

DZHIKIYA (SERGEI SIMONOVICH). *See* JIKʿIA (S. S.)

DZHORDZHADZE (ARCHIL). *See* JORJADZE (A.)

DZHUGASHVILI-STALIN (JOSEPH). *See* STALIN (I. V.)

DZIDZARIA (GIORGI ALEKʿSIS-DZE). Народное хозяйство и социальные отношения в Абхазии в XIX веке, до крестьянской реформы 1870 г. pp. 511. *Сухуми*, 1958. 8⁰.   **17075. e. 48**

DZIDZIGURI (SHOTʿA VARLAMIS-DZE). [Compiler of glossary to works of A. M. Qazbegi.] *See* QAZBEGI (A. M.)

—— ძიებანი ქართული დიალექტოლოგიიდან. [Dziebani kʿartʿuli dialekʿtologiidan. Researches in Georgian dialects. Edit. by S. Zhghenti.] pp. 271. თბილისი [*Tiflis*,] 1954. 8⁰.   **17076. f. 14**

—— ქართული დიალექტების ქრესტომათია ლექსიკონითურთ. [Kʿartʿuli dialekʿtebis kʿrestomatʿia lekʿsikonitʿurtʿ. An anthology of texts in various Georgian dialects, with glossary. Edit. by G. Akhvlediani.] pp. 401, 3. თბილისი [*Tiflis*,] 1956. 8⁰.   **17076. c. 17**

—— მწერლის ენა. [Mdserlis ena. The language of the writer. Essays on Georgian literary style.] pp. 205, 3. თბილისი [*Tiflis*,] 1957. 8⁰.   **17073. a. 5**

DZIDZIGURI (VALENTINA). [Joint trans. of 'Bukhara: mogonebani'.] *See* ʿAINĪ (ṢADR UD-DĪN).

DZODSENIDZE (LALI GIORGIS-ASULI). რუსული "აპოვთʿეგმატას" ქართული რედაქციები. [Rusuli "apovtʿegmatas" kʿartʿuli redakʿtsiebi. The Georgian recensions of the Russian "Apophthegmata".

A critical study.] pp. 97. თბილისი [*Tiflis*,] 1959. 8⁰.

17076. f. 34. (1.)

EKALADZE (IA) *pseud.* [i. e. IAKOB TSINTSADZE]. *See* TꞋOMAANTꞋ KOBA, *pseud.*

EKBA (NAZIR BEKMURZOVICH). [Joint edit. of Russian-Abaza dictionary.] *See* CHERKESSK.—*Cherkessky Nauchno-Issledovatel'sky Institut.*

ELBRUZ, *Mount.* [For 'TꞋovlian mtꞋebshi. Ialbuzi':] *See* KETSKHOVELI (N. N.)

ELEUSIPPUS, *Saint and Martyr, of Cappadocia.* [For Acts of St. Eleusippus:] *See* SPEUSIPPUS, ELEUSIPPUS AND MELEUSIPPUS, *Saints and Martyrs, of Cappadocia.*

EPHRAIM, *Mtsire.* უწყებაჲ მიზეზსა ქართველთა მოქცევისასა, თუ რომელთა წიგნთა შინა მოჲსჷნების. [Udsqebay mizezsa KꞋartꞋveltꞋa mokꞋtsevisasa, tꞋu romeltꞋa dsigntꞋa shina moikhsenebis. Discourse on the conversion of the Georgians, and the books in which this is mentioned. With Greek and Russian parallel texts. Edit. by TꞋ.M. Bregadze.] (Повествование об обращении грузин, *etc.*) pp. 021. 61. თბილისი [*Tiflis*,] 1959. 8⁰.

17076. f. 34. (3.)

EPHRAIM, *Saint, the Syrian.* [For 'Notice sur une version géorgienne de la Caverne des Trésors, apocryphe syriaque attribué à Saint Éphrem':] *See* AVALISHVILI (Z. D.)

—— Vie de S. Éphrem. [The Georgian Life of St. Ephraim, itself a translation from the Syriac. Edited from Brit. Mus. MS. Add. 11281, with a Latin version, by G. Garitte.] *See* SIMEON, *Stylites, Saint.* Vies géorgiennes de S. Syméon Stylite l'Ancien et de S. Éphrem. pp. 78–117; 54–81. 1957. 8⁰. [*Corpus Scriptorum Christianorum Orientalium.* vol. 171–172. Scriptores Iberici. tom. 7–8.]   **14005. a**

EPIPHANIUS, *Saint, Bishop of Constantia in Cyprus.* Epiphanius de gemmis. The Old Georgian version and the fragments of the Armenian version, [edited and translated] by Robert P. Blake; and the Coptic-Sahidic fragments, [edited with Latin

translation] by Henri de Vis. pp. cxxiii. 335. 51. *Christophers: London; Wetteren* printed, 1934. 8⁰. [*Studies and Documents.* no. 2.]   **W.P. 11331/2**

EPIPHANIUS, *Catholicos of Georgia.* L'inscription d'Épiphane, Catholicos de Géorgie. [A translation by E. TꞋaqaishvili of the article by N. Y. Marr.] pp. 216–24. 4 *plates. Paris,* 1938. 8⁰. [*Revue de l'Orient Chrétien.* tom. 10 (30).]   **P.P. 37. ck**

—— Надпись Епифанія, католикоса Грузіи. [Edit. with commentary by N. Y. Marr.] pp. 1433–42. 2 *plates.* С.-Петербургъ, 1910. 8⁰. [*Извѣстія Академіи Наукъ.* серія 6. томъ 4.]   **Ac. 1125/44**

ERCKERT (RODERICH von). Die Sprachen des kaukasischen Stammes, *etc.* 2 Thle. *Wien,* 1895. 8⁰.

2056. c

EREKLE II, *King of Georgia.* [For letters of King Erekle II, trans. into French by M.-F. Brosset, and published in the second part of 'Histoire de la Géorgie':] *See* BROSSET (M.-F.)

—— [For 'MepꞋe Erekles sakhsovari':] *See* JANASHVILI (M. G.)

—— [For 'Dabadeba da aghzrda Erekle Batonishvilisa, legenda':] *See* RAZIKASHVILI (N.), known as BACHANA.

—— [For decrees and other historical documents of the 18th century, relative to Georgia during the reign of Erekle II:] *See* TSAGARELI (A. A.)

—— მეფე ერეკლე მეორის დოკუმენტები. [MepꞋe Erekle meoris dokumentebi. Documents of King Erekle II, comprising Charters, official letters, etc.] pp. 46–54. ტფილისი [*Tiflis*,] 1894. 8⁰. [*Moambe.* tom. I. no. 10.]   **17089. b. 1**

—— მეფე ირაკლი მეორის დროის წერილები. [MepꞋe Irakli meoris drois dserilebi. Letters of the time of King Irakli II, consisting of correspondence of 18th century Georgian princes and notables.] pp. 40–48. ტფილისი [*Tiflis*,] 1894. 8⁰. [*Moambe.* tom. I. no. 1.]   **17089. b. 1**

ERIST'AVI (DAVIT') *Prince.* [*Life.*] *See* TCHI-TCHINADZE (Z. E.)

ERIST'AVI (RAP'IEL DAVIT'IS-DZE)*Prince.* [*Life.*] *See* QIP'SHIDZE (G. T'.)

—— Краткій грузино-русско-латинскій словарь изъ трехъ естественныхъ царствъ природы, *etc.* pp. vii. 167. Тифлисъ, 1884. 8⁰.   **12975. k. 35**

ERIST'AVI-MDIVANI (DOMINIKA ZURABIS-ASULI). [Edit. 'Nobat'i'.] *See* PERIODICAL PUBLICATIONS.—*Tiflis.*

ESADZE (BORIS SPIRIDONIS-DZE). Лѣтопись Грузіи. Юбилейный сборникъ къ 300-лѣтію царствованія дома Романовыхъ... 1613–1913, *etc.* [With illustrations and bibliographies.] вып. 1. pp. xv. 366. 13 *plates.* [Тифлисъ, 1913.] 4⁰. *No more published.*   **9057. i. 6**

ESDRAS. [The Books of Esdras.] *See* BIBLE.—Old Testament.—*Apocrypha.*

ESTATE, *Saint and Martyr. See* EUSTACE, *Saint and Martyr, of Mtskhet'a.*

EUBULUS, *Saint.* [For 'La Passion géorgienne des SS. Théodore ... Eubulus, *etc.*':] *See* THEODORE, *Saint and Martyr, of Pella.*

EULI-K'URIDZE (SANDRO KISHVARDIS-DZE). [Edit. of works of the Karl Marx State Library.] *See* TIFLIS.—*Karl Marx State Library.*

—— რჩეული. ლექსები, პოემები, 1934–1953. [Rcheuli. Lek'sebi, poemebi, 1934–1953. Selections. Verses and poems, 1934–1953.] pp. 263. 1 *plate.* თბილისი [*Tiflis,*] 1954. 8⁰.   **17075. c. 8**

EUROPEAN WAR, *1914–1919.* ბრიტანეთის და გერმანეთის სამხედრო ბრძანებანი. [Britanet'is da Germanet'is samkhedro brdzanebani. British and German military orders. A poster, 2′ 5¼″ in height and 1′ 7″ in width, issued by the British Government, containing in parallel columns the proclamations of General Allenby at Jerusalem (in English and Georgian) and the German Comman-

dant Gloss at Holnon (in French and Georgian), with comments in Georgian]. [*n. p. and d.* London, 1917 ?]   **O.P. 219. (64)**

—— [Another copy.]   **O.P. 219. (64*)**

EUSEBIUS,*Pamphili, Bishop of Caesarea in Palestine.* Version géorgienne de la Passion de S. Procope par Eusèbe. [Edit., with Latin trans., by] G. Garitte. pp. 245–66. *Louvain,* 1953. 8⁰. [*Le Muséon* tom. 66.]   **P.P. 4453**

EUSTACE, *Saint and Martyr, of Mtskhet'a.* Das Martyrium des heiligen Eustatius von Mzchetha. Aus dem Georgischen übersetzt. Von Dschawachoff. Vorgelegt und bearbeitet von Hrn. Harnack. pp. 875–902. *Berlin,* 1901. 4⁰. [*Sitzungsberichte der K. Preussischen Akademie der Wissenschaften.* 1901, Juli-Dec., No. 38.]   **Ac. 855**

EUTHYMIUS, *of Mt'a-dsminda, Saint.* [Trans. life of St. Pancras, Bishop of Taormina.] *See* EVAGRIUS, *Bishop of Taormina.*

—— [For 'St. Euthymius the Georgian and the Barlaam and Ioasaph Romance':] *See* LANG (D. M.)

—— [*Life.*] *See* PEETERS (P.). Histoires monastiques géorgiennes. 1917–19. 8⁰.   **2002. f**

—— [For 'Die Anfänge der schriftstellerischen Tätigkeit des hl. Euthymius, *etc.*':] *See* T'ARKHNISHVILI (M.)

—— Notice sur un Nomocanon géorgien რჯულის-კანონი [Rjulis-kanoni]. Par M. Brosset. [Being extracts translated and edited by M.-F. Brosset from the Georgian translation of the Greek Nomocanon made by St. Euthymius.] pp. 113–66. *St.-Pétersbourg,* 1874. 8⁰. [*Mélanges Asiatiques de l'Académie des Sciences.* tom. 7. livr. 2–3.]   **Ac. 1125/11**

EVAGRIUS, *Bishop of Taormina.* Багратъ, епископъ Тавроменійскій. Грузинскій текстъ по рукописямъ XI в. Съ предисловіемъ и переводомъ издалъ А. Хахановъ. [Georgian version by St. Euthymius of Mt'a-dsminda of the life of St. Pancras of Taormina composed by Evagrius, his disciple.] pp. xvii. 111. *Москва*, 1904. 8⁰. *Georgian text only; no more published.* [*Лазаревскій Институтъ. Труды по Востоковѣдѣнію.* вып. 19.]

17068. g. 1

FAKHR AL-DIN, *Gurgānī. See* As'AD (FAKHR AL-DĪN), *Gurgānī.*

FIRDAUSĪ. [For a Georgian version of the 'Shāh-nāmeh':] *See* ḤASAN (ABU'L-Ḳ̄ĀSIM), called FIRDAUSĪ, *Ṫūsī.*

FRAEHN (CHRISTIAN MARTIN). Über ein merk-würdiges Volk des Kaukasus, die Kubetschi. 2 pt. pp. 33–45; 49–53. *St.-Pétersbourg*, 1838. 4⁰.[*Bulletin Scientifique de l'Académie des Sciences.* tom. 4.]

Ac. 1125/6

FRANK-KAMENETSKY (IZRAIL' GRIGOR'E-VICH). Грузинская параллель к древне-египетской повести "О двух братьях". pp. 39–71. *Ленинград*, 1926. 8⁰. [*Яфетический сборник.* вып. 4.]   **Ac. 1125. t**

GABASHVILI (BESARION IOBIAN) called BESIKI. [For historical novel based on the life of B. Gabashvili:] *See* BELIASHVILI (A. I.)

—— [For selected poems, in Russian translation:] *See* GOL'TSEV (V. V.) and CHIK'OVANI (S. I.). Поэзия Грузии. 1949. 4⁰.   **17075. dd. 1**

—— ლექსნი. [Lek'sni. Poems of B. Gabashvili, edited with biographical introduction by Z. E. Tchitchinadze.] pp. 66. თფილისი [*Tiflis*,] 1885. 8⁰.

17075. d. 2. (1.)

GABASHVILI (GIORGI IVANES-DZE). [*Life.*] *See* DUDUCHAVA (M. I.)

GABASHVILI (TIMOT'E) *Metropolitan of K'ut'aisi.* მიმოსლვა. [Mimoslva. Travels to Mount Athos, Jerusalem and other Holy Places, under-taken in 1755–59. Edited, with a biographical and critical introduction, by E. P. Metreveli. With a map.] (Путешествие.) pp. 0253. 158, 2. 14 *plates.* თბილისი [*Tiflis*,] 1956. 8⁰.   **17075. e. 34**

GABASHVILI (TSIALA REVAZIS-ASULI). პორ-

ტალები ქართულ არკიტექტურაში. [Portalebi k'art'ul ark'itek'turashi. Portals in Georgian Architecture.] (Порталы в грузинской архитектуре.) [Georgian and Russian texts. Edit. by B. Lort'-k'ip'anidze.] pp. 80, 2. 63 *plates.* თბილისი [*Tiflis*,] 1955. 4⁰.   **17080. f. 6**

GABASHVILI (VALERIAN NIKOLOZIS-DZE). ქარ-თული ფეოდალური წყობილება XVI–XVII საუ-კუნეებში. [K'art'uli p'eodaluri dsqobileba XVI–XVII saukuneebshi. A comparative study of Georgian feudal institutions in the 16th and 17th centuries.] pp. 440. თბილისი [*Tiflis*,] 1958. 8⁰.

17075. e. 44

GABESKIRIA (VIK'TOR IPATES-DZE). ერთ-ტომეული. [Ert'tomeuli. Collected poems, in one volume, including translations, and a dramatic poem on the martyrdom of Queen K'et'evan.] pp. 301. თბილისი [*Tiflis*,] 1955. 8⁰.   **17075. c. 9**

GABILAIA (IASON). [Trans. '50 dselidsadi samomkhmareblo kooperatsiisa Ruset'shi'.] *See* KHEISIN (M. L.)

—— [Edit. bi-weekly journal 'Kooperatsia'.] *See* PERIODICAL PUBLICATIONS.—*K'ut'aisi.*

GACHECHILADZE (AMBERKI NIKOLOZIS-DZE). გადმოცემა "ხოგაის მინდიზე" და პოემა "გველის მჭამელი". [Gadmotsema "Khogais Mindize" da poema "Gvelis mtchameli". The legend of Khogais Mindi and the poem, 'The Snake-eater', by Vazha-P'shavela.] pp. 68. თბილისი [*Tiflis*,] 1959. 8⁰.

17075. c. 40

GACHECHILADZE (GIVI RAZHDENIS-DZE). [Trans. 'Robin Hood'.] *See* HOOD (R.)

—— [Edit. of Georgian translation of 'Paradise Lost. Paradise Regained'.] *See* MILTON (J.)

—— [Trans. Shakspere's Sonnets.] *See* SHAKSPERE (W.)

—— [Editor and joint trans. of works of Shakspere.] *See* SHAKSPERE (W.)

GAGUA (Oʻtar Evmenis-dze). [Joint author of 'Tʻbilisis ghrmad mokhutsebuli adamianebi', or essays about the oldest inhabitants of Tiflis:] *See* Shapʻiro (I. B.) *and others*.

GAIOZ, *the Archdeacon. See* Gaius, *Archbishop of Astrakhan and Stavropolʼ*.

GAIUS, *Archbishop of Astrakhan and Stavropolʼ*. [*Life*.] *See* Palʼmov (N. N.)

GALAKTIONOV (Mikhail Romanovich). [Joint author of short biography of Stalin.] *See* Aleksandrov (G. F.) *and others*.

GAMEZARDASHVILI (Davitʻ Minas-dze). [Joint edit. of works of Niko Lortʻkʻipʻanidze.] *See* Lortʻkʻipʻanidze (N. M.)

—— ნარკვევები ქართული რეალიზმის ისტორიიდან. [Narkvevebi kʻartʻuli realizmis istoriidan. Studies in the history of realism in Georgian literature.] tom. 2. pp. 668, 4. თბილისი [*Tiflis*,] 1957. 8⁰.   **17075. f. 43**

GAMQRELIDZE (Tʻamaz Valerianis-dze). სიბილანტთა შესატყვისობანი და ქართველურ ენათა უძველესი სტრუქტურის ზოგი საკითხი. [Sibilanttʻa shesatqvisobani da kʻartʻvelur enatʻa udzvelesi strukʻturis zogi sakitʻkhi.] (Sibilant correspondences and some questions of the ancient structure of Kartvelian languages.) [With Russian and English summaries.] pp. 86. თბილისი [*Tiflis*,] 1959. 8⁰.   **17076. f. 34. (5.)**

GAMREKELI (Nikoloz). Саба Орбеліани и его грузинскій "Лексиконъ". Критическій очеркъ. pp. 30. *Тифлисъ*, 1885. 8⁰.   **011824. f. 29. (1.)**

GAMSAKHURDIA (Konstantine Svimonis-dze). Давид Строитель. Трилогия. кн. 1. Перевод с грузинского Элисбара Ананиашвили. pp. 358. *Москва*, 1945. 8⁰.   **17076. b. 41**

—— დავით აღმაშენებელი. ტეტრალოგია. [Davitʻ aghmashenebeli. Tetralogia. A historical novel cycle, based on the life of King David II of Ge-

orgia, surnamed the Builder.] bk. 1, *etc.* თბილისი [*Tiflis*,] 1954. 8⁰. *In progress*.   **17076. b. 14**

—— Десница великого мастера. Роман. [A historical novel, trans. into Russian by Pʻ. A. Tʻvaltʻvadze]. pp. 326. 1 *plate*. *Тбилиси*, 1955. 8⁰.   **17076. b. 17**

—— დიდოსტატის კონსტანტინეს მარჯვენა. რომანი. [Didostatis Konstantines marjvena. Romani. The right hand of Constantine, the great master. A historical novel.] pp. 398, 4. თბილისი [*Tiflis*,] 1958. 8⁰.   **17076. b. 39**

—— დიონისოს ღიმილი. რომანი. [Dionisos ghimili. Romani. The smile of Dionysos. A novel. With a preface by P. Kʻikʻodze. Second edition.] pp. ii. ix. 459. ტფილისი [*Tiflis*,] n. d. [1933]. 8⁰.   **17076. c. 10**

—— კრიტიკა. [Kritika.] Essays. [A collection of articles and essays on literary and historical themes.] 2 tom. თბილისი [*Tiflis*,] 1956–59. 8⁰.   **17076. f. 26**

GAPʻRINDASHVILI (Givi Mikheilis-dze). კლდის სახლები ნასოფლარ ფიაში. ქვაბთა საცხოვრისის ნიმუშები ფეოდალურ საქართველოში. [Kldis sakhlebi nasopʻlar Pʻiashi. Kʻvabtʻa satskhovrisis nimushebi pʻeodalur Sakʻartʻveloshi. Cliff dwellings at the ancient settlement of Pʻia. Specimens of underground habitations in feudal Georgia. Georgian text, with summary in Russian and sketches in the text.] ("Клдис сахли"—скальные дома селища Пиа.) pp. 70. 43 *plates*. თბილისი [*Tiflis*,] 1959. 8⁰.   **17075. e. 49**

GAPʻRINDASHVILI (Valerian Ivanes-dze). [Edit. 'Meotsnebe niamorebi'.] *See* Periodical Publications.—*Tiflis*.

—— ლექსები. ტომი პირველი. [Lekʻsebi. Tomi pirveli. Poems. Volume I.] pp. 220, v. ტფილისი [*Tiflis*,] 1926. 8⁰.   **17075. c. 28**

—— რჩეული. [Rcheuli. Selected poems.] pp. 243. თბილისი [*Tiflis*,] 1956. 8⁰.   **17075. d. 39**

GARAQANIDZE (Mikheil Kasianis-dze). Грузинское деревянное зодчество. (საქართველოს ხით

ხურㄴთმოძღვრება. [Sak'art'velos khit' khuro-t'modzghvreba. Georgian architecture in wood. Illustrated.]) pp. 169. 233 *plates. Государственное издательство "Искусство", etc.*: [*Tiflis*,] 1959. 4⁰.

17080. g. 6

GARITTE (GÉRARD). [Edit. and trans. Georgian version of letters of St. Antony.] *See* ANTONY, *Saint, the Monk.*

—— [Edit., with Latin trans., of an Epistle attributed to St. Arsenius.] *See* ARSENIUS, *Saint,* called *the Great.*

—— [Edit., with Latin trans., of Georgian version of the discovery of the relics of the Three Children of Babylon.] *See* BABYLON.—*Three Children of.*

—— [Edit., with Latin translation, of the Georgian version of Acts.] *See* BIBLE.—New Testament.—*Acts.*

—— [Edit. with Latin trans. the Georgian version of the Protevangelium Jacobi.] *See* BIBLE.—New Testament.—*Apocrypha.*

—— [Trans. 'Le fragment géorgien de l'Évangile de Thomas'.] *See* BIBLE.—New Testament.—*Apocrypha.*

—— [Compiler of 'Catalogue des manuscrits géorgiens littéraires du Mont Sinaï'.] *See* CATHARINE, *Saint of Alexandria.*—CONVENT OF, ON MOUNT SINAI.

—— [Edit., with Latin trans., of the Georgian version of the Passion of St. Procopius by Eusebius.] *See* EUSEBIUS, *Pamphili, Bishop of Caesarea in Palestine.*

—— [Trans. Georgian version of the Passion of St. Golindukh.] *See* GOLINDUKH, *Saint.*

—— [Edit. and trans. 'Le calendrier palestino-géorgien du Sinaiticus 34'.] *See* LITURGIES.—Greek Rite.—*Calendar.*

—— [Edit., with Latin trans., of the Life of St.

Orentius as contained in the Synaxary of the Georgian Church.] *See* ORENTIUS, *Saint, of Rize.*

—— [Edit., with Latin trans., of a fragment of the 9th Homily of Severian of Gabala.] *See* SEVERIAN, *Bishop of Gabala.*

—— [Edit. Georgian version of Sentences of Sextus.] *See* SEXTUS, *Pythagoraeus.*

—— [Edit., with Latin translation, of the Georgian Lives of St. Simeon Stylites and St. Ephraim.] *See* SIMEON, *Stylites, Saint.*

—— [Edit. and trans. of a portion of the Georgian version of the biography of Stephen of the Monastery of St. Savva.] *See* STEPHEN, *Laurae S.Sabae Monachus,* called THAUMATURGUS.

—— [For 'À propos des travaux de philologie géorgienne de M. G. Garitte':] *See* T'ARKHNISHVILI (M.)

—— La collection "Monuments de l'ancienne langue géorgienne". pp. 443–61. *Louvain,* 1959. 8⁰. [*Le Muséon.* tom. 72.] **P.P. 4453**

—— Les lettres de saint Antoine en géorgien. pp. 267–78. 2 *plates. Louvain,* 1951. 8⁰. [*Le Muséon.* tom. 64.] **P.P. 4453**

—— La littérature géorgienne et l'histoire culturelle du Moyen Âge. pp. 431–37. *Roma,* 1957. 8⁰. [*Accademia Nazionale dei Lincei, Fondazione Alessandro Volta. Atti dei Convegni, no. 12: Convegno di Science Morali, Storiche e Filologiche,* 1956. Tema: Oriente ed Occidente nel Medio Evo.] **Ac. 104. fd**

—— La mort de S. Jean l'Hésychaste d'après un texte géorgien inédit. pp. 75–84. *Bruxelles,* 1954. 8⁰. [*Analecta Bollandiana.* tom. 72.] **2002. g**

—— La sépulture de Modeste de Jérusalem. [Based mainly on Georgian sources.] pp. 127–33. *Louvain,* 1960. 8⁰. [*Le Muséon.* tom. 73.] **P.P. 4453**

—— Sur un fragment géorgien d'Agathange. pp.

GARITTE *(cont.)*
89–102. 2 *plates. Louvain*, 1948. 8⁰. [*Le Muséon.*
tom. 61.]   **P.P. 4453**

—— Le témoignage de Georges l'Hagiorite sur
l'origine du "Barlaam" grec. pp. 57–63. *Louvain,*
1958. 8⁰. [*Le Muséon.* tom. 71.]   **P.P. 4453**

—— and **DE HALLEUX** (André). [For 'Le sermon géorgien du moine Martyrius et son modèle
syriaque', being the Georgian text of a Homily De
paenitentia et humilitate by Martyrius-Sāhdōnā,
edited and trans. by G. Garitte, and accompanied
by the corresponding passages of the Syriac original
in a Latin trans. by A. de Halleux:] *See* Sāhdōnā,
Bishop of Māḫōzē dh-Arēwān in Bēth Garmai.

GARRY (Stephen). [Trans. 'Тьади Бигва'.] *See*
Kʻiacheli (L.) *pseud.*

GEBHARDT (Oscar von) and **HARNACK**
(Carl Gustav Adolf von). Texte und Unter-
suchungen zur Geschichte der altchristlichen Li-
teratur... herausgegeben von O. v. Gebhardt und
A. von Harnack. Bd. 1, *etc.. Leipzig*, 1882–. 8⁰.
In progress.   **3628. d. 1/1 —**

GEGESHIDZE (Mikheil Kiriles-dze). ქართული ხალხური ტრანსპორტი. I. სახმელეთო
საზიდი საშუალებანი. [Kʻartʻuli khalkhuri transporti. I. Sakhmeletʻo sazidi sashualebani.] (Грузинский народный транспорт. I. Сухопутные средства
перевозки. Georgischer Volkstransport. I. Landsbeförderungsmittel.) [Georgian text, with Russian
and German summaries.] pp. 230, 2. 74 *plates.*
თბილისი [*Tiflis,*] 1956. 8⁰.   **17080. e. 6**

GEGETCHKORI (Evgeni Petres-dze). L'Avenir
de la Géorgie. pp. 13. *Genève*, 1927. 8⁰. **17075. f.2 (3.)**

GEGETCHKORI (Lado). ქართული ხალხური
სიმღერის ოსტატები.[Kʻartʻuli khalkhuri simgheris
ostatebi. Masters of Georgian folk-song. Biographical sketches. Edit. by G. Chkhikvadze.] pp. 145,
2. 14 *plates.* თბილისი [*Tiflis,*] 1954. 8⁰. **17075. d.31**

GEIGER (Bernard) *and others.* Peoples and
languages of the Caucasus. A synopsis, by Bernard

Geiger, Tibor Halasi-Kun, Aert H. Kuipers, Karl
H. Menges. pp. 77. 1 *map. The Hague*, 1959. 8⁰.
[*Janua Linguarum.* no. 6.]   **17076. f. 28**

—— [Another copy.]   **W.P. 3312/6**

GELAZANIA (Gela). ღრუბლიან დღეებში.
ლექსები და პოემები. [Ghrublian dgheebshi.
Lekʻsebi da poemebi. In foggy days. Verses and
poems. With an introduction by V. Bakʻradze.]
pp. 192. პარიზი [*Paris,*] 1934. 8⁰.   **17076. d. 11**

GENCKO (Anatoly Nestorovich). *See* Genko
(A. N.)

GENKO (Anatoly Nestorovich). Абазинский
язык. Грамматический очерк наречия Тапанта.
pp. 202. *Москва*, 1955. 8⁰.   **012977. h. 12**

—— Абхазский вокализм. pp. 45–54. *Ленинград,*
1928. 8⁰. [*Известия Акад. Наук.* VII серия. *Отделение Гуманитарных Наук.*]   **Ac. 1125/44. (2)**

—— Из культурного прошлого ингушей. pp. 681–761.
Ленинград, 1930. 8⁰. [*Записки Коллегии Востоковедов.*
том 5.]   **Ac. 1125/qb**

—— Материалы по лезгинской диалектологии. Ку-
бинское наречие. pp. 317–42. *Ленинград*, 1929. 8⁰.
[*Известия Академии Наук.* VII серия. *Отделение
Гуманитарных Наук.*   **Ac. 1125/44 (2)**

—— Несколько образцов южно-дагестанского словесного творчества. pp. 182–189. *Ленинград*, 1927. 8⁰.
[*Восточные Записки.* том I.]   **Ac. 1096. d/3**

—— О языке убыхов. pp. 227–42. *Ленинград*, 1928. 8⁰.
[*Известия Акад. Наук.* VII серия. *Отделение Гуманитарных Наук.*]   **Ac. 1125/44. (2.)**

—— Оксфордский фрагмент древне-грузинской версии Иеремии. [A description and critical study
of the Georgian palimpsest fragment of the Book
of Jeremiah in the Bodleian Library.] pp. 345–52.
Ленинград, 1925. 8⁰. [*Записки Коллегии Востоковедов.*
том I.]   **Ac. 1125. qb**

—— По поводу работы проф. И. А. Джавахишвили,

касающейся грузинских палимпсестов с библейскими текстами. pp. 35–49. 1 *plate*. *Ленинград*, 1925. 4⁰. [*Тексты и разыскания по кавказской филологии*. том I.]   **Ac. 1125/228**

GEORGE. [For the Georgian form of this Christian name:] *See* Giorgi.

GEORGE, *Saint,* surnamed The Hagiorite. [For 'Le témoignage de Georges l'Hagiorite sur l'origine du "Barlaam" grec':] *See* Garitte (G.)

—— [For 'К исторіи церковныхъ реформъ въ древней Грузіи.—Георгій Аѳонскій':] *See* Javakhishvili (I. A.)

—— [*Life.*] *See* Peeters (P.). Histoires monastiques géorgiennes. 1917–19. 8⁰.   **2002. f**

GEORGIA. [For 'L'Avenir de la Géorgie':] *See* Gegetchkori (E. P.)

—— *Descriptions and Travels.* [For 'Gurjistanis vilaiet'is didi davt'ari', being a Turkish census return and cadastral survey of the provinces of Georgia occupied by the Ottomans in the 16th century:] *See* Jik'ia (S. S.)

—— Extraits d'une Topographie de la Géorgie, (traduits) par M. Klaproth. 3 pt. tom. 2. pp. 203–34; 349–75; tom. 5. pp. 20–59. *Paris*, 1828–30. 8⁰. [*Nouveau Journal Asiatique*. tom. 2, 5.]   **R. Ac. 8808**

—— *Filial of the U.S.S.R. Academy of Sciences.* *See* Tiflis.—*Academy of Sciences of the U.S.S.R. —Georgian Filial.*

—— *Foreign Relations.* [For decrees and other historical documents of the 18th century relative to Georgia:] *See* Tsagareli (A. A.)

—— *Georgian Communist Party.—Central Committee.* [For 'Sakavshiro komunisturi partiis (bolshevikebis) istoria', trans. by a commission of the Georgian Communist Party Central Committee:] *See* Russia. —*Российская Коммунистическая Партия.*

—— *Georgian Fascist Front.* დებულებანი მოღვაწეობისა და ბრძოლისათვის.[Debulebani moghvadseobisa da brdzolisat'vis. Principles for Action and Struggle. Signed by the Chairman of the Front, Sh. Maghlakelidze, and with a preface by V. Nozadze.] pp. 32. პარიზი [*Paris,*] 1937. 12⁰.   **17075. f. 37**

—— *Georgian Legion.* ჩვენი სიმღერები. [Chveni simgherebi. Our songs. A collection of war-time ballads, etc., edited with an introduction by L. Lini.] pp. 93. 8 *plates.* ბერლინი [*Berlin,*] 1943. 8⁰. [*K'art'uli legionis savele bibliot'eka.* no. 1.]   **17080. b. 10**

—— *Laws.* [For 'Notice du Code géorgien, manuscrit de la Bibliothèque royale':] *See* Brosset (M.-F.)

—— [For 'Sak'art'velos samart'lisa da kanont'mtsodneobis mimokhilva':] *See* David, *Prince-Regent of Georgia.*

—— [For 'Zwei Grundsteine zu einer grusinischen Staats- und Rechtsgeschichte':] *See* Holldack (F.)

—— [For 'Détails sur le droit public arménien, extraits du Code géorgien du roi Wakhtang, *etc.*':] *See* Vakhtang VI, *King of Georgia.*

—— Le Code de Vakhtang VI, édité en version française et annoté par Joseph Karst ... Avec un supplément: texte géorgien du Code V. établi d'après le manuscrit de la Bibliothèque Nationale de Paris, *etc.* [Followed by editions and translations of other Georgian mediaeval legal codes. With maps.] *Strasbourg*, 1934–40. 8⁰. [*Corpus Juris Ibero-Caucasici*. tom. 1–4, 6.]   **W. P. 5873/1,2**

—— *Ministry of Education.* [For 'T'khzulebani' or collected works of Iakob Gogebashvili, published under the auspices of the Institute of Pedagogic Sciences of the Georgian Ministry of Education:] *See* Gogebashvili (I. S.)

—— *Museum of Georgia. See* Tiflis.—*Museum of Georgia.*

GEORGIA *(cont.)*

—— *Muslim Georgian Liberation Committee.* [Newspaper 'Samuslimano Sak'art'velo'.] *See* PERIODICAL PUBLICATIONS.—*Batum.*

—— *National Boundaries.* [For 'Sak'art'velos teritoriis sazghvrebis shesakheb':] *See* I. (P.)

—— *National-Democratic Party.* [For journal of the Georgian National-Democratic Party, 'Iveria':] *See* PERIODICAL PUBLICATIONS.—*Paris.*

—— [For journal of the Georgian National-Democratic Party, 'Samshoblo':] *See* PERIODICAL PUBLICATIONS.—*Paris.*

—— *National Theatre.* ქართული თეატრის აღდგენის 100 წელი. [K'art'uli t'eatris aghdgenis 100 dseli. A jubilee symposium compiled in honour of the centenary of the revival of the Georgian national theatre.] pp. 239. 13 *plates* თბილისი [*Tiflis,*] 1953. 8⁰. **17076. e. 2**

—— *Republican Government.* [For government newspaper 'Sak'art'velos respublika':] *See* PERIODICAL PUBLICATIONS.—*Tiflis.*

—— მემუარი საქართველოს რესპუბლიკის მთავრობისა სახელმწიფოებსა და ერებს. [Memuari Sak'art'velos respublikis mt'avrobisa sakhelmdsip'oebsa da erebs. Memoir of the Government of the Georgian Republic to the States and Nations.] pp. 12. [*Tiflis ?,*] [1918.] 4⁰. **17080. e. 1**

—— *Scientific Conference of Young Scholars.* [For Proceedings of 9th Conference, held in Tiflis in 1958:] *See* TIFLIS.—*Academy of Sciences of the Georgian S.S.R.*

—— *Social-Democratic Workers' Party.* [For 'Sak'art'velos sots.-dem. mushat'a partiis mushaoba sazghvar-garet':] *See* GVARJALADZE (K.I.)

—— [For party organ 'Ert'oba':] *See* PERIODICAL PUBLICATIONS.—*Tiflis.*

—— *Socialist-Federalist Revolutionary Party.* [For party newspaper 'Sakhalkho sak'me':] *See* PERIODICAL PUBLICATIONS.—*Tiflis.*

—— ქართველ გლეხს. [K'art'vel glekhs. To the Georgian peasant.] pp. 16. პარიზი [*Paris,*] 1905. 8⁰. ['*Sak'art'velos' redak'tsiis gamotsema.* no. 2.] **17075. f. 1. (4.)**

—— ოქმები ქართველ რევოლუციონერთა პირველ კონფერენციისა. [Ok'mebi k'art'vel revolutsionert'a pirvel konp'erentsiisa. Protocols of the first conference of Georgian revolutionaries.] პარიზი [*Paris,*] 1904. pp. 259. 8⁰. ['*Sak'art'velos' redak'tsiis gamotsema.* no. 3.] **17075. f. 1. (3.)**

—— როგორ უნდა გადაწყდეს ჩვენში მიწის მფლობელობის საქმე. [Rogor unda gadadsqdes chvenshi midsis mp'lobelobis sak'me. How the agrarian problem should be settled in our country.] pp. 49. პარიზი [*Paris,*] 1905. 8⁰. ['*Sak'art'velos' redak'tsiis gamotsema.* no. 4.] **17075. f. 1. (2.)**

—— *Society for the Spreading of Literacy among the Georgians. See* TIFLIS.

—— *Soviet Socialist Republic.* საბჭოთა საქართველო 17 წლის მანძილზე. [Sabtchot'a Sak'art'velo 17 dslis mandzilze. Soviet Georgia over a period of 17 years; a political and economic survey.] pp. 101. 2 *plates.* [*Tiflis*; *Orjonikidze* printed,] 1938. 8⁰. **17075. ee. 3**

—— *State Publishing House.* [For 'Dsignis matiane', a bibliographical chronicle:] *See* PERIODICAL PUBLICATIONS.—*Tiflis.*

GEORGIAN ALPHABET. [For 'Das Alter der georgischen Schrift':] *See* DEETERS (G.)

—— [For 'Alphabetum Ibericum, sive Georgianum':] *See* IBERIAN ALPHABET.

—— [For 'Shrip'tebi nakhatebze dsardserebisat'vis':] *See* MIK'ELADZE (M. D.)

—— [For 'Армазское письмо и проблема происхождения грузинского алфавита':] *See* TSERET'ELI (G. V.)

GEORGIAN ANNALS. [For 'Histoire de la Géorgie depuis l'Antiquité jusqu'au XIXᵉ siècle':] *See* BROSSET (M.-F.)

GEORGIAN *(cont.)*

—— [For 'K'art'lis tskhovreba', being an edition of the Georgian annals, with critical notes and commentary:] *See* Brosset (M.-F.) and Chubinov (D. I.)

—— [For 'Akhali K'art'lis tskhovreba', a study of the sources and various redactions of the Georgian Annals:] *See* Grigolia (K. G.)

—— [For 'K'art'lis tskhovreba', being a re-edition of the early portion of the Georgian annals:] *See* Tchitchinadze (Z. E.)

—— ქართლის ცხოვრება. ტექსტი დადგენილი ყველა ძირითადი ხელნაწერის მიხედვით ს. ყაუხჩიშვილის მიერ. [K'art'lis tskhovreba. Tek'sti dadgenili qvela dzirit'adi khelnadseris mikhedvit' S. Qaukhchishvilis mier. The Georgian Annals. Text established on the basis of all the fundamental manuscripts by S. Qaukhchishvili.] (Картлис цховреба. История Грузии. Грузинский текст.) tom. 1, 2. თბილისი [*Tiflis*,] 1955– 4⁰. *In progress.*

17075. dd. 4

—— [Another copy of tom. 2.]   **17075. dd. 4***

GEORGIAN FOLKTALES. [For 'Khalkhuri zghaprebi':] *See* Aghniashvili (L.)

—— [For 'Georgian Folk Tales':] *See* Wardrop (M. S.)

GEORGIAN ORTHODOX CHURCH.—*Monastic Rules.* [For 'Typicon Gregorii Pacuriani', being a book of monastic rules drawn up for the Georgian monastery at Petritzos in Bulgaria:] *See* Bakuriani (G.)

—— [For 'La destinée du Typikon de Grégoire Bakouriani':] *See* Nikolaev (V.)

—— *Nomocanon.* [For 'Notice sur un Nomocanon géorgien ... Par M. Brosset':] *See* Euthymius, *of Mt'a-dsminda, Saint.*

—— Грузинскій великій номоканонъ по спискамъ Тифлисскаго Церковнаго Музея. [Extracts, with

Greek and Russian trans., edit. by V. N. Beneshevich.] pt. 2. pp. 112–27. Петроградъ, 1917. 4⁰. [*Христіанскій Востокъ.* том. 5. вып. 2.] *Lacks the first part.*   **Ac. 1125/105**

GEORGIAN THEATRE.—*Jubilee Committee.* [For 'K'art'uli t'eatris aghdgenis 100 dseli', a jubilee symposium compiled in honour of the centenary of the revival of the Georgian national theatre:] *See* Georgia.—*National Theatre.*

GERMANY. [For publications of Georgian antiBolshevik forces in the German army:] *See* Georgia.—*Georgian Legion.*

GHAMBASHIDZE (Davit'). [Edit. 'Mdsqemsi'.] *See* Periodical Publications —*K'ut'aisi.*

GHAMBASHIDZE (Rogneda Bidzinas-asuli). [Joint compiler of dictionary of metallurgical terminology.] *See* K'ashakashvili (N. V.) and Ghambashidze (R. B.)

GHĀZGHĪ-UMŪK̇. [For studies on the language of this region of Daghestan:] *See* Lak Language.

GHOGHOBERIDZE (Elene Davit'is-asuli). [Trans. 'Твади Бигва'.] *See* K'iacheli (L.) *pseud.*

—— [Trans. selected tales by Niko Lort'k'ip'anidze.] *See* Lort'k'ip'anidze (N. M.)

—— [Trans. selected tales by Qazbegi.] *See* Qazbegi (A. M.)

—— [Trans. 'О мудрости вымысла'.] *See* Savva, *the Monk* [*Prince* Sulkhan Orbeliani].

—— [Trans. selected works by Ilia Tchavtchavadze.] *See* Tchavtchavadze (I. G.) *Prince.*

—— [Trans. 'Пережитое'.] *See* Tseret'eli (A.R.) *Prince.*

GIGINEISHVILI (Ivane Moses-dze). [Joint compiler of 'Ort'ograp'iuli lek'sikoni'.] *See* T'op'uria (V. T.) and Gigineishvili (I. M.)

GIOFFI (Bernardo Maria). [Translator of Cardinal Bellarmino's 'Dottrina Christiana breve'.] *See* Robert [Bellarmino] *Saint, Cardinal, Archbishop of Capua.*

GIORGI V, *King of Georgia,* called The Brilliant. Laws of King George V, of Georgia, surnamed "The Brilliant". From the Bodleian Ms. of the Code of Vakhtang VI, formerly the Property of Prince David of Georgia. Translated by Oliver Wardrop. pp. 607–26. London, 1914. 8⁰. [*Journal of the Royal Asiatic Society* for 1914.]

                                   R. Ac. 8820/3

GIORGI VI, *King of Georgia.* [For 'Георгий Шестой. Поэма':] *See* Abashidze (G.G.)

GIORGI XII, *King of Georgia.* [For decrees and other historical documents relative to Georgia during the reign of Giorgi XII:] *See* Tsagareli (A. A.)

GIORGI, *Merchule.* [For critical study of the Latin trans. by P. Peeters of the biography of Gregory of Khandzt'a by Giorgi Merchule:] *See* Dondua (K. D.)

—— [*Life.*] *See* Ingoroqva (P. I.)

—— [For 'Histoires monastiques géorgiennes', containing a Latin translation of the Life of St. Gregory of Khandzt'a by Giorgi Merchule:] *See* Peeters (P.)

—— Житіе св. Григорія Хандзтˇійскаго. Грузинскій текстъ. Введеніе, изданіе, переводъ Н. Марра, съ Дневникомъ поѣздки въ Шавшію и Кларджію. pp. 012. lxx. 151. 216. 59 *plates.* С.-Петербургъ, 1911. 8⁰. [*Тексты и разысканія по армяно-грузинской филологіи.* кн. 7.]   **14005. f. 5**

GIORGIJANIDZE (Pˇarsadan). [For a French trans. of extracts from the chronicle of Pˇarsadan Giorgijanidze, incorporated in 'Histoire de la Géorgie':] *See* Brosset (M.-F.)

—— [For extracts from the chronicle of, incorporated as a continuation to 'Kˇartˇlis tskhovreba':] *See* Brosset (M.-F.) and Chubinov (D. I.)

GLOSS, *German Commandant in Palestine.* [For Georgian text of Commandant Gloss's proclamation at Holnon:] *See* European War, 1914–1919.

GOFFENSHEFER (V.). [Introduction to 'Заря над Эльбрусом'.] *See* Shogentsukov ('Ali) *and others.*

GOGEBASHVILI (Iakob Svimonis-dze). [For new version of 'Deda ena':] *See* Botsvadze (N.I.) and Burjanadze (E. I.)

—— [*Life.*] *See* Tˇavzishvili (G. I.)

—— ასპინძის ომი. ისტორიული ამბავი. [Aspindzis omi. Istoriuli ambavi. The Battle of Aspindza, a historical narrative. With a portrait of King Erekle II, and a map of the battle area.] pp. 31. თბილისი [*Tiflis,*] 1892. 8⁰. **17075. e. 4. (3.)**

—— ბურჯი ეროვნებისა. [Burji erovnebisa. The pillar of nationality. An essay on the importance of the mother tongue as basis for national life. Second, enlarged edition.] pp. 64. ტფილისი [*Tiflis,*] 1903. 8⁰.   **17075. f. 3**

—— ძირითადი უკუღმართობა. [Dziritˇadi ukughmartˇoba. Fundamental perversion. A pamphlet on the need for safeguarding the Georgian mother tongue.] pp. 62. ტფილისი [*Tiflis,*] 1892. 8⁰.   **17075. f. 1. (1.)**

—— Избранные педагогические сочинения. [Trans. from Georgian.] (Под редакцией ... Н. А. Константинова. [With a portrait.] pp. 293. *Москва,* 1954. 8⁰.   **8313. ee. 20**

—— თხზულებანი. [Tˇkhzulebani. Collected works.] tom. 2. [comprising essays on political and pedagogic subjects.] pp. 488. თბილისი [*Tiflis,*] 1954. 8⁰.   **17075. e. 13**

GOGIAVA (Klimenti). ახალი ნერგი : რომანი. [Akhali nergi: romani. Young growth: a novel.] pp. 222. თბილისი [*Tiflis,*] 1954. 8⁰.   **17077. a. 11**

GOGIBERIDZE (Simon). ბრძოლა სამშობლოსათვის. [Brdzola samshoblosatˇvis. The struggle for the homeland.] pp. 140. ვარსზი [*Paris*,] 1938. 8⁰.

———— [Joint edit. of poems by Vazha-P'shavela in Russian trans.] *See* VAZHA-P'SHAVELA, *pseud.*

17075. f. 19 (1)

GOGOBERIDZE. [For the surname of this form:] *See* GHOGHOBERIDZE.

GOLIATH, *the Philistine.* [For 'Hippolyts Erklärung in betreff Davids und Goliaths':] *See* HIPPOLYTUS, *Saint, of Rome.* Drei georgisch erhaltene Schriften von H., herausgegeben von G. Nath. Bonwetsch. 1904. 8⁰.   **3628. d. 1/26**

GOLINDUKH, *Saint.* La Passion géorgienne de Sainte Golindouch. [Georgian version, trans. into Latin, with introduction and notes by G. Garitte.] pp. 405–40. *Bruxelles,* 1956. 8⁰. [*Analecta Bollandiana.* tom. 74.]   **2003. a**

GOL'TSEV (VIKTOR VIKTOROVICH). [Edit. Boris Pasternak's trans. of poems by N. Barat'ashvili.] *See* BARAT'ASHVILI (N. M.) *Prince.*

———— [Edit. 'Песнь о Давиде Гурамишвили'.] *See* CHIK'OVANI (S. I.)

———— [Edit. novel 'Арсен из Марабды'.] *See* JAVAKHISHVILI (M. S.)

———— [Edit. selected fiction of L. K'iacheli in Russian translation.] *See* K'IACHELI (L.) *pseud.*

———— [Edit. 'Грузинские новеллы'.] *See* KLDIASHVILI (S. D.)

———— [Edit. poems by Giorgi Leonidze.] *See* LEONIDZE (G. N.)

———— [Edit. G. Tsagareli's translation of the epic poem 'Витязь в тигровой шкуре'.] *See* RUST'AVELI (SHOT'A).

———— [Edit. selected works of Ilia Tchavtchavadze in Russian trans.] *See* TCHAVTCHAVADZE (I. G.) *Prince.*

———— [Joint edit. of selected works of Akaki Tseret'eli in Russian translation.] *See* TSERET'ELI (A. R.) *Prince.*

———— Георгий Леонидзе. Критико-биографический очерк. pp. 106. 1 *plate. Москва,* 1955. 8⁰.

11872. aa. 17

———— Поэты советской Грузии в переводах Бориса Брика. (Редактор В. Гольцев.) [An anthology. With biographical notes on the poets represented.] pp. 140. *Москва,* 1936. 8⁰.   **11587. a. 4**

———— Шота Руставели и его поэма. pp. 156. *Москва,* 1940. 8⁰.   **11863. aa. 18**

———— Шота Руставели. Издание второе, доработанное. pp. 118. *Москва,* 1956. 8⁰.   **012977. i. 40**

———— Шота Руставели и его время. Сборник статей. (Редактор В. Гольцев.) [With a portrait.] pp. 275. *Москва,* 1939. 8⁰.   **10796. a. 59**

———— and **CHIK'OVANI** (SIMON IVANES-DZE). Поэзия Грузии, [Georgian poetry by various authors, translated into Russian. With illustrations by Irakli T'oidze.] pp. xxxi. 507. 14 *plates. Москва, Ленинград,* 1949. 4⁰.   **17075. dd. 1**

———— [Another copy.]   **11586. i. 22**

GOMART'ELI (IVANE GEDEVANIS-DZE). ეროვნული საკითხი. [Erovnuli sakit'khi. The National Question.] pp. 55. თფილისი [*Tiflis*,] 1906. 8⁰.

17075. f. 2. (2.)

GOMIASHVILI (ALEK'SANDRE KONSTANTINES-DZE) and **GVETADZE** (RAZHDEN MAT'ES-DZE). ხალხური პოეზია. რჩეული. [Khalkhuri poezia. Rcheuli. Folk poetry. A selection. Includes a representative collection of ballads, historical poems, etc., from mediaeval times to the present day.] pp. 575. თბილისი [*Tiflis*,] 1950. 8⁰.   **17075. d. 14**

GONCHAR (ALEKSANDR TERENTIEVICH). *See* HONCHAR (O. T.)

GONOV (S. Кн.) *and others.* [Joint compilers of Russian-Abaza dictionary.] *See* CHERKESSK.— *Cherkessky Nauchno-Issledovatel'sky Institut.*

GORDEEV (Dmitry). Описаніе пяти эмалевыхъ медальоновъ съ грузинскими надписями. pp. 209–16. 1 *plate. Петроградъ*, 1917. 4⁰. [*Христіанскій Востокъ*. томъ 5. вып. 3.]   **Ac. 1125/105**

GORDON (V.O.). [Edit. 'Shrip'tebi nakhatebze dsardserebisat'vis'.] *See* Mik'eladze (M. D.)

GORGADZE (Vasil Vasilis-dze). [Trans. 'Mebadurisa da t'evzis zghapari'.] *See* Pushkin (A.S.)

GORGANELI (Vakhtang). სიცოცხლის ტალღები. ლექსები. [Sitsotskhlis talghebi. Lek'sebi. Waves of life. Poems.] pp. 95. თბილისი [*Tiflis*,] 1953. 8⁰.   **17075. d. 10**

GOR'KY (Maksim) *pseud.* [i. e. Aleksyei Maksimovich Pyeshkov] *and others.* სამოქალაქო ომის ისტორია სსრ კავშირში. [Samok'alak'o omis istoria S.S.R. Kavshirshi. History of the Civil War in the U.S.S.R. Trans. from the Russian by B. Barat'ashvili and others. Illustrated.] tom. 1. pp. 558. 4 *plates.* თბილისი [*Tiflis*,] 1938. 8⁰.   **17075. e. 17**

GORNOSTAEV (G.). [Trans. 'Тайна Дюрка. Поэма'.] *See* Jafarov (A. M.)

GOTSADZE (Mikheil Kalistrates-dze). სოლომონ დოდაშვილი, ცხოვრება და მოღვაწეობა. [Solomon Dodashvili, tskhovreba da moghvadseoba. The life and career of S. Dodashvili, the 19th century pedagogue and man of letters.] pp. 268. სახელგამი [*State Publishing House: Tiflis*,] 1955. 8⁰.   **17075. e. 24**

GOUSSEN (Heinrich). [Trans. and edit. of the Georgian version of the Liturgy of St. Peter.] *See* Liturgies.—Greek Rite.—*Leitourgikon I.*

—— Die georgische Bibelübersetzung. A) Alte kirchliche Abhängigkeit Georgiens von Armenien. Die alte Übersetzung. pp. 300–18. 2 *plates. Rom*, 1906. 8⁰. [*Oriens Christianus.* Jahrg. 6.] *No more published.*   **Ac. 2002. b**

GRACH (A. D.). Кубачинский котел из археологического собрания Музея антропологии и этно-

графии. [Illustrated.] pp. 317–31. *Москва, Ленинград*, 1953. 8⁰. [*Сборник Музея Антропологии и Этнографии.* том 15.]   **Ac. 1126**

GRAF (Georg) *Dr. theol. et phil.* [Trans. Georgian version of the Physiologus.] *See* Physiologus.

GRAFFIN (René Léger Marie). [Edit. of 'Revue de l'Orient chrétien'.] *See* Periodical Publications.—*Paris.*

—— and **NAU** (François). Patrologia Orientalis. [Edited by R. Graffin and F. Nau.] tom. 1—*Paris*, 1903– 4⁰. *In progress. Tom. 10 contains an index to tom. 1–10; tom. 20 contains an index to tom. 11–20.*
                   2002. c—2002. d

—— [Another set.]   **14005. c**

GRAHAM (Cyril Clerke). The Avâr Language. pp. 291–352. *London*, 1881. 8⁰. [*Journal of the Royal Asiatic Society.* New ser. vol. 13.]
                   R. Ac. 8820/3

GRAY (Basil) *Keeper of Oriental Antiquities, British Museum.* 'The Man in the Panther Skin'. [A study of a 17th century manuscript of the epic by Shot'a Rust'aveli, acquired by the Bodleian Library.] pp. 194–98. 1 *plate. Oxford*, 1951. 8⁰. [*The Bodleian Library Record.* vol. 3. no. 32.]
                   P. P. 6481. bi

GREBNEV (Naum). Дагестанская народная лирика. В переводах Наума Гребнева. pp. 279. *Москва*, 1957. 8⁰.   **17075. c. 30**

GREGORY, *Bakuriani. See* Bakuriani (G.)

GREGORY, *Saint, of Khandzt'a.* [For critical study of the Latin trans. by P. Peeters of the biography of Gregory of Khandzt'a:] *See* Dondua (K. D.)

—— [*Life.*] *See* Giorgi, *Merchule.*

—— [*Life.*] *See* Peeters (P.). Histoires monastiques géorgiennes. 1917–19. 8⁰.   **2002. f**

GREN (Aleksei Nikolaevich). Грузинская повѣсть объ Амиранѣ, сынѣ Дареджана и остатки сказаній о немъ въ Картвельской народной литературѣ. pp. 1–40. С.-Петербургъ, 1895. 8⁰. [*Журналъ Министерства Народнаго Просвѣщенія.* часть 298. отд. 2.]

P. P. 1213

GRIBOMONT (Jean). Histoire du texte des Ascétiques de S. Basile. [With a chapter on the Georgian versions of the 'Regulae monasticae'.] pp. xix. 348, 2. *Louvain,* 1953. 4⁰. [*Bibliothèque du Muséon.* vol. 32.]

P. P. 1927. d

—— [Another copy.]   **753. ee. 18**

GRIGOL, *Bakuriani. See* BAKURIANI (G.)

GRIGOLIA (Konstantine Grigolis-dze). [Edit. Guide to the collections of ancient manuscripts in the Georgian State Museum.] *See* TIFLIS.—*Museum of Georgia.*

—— ახალი ქართლის ცხოვრება. [Akhali K'art'lis tskhovreba. A study of the sources and various redactions of the Georgian Annals. Edit. by N. A. Berdzenishvili.] pp. 363. თბილისი [*Tiflis,*] 1954. 8⁰. [*Narkvevebi Sak'art'velos istoriis dsqarot'mtsodneobidan.* no. 1.]

17075. e. 20

GRIGOLIA (Lado Davit'is-dze). [For a biography in pictures of the Georgian writer Ilia Tchavtchavadze, compiled under the artistic direction of L. Grigolia:] *See* TCHAVTCHAVADZE (I. G.) *Prince.*

GRIGOR, *of Akanc'.* [For the History of the Nation of the Archers, i. e. the Mongols, and their invasion of Georgia, formerly attributed to Małak'ia the Monk, and now ascribed to Grigor of Akanc', translated from the Armenian by M.-F. Brosset, and included as an appendix to 'Histoire de la Géorgie':] *See* BROSSET (M.-F.)

GRIGOR, *Saint,* called LUSAWORIČ, *Catholicos of Armenia.* [For 'Крещеніе армянъ, грузинъ, абхазовъ и алановъ святымъ Григоріемъ':] *See* MARR (N. Y.)

GRIMM LIBRARY. [For 'Georgian Folk Tales',

translated by M. S. Wardrop, and published in the Grimm Library series.] *See* WARDROP (M. S.)

GRISHASHVILI (Ioseb Grigolis-dze). ერთტომეული. [Ert'tomeuli. Collected poems in one volume. Edit., with a biography of the author, by G. Jibladze.] pp. xxxvii. 673. 1 *plate.* თბილისი [*Tiflis,*] 1955. 8⁰.   **17075. c. 18**

—— Избранные стихи. [Selected poems in Russian translation by various hands, edited by I. Postupal'sky.] pp. 251. 1 *plate.* Москва, 1951. 8⁰.

17076. h. 1

—— Ein polyglottes Liebeslied. Ein Beitrag zur Volkskunde Transkaukasiens. [Text edited, with translation and commentary, by A. Dirr.] pp. 55–59. *Leipzig,* 1928. 8⁰. [*Caucasica.* fasc. 5.]

P. P. 3803. eba

GUEGUETCHKORI (Eugène). *See* GEGETCHKORI (Evgeni).

GUELDENSTAEDT (Johann Anton). Reisen nach Georgien und Imerethi... herausgegeben... von Julius von Klaproth. pp. vi. 305. 1 *map.* *Berlin,* 1815. 8⁰.   **10075. c. 4**

GUGUNAVA (Svimon) *Prince.* თამარიანი. [T'amariani. The lay of T'amar. A historical poem. Second edition.] pp. 160, ii. ახალ-სენაკი [*Akhal-Senaki,*] 1893. 8⁰.   **17075. d. 2.(5.)**

GUGUSHVILI (Andro Iulonis-dze). [Joint edit. of 'Georgica'.] *See* LONDON.—*Georgian Historical Society.*

—— [Trans. 'Bahai-s sardsmunoeba'.] *See* BAHAISM.

—— The Chronological-Genealogical Table of the Kings of Georgia. pp. 109–53. *London,* 1936. 8⁰. [*Georgica.* vol. 1. nos. 2–3.]   **Ac. 8821. e**

—— Ethnographical and Historical Division of Georgia. [With a map.] pp. 53–71. *London,* 1936. 8⁰. [*Georgica.* vol. 1. nos. 2–3.]   **Ac. 8821. e**

GUGUSHVILI *(cont.)*

—— The Georgian alphabet: Transliteration, pronunciation, and classification of Georgian speech-sounds. 2 pt. no. 1. pp. 126–36; nos. 2–3. pp. 181–88. *London*, 1935. 8⁰. [*Georgica.* vol. 1. nos. 1–3.]

                 Ac. 8821. e

GUGUSHVILI (Paata Besarionis-dze). საქართველოსა და ამიერკავკასიის ეკონომიკური განვითარება XIX–XX სს. — მონოგრაფიები. [Sak'art'velosa da Amierkavkasiis ekonomikuri ganvit'areba XIX–XX ss.—Monograp'iebi. Studies on the economic development of Georgia and Transcaucasia in the 19th and 20th centuries.] Экономическое развитие Грузии и Закавказья в XIX–XX вв.—Монографии. tom. 2. pp. xv. 985. თბილისი [*Tiflis*,] 1956. 8⁰.   **17075. e. 33**

GULEKARI. [For description of antiquities in church at Gulekari:] *See* T'aqaishvili (E. S.)

GULIA (Dimitri Iosebis-dze). [For 'D. Gulias sakhelobis Ap'khazet'is enis, literaturis da istoriis institutis shromebi':] *See* Sukhumi.—*Abkhazian Linguistic, Literary and Historical Institute.*

—— Избранное. Перевод с абхазского. [Translations by A. Drozdov and others. With a portrait.] pp. 415. *Москва*, 1950. 8⁰.   **12266. de. 5**

—— Избранные произведения. Перевод с абхазского. (Стихотворения.—Камачич. Роман.—Из 'Коротких рассказов'.—Призраки. Драма.) [With a portrait.] pp. 414. *Москва*, 1953. 8⁰.   **12266. i. 11**

—— რჩეული. [Rcheuli. Selections, comprising poems and tales; 'Achrdilebi': 'The Half-Shadows', a drama in 3 acts, translated by I. K'avzharadze. With a biographical postscript by K. Bobokhidze.] pp. 214. 1 *plate.* სახელგამი [*State Publishing House*: *Tiflis*,] 1956. 8⁰.   **17076. b. 20**

GURAMISHVILI (Davit'). [For 'Песнь о Давиде Гурамишвили':] *See* Chik'ovani (S. I.)

—— [For selected poems, in Russian translation:] *See* Gol'tsev (V. V.) and Chik'ovani (S. I.). Поэзия Грузии. 1949. 4⁰.   **17075. dd. 1**

—— [*Life.*] *See* Nasidze (M.)

—— დავითიანი. [Davit'iani. A collection of poems, partly autobiographical, edited by Z. E. Tchitchinadze, with introductory essays by G. E. Tseret'eli and Petre Umikashvili. Third edition.] pp. xxx. xxv. 294, vii. ტფილისი [*Tiflis*,] 1894. 8⁰.

                 17075. d. 2. (6.)

—— დავითიანი. თხზულებათა სრული კრებული. [Davit'iani. T'khzulebat'a sruli krebuli. The Lay of David, comprising autobiographical and other poems. Complete collected edition, edited by a committee headed by A. G. Baramidze.] pp. 386. თბილისი [*Tiflis*,] 1955. 4⁰.   **17075. c. 19**

—— Давитиани. Стихотворения и поэмы. [A collection of poems, partly autobiographical. Trans. into Russian by N. A. Zabolotsky.] pp. 222. *Москва*, 1953. 8⁰.   **17075. d. 23**

GURGENIDZE (Mikheil). [Trans. 'Ukana-sknelni zhamni tskhovrebisa Imperatoris Nikolooz pirvelisa'.] *See* Nicholas I, *Tsar of Russia.*

GURIA. [For 'Археологическое путешествіе по Гуріи, *etc.*':] *See* Bak'radze (D. Z.)

—— [For 'Краткій отчетъ объ археологической поѣздкѣ въ Гурію':] *See* Bak'radze (D. Z.)

—— [For 'Beiträge zur Sprach- und Volkskunde . . . der Gurier':] *See* Bleichsteiner (R.)

—— [For 'Rapport sur les recherches archéologiques faites par M. Bakradzé dans le Gouria, en 1873':] *See* Brosset (M.-F.)

—— [For 'Rapport sur l'ouvrage manuscrit de M. Bakradzé, contenant l'exposé des recherches archéologiques faites par l'auteur, dans. . . le Gouria':] *See* Brosset (M.-F.)

—— [For 'Возстаніе въ Гуріи. Историческій романъ':] *See* Ninoshvili (E.) *pseud.*

GURIELI (Grigol Davit'is-dze) *Prince.* ქართველთ მაჰმადიანთ ლოცვები. [K'art'velt' Mahmadiant' lotsvebi. Prayers used by Georgian Muslims.] pp. 23. თბილისი [*Tiflis*,] 1891. 8⁰.

17071. d. 1

GURKO-KRYAZHIN (VLADIMIR ALEKSANDRO-VICH). Абхазия. pp. 93–116. *Москва*, 1926. 8⁰. [*Новый Восток.* кн. 13–14.]   **Ac. 1096. b/5**

—— Хевсуры. [With a bibliography.] pp. 258–96. *Москва*, 1928. 8⁰. [*Новый Восток.* кн. 20–21.].

Ac. 1096. b/5

GVARAMADZE (KONSTANTINE) called MESKHI. ხალხური მესხური ლექსები. [Khalkhuri meskhuri lek'sebi. Meskhian popular verses and folk poetry.] pp. 26. ახალ-სენაკი [*Akhal-Senaki*,] 1894. 12⁰.

17075. d. 5. (4)

GVARJALADZE (ISIDORE SILOVANIS-DZE). [Joint compiler of French-Georgian Dictionary.] *See* MATCHAVARIANI (I. N.) and GVARJALADZE (I. S.)

GVARJALADZE (KONSTANTINE IAGORAS-DZE). საქართველოს სოც.-დემ. მუშათა პარტიის მუშაობა საზღვარ-გარეთ. [Sak'art'velos sots.-dem. mushat'a partiis mushaoba sazghvar-garet'. The work abroad of the Georgian Social-Democratic Workers' Party.] pp. 68. პარიზი [*Paris*,] 1936. 8⁰.

17075. f. 25

GVAZAVA (GIORGI). [Edit. journal 'La Géorgie, organe de défense nationale'.] *See* PERIODICAL PUBLICATIONS.—*Paris*.

—— [Trans. the 'Prometheus Bound' of Aeschylus.] *See* AESCHYLUS.

—— [Trans. the tragedy 'Mithridate'.] *See* RACINE (J.)

—— [Joint translator of the epic 'The Man in the Panther's Skin'.] *See* RUST'AVELI (SHOT'A).

—— Rust'aveli and his Poem. pp. 3–9. 1 *plate*. *London*, 1937. 8⁰. [*Georgica.* vol. 1. nos. 4–5.]

Ac. 8821. e

GVETADZE (RAZHDEN MAT'ES-DZE). [Joint edit.

of Anthology of Soviet Georgian poetry.] *See* ABASHELI (A. B.) *and others.*

—— [Joint compiler of 'Khalkhuri poezia':] *See* GOMIASHVILI (A. K.) and GVETADZE (R. M.)

—— მოთხრობები. [Mot'khrobebi. Three tales.] pp. 199. ტფილისი [*Tiflis*,] 1930. 8⁰. **17076. b. 34**

—— Повести. [Stories. Russian translation by B. I. Korneev.] pp. 285. *Тбилиси*, 1950. 8⁰.

17076. a. 8

—— თხზულებანი ორ ტომად.[T'khzulebani or to-mad. Prose writings, in two volumes. Edit. by I. Khoshtaria with a biographical introduction by B. D. Zhghenti. With a portrait.] tom. 1. თბილისი [*Tiflis*,] 1955. 8⁰. *In progress.* **17076. b. 21**

GVRITISHVILI (DAVIT' VLADIMERIS-DZE). ფეოდალური საქართველოს სოციალური ურთიერთობის ისტორიიდან : ქართლის სათავადოები. [P'eodaluri Sak'art'velos sotsialuri urt'iert'obis isto-riidan: K'art'lis sat'avadoebi. From the history of the social relationships of feudal Georgia: The K'art'lian principalities. Edit. by Sh. A. Meskhia.] pp. 511. სახელგამი [*State Publishing House: Tiflis,*] 1955. 8⁰ **17075. e. 23**

HALASI-KUN (TIBOR). [Joint author of 'Peoples and languages of the Caucasus'.] *See* GEIGER (B.) *and others.*

HARNACK (CARL GUSTAV ADOLF von). [For 'Das Martyrium des heiligen Eustatius von Mzchetha... bearbeitet von Hrn. Harnack':] *See* EUSTACE, *Saint and Martyr, of Mtskhet'a.*

—— [Joint edit. of 'Texte und Untersuchungen zur Geschichte der altchristlichen Literatur'.] *See* GEBHARDT (O. von) and HARNACK (C. G. A. von).

—— [For 'Ein in georgischer Sprache überliefertes Apokryphon des Joseph von Arimathia', trans. by A. von Harnack:] *See* JOSEPH, *of Arimathea.*

—— Harnack-Ehrung: Beiträge zur Kirchen-geschichte ihrem Lehrer Adolf von Harnack zu seinem siebzigsten Geburtstage, 7. Mai 1921, dargebracht von einer Reihe seiner Schüler. pp. xxii. 483. *Leipzig*, 1921. 8⁰.   **04530. i. 7**

HASAN (Abu'l-Kāsim) called Firdausī, *Ṭūsī*. [For 'Из грузино-персидских литературных связей', containing a study of the Georgian version of the Shāhnāmeh:] *See* Marr (N. Y.)

—— შაჰნამე. ქართული ვერსიები. [Shahname. K'art'uli versiebi. The Old Georgian verse and prose versions of sections of the Shāhnāmeh, edit. by I. I. Abuladze and others.] (Le Chahnaméh. Versions géorgiennes.) tom. 2. pp. x. 649. 10 *plates*. ტფილისი[*Tiflis*,] 1934. 4⁰. *Note: tom. 1, containing vv. 1–2941, was published by I. I. Abuladze in 1916.*   **14807. g. 25**

HEGEL (Georg Wilhelm Friedrich). [For 'Ratsionaluri martsvali Hegelis daskvnis t'eoriashi':] *See* Tseret'eli (S. B.)

HENCKO (Anatoly Nestorovich). *See* Genko (A. N.)

HILARION, *the Priest*. [For 'Notice sur le couvent ibérien du Mont Athos', with a list of the Georgian manuscripts in the Iviron Monastery, compiled by the Priest Hilarion:] *See* Langlois (V.)

HILARION, *Saint, of Iberia*. S. Hilarion d'Ibérie. [Georgian text of the Life of St. Hilarion, trans. into Latin with introduction by P. Peeters.] pp. 236–69. *Bruxelles*, 1913. 8⁰. [*Analecta Bollandiana*. tom. 32.]   **2002 f**

—— [Another copy, being an offprint.] **4829. g. 37**

HIPPOLYTUS, *Saint, of Rome*. Drei georgisch erhaltene Schriften von H., herausgegeben von G. Nath. Bonwetsch: Der Segen Jakobs, Der Segen Moses, Die Erzählung von David und Goliath. pp. xvi. 98. *Leipzig*, 1904. 8⁰. [*Texte und Untersuchungen zur Geschichte der altchristlichen Literatur*. Neue Folge. Bd. 11, Hft. 1a.]   **3628. d. 1/26**

—— Hippolyts Kommentar zum Hohenlied, auf

Grund von N. Marrs Ausgabe des grusinischen Textes herausgegeben von G. Nathanael Bonwetsch. pp. 108. *Leipzig*, 1902. 8⁰. [*Texte und Untersuchungen zur Geschichte der altchristlichen Literatur*. Neue Folge. Bd. 8, Hft. 2.] **3628. d. 1/23**

—— Une page de saint Hippolyte retrouvée. (Ms. Hib. Hieros. 44), par Robert P. Blake. [Text and translation of a fragment of the Georgian version of the Benedictions of Moses.] pp. 225–31. *Paris*, 1925–26. 8⁰. [*Revue de l'Orient Chrétien*. tom. 5 (25).]   **P. P. 37. ck**

—— Sur les bénédictions d'Isaac, de Jacob et de Moïse. Sur les bénédictions d'Isaac et de Jacob: texte grec; versions arménienne et géorgienne. Sur les bénédictions de Moïse: versions arménienne et géorgienne. Traduction française résultante et notes par Maurice Brière, Louis Mariès, B.-Ch. Mercier. pp. xl. 274. *Paris*, 1954. 4⁰. [*Patrologia Orientalis*. tom. 27. fasc. 1 & 2.] **14005. c**

—— [Another copy.]   **2002. d**

—— Толкованіе Пѣсни пѣсней. Грузинскій текстъ … изслѣдовалъ, перевелъ и издалъ Н. Марръ. [With fragments of Hippolytus taken from the Armenian commentary on the Song of Solomon by Vardan Bardzrberdaçi.] pp. cxiv. 32. 67. 1 *plate*. С.-Петербургъ, 1901. 8⁰. [*Тексты и разысканія по армяно-грузинской филологіи*. кн. 3.] **14005. f. 5**

—— Die unter Hippolyts Namen überlieferte Schrift 'Über den Glauben', nach einer Übersetzung der in einer Schatberder Handschrift vorliegenden georgischen Version herausgegeben von G. N. Bonwetsch. pp. 1–36. Leipzig, 1907. 8⁰. [*Texte und Untersuchungen zur Geschichte der altchristlichen Literatur*. ser. 3. Bd. 1. Hft. 2.] **3628. d. 1/31**

HOLLDACK (Felix). Zwei Grundsteine zu einer grusinischen Staats- und Rechtsgeschichte. pp. xii. 256. *Leipzig*, 1907. 8⁰. **06005. h. 9**

HONCHAR (Oles' Terentievich). მედროშენი. [Medrosheni. The Standard-bearers. A novel. Trans. by D. Kasradze and S. P'ashalishvili. With a portrait.] pp. 594. სახელმწიფო გამომცემლობა [*State Publishing House: Tiflis,*] 1952. 8⁰.

17077. a. 14

HOOD (Robin). რობინ ჰუდი. ინგლისური ხალხური ბალადები. [Robin Hudi. Inglisuri khalkhuri baladebi.] (Robin Hood. English popular ballads. Translated into Georgian by Givi Gachechiladze.) [With illustrations by A. Bandzeladze.] pp. 129. თბილისი [*Tiflis,*] 1954. 8⁰.

17076. d. 14

I. (P.). საქართველოს ტერიტორიის საზღვრების შესახებ. — მოკლე სამოხსოვრო ცნობა. [Sak'art'velos teritoriis sazghvrebis shesakheb. — Mokle samokhsovro tsnoba. Concerning the frontiers of the territory of Georgia.—A brief memorandum.] (Court aperçu sur les frontières de la Géorgie.) [By P. I.] pp. 13. 2 *tables.* კონსტანტინეპოლი [*Constantinople,*] 1918. 4⁰.

17080. c. 2

IBERIAN ALPHABET. Alphabetum Ibericum, sive Georgianum, cum Oratione Dominicali, Salutatione Angelica, Symbolo Fidei, Præceptis Decalogi, Ecclesiæ Sacramentis, & Operibus Misericordiæ. Latina, & Iberica lingua compositis, & charactere Georgiano impressis: accesserunt Litaniæ B. V. eisdem lingua, & characteribus Ibericis. [The Georgian portion being attributed to Nicephorus the Monk, i. e. Nikoloz Irubak'idze-Choloqashvili.] pp. 16. *Typis Sac. Congr. de Propag. Fide: Romæ,* 1629. 8⁰.

621. b. 4. (12.)

—— [Another copy.]   **58. b. 31. (9.)**

—— [Another copy.]   **621. c. 33. (1.)**

—— [Another copy.]   **673. b. 11. (12.)**

—— [Another copy.]   **G. 16832. (12.)**

IEVLEV (Aleksei Ivanovich). [For a report on the diplomatic mission of Tolochanov and Ievlev to Imeret'i:] *See* Polievktov (M. A.)

IMEDASHVILI (Gaioz). რუსთველოლოგიური ლიტერატურა, 1712-1956 წლები. [Rust'velologiuri literatura, 1712–1956 dslebi. Bibliography of literature on Shot'a Rust'aveli, 1712–1956.] (Руствело-

логическая литература, 1712–1956 годы.) pp. xvi. 948, 4. თბილისი [*Tiflis,*] 1957. 8⁰.   **17075. c. 23**

IMNAISHVILI (Grigol Moses-dze). [Joint author of 'K'art'uli enis kakhuri dialek'ti'.] *See* Martirosov (A. G.) and Imnaishvili (G. M.)

IMNAISHVILI (Ivane Besarionis-dze). ქართული ოთხთავის სიმფონია - ლექსიკონი. [K'art'uli ot'kht'avis simp'onia-lek'sikoni. Concordance and dictionary to the Georgian Gospels.] (Симфония-словарь к грузинскому четвероглаву.) [Edit. by A. G. Shanidze]. pp. 032. 839. თბილისი [*Tiflis,*] 1948-1949. 4⁰. [*Dzveli k'art'uli enis dzeglebi.* no. 6.]

17071. c. 2

—— სახელთა ბრუნება და ბრუნვათა ფუნქციები ძველ ქართულში. [Sakhelt'a bruneba da brunvat'a p'unk'tsiebi dzvel k'art'ulshi. The declension of nouns and the functions of grammatical cases in Old Georgian.] (Склонение имен и функции падежей в древнегрузинском.) pp. 028. 781. თბილისი [*Tiflis,*] 1957. 4⁰. [*Dzveli k'art'uli enis kat'edris shromebi.* no. 4.]   **17076. h. 13**

IMPERATORSKAYA PUBLICHNAYA BIBLIOTEKA. *See* Saint Petersburg.

INASARI (Indo). ჩრდილი ერთი სინამდვილის. [Chrdili ert'i sinamdvilis. The shadow of a reality. An autobiographical novel.] pp. 215, 1. პარიზი [*Paris,*] 1936. 8⁰.   **17075. e. 36**

INGOROQVA (Egnate Fomich). *See* Ninoshvili (E.) *pseud.*

INGOROQVA (Pavle Ieses-dze). [Joint edit. of Georgian version of the Shāhnāmeh.] *See* Hasan (Abu'l-Ḳāsim) called Firdausī, *Ṭūsī.*

—— [Edit. 'Vep'khistqaosani'.] *See* Rust'aveli (Shot'a).

—— [Introductory essay to the epic poem 'The Knight in the Tiger's Skin':] *See* Rust'aveli (Shot'a).

—— [Edit. complete works of Ilia Tchavtchavadze.] *See* Tchavtchavadze (I. G.) *Prince.*

INGOROQVA *(cont.)*

—— [Edit. selected works by Ilia Tchavtchavadze.] *See* TCHAVTCHAVADZE (I. G.) *Prince.*

—— [Edit. Russian trans. of poems by Vazha-P'shavela.] *See* VAZHA-P'SHAVELA, *pseud.*

—— [Edit. tom. 7 of complete works of Vazha-P'shavela.] *See* VAZHA-P'SHAVELA, *pseud.*

—— გიორგი მერჩულე, ქართველი მწერალი მეათე საუკუნისა. ნარკვევი ძველი საქართველოს ლიტერატურის, კულტურის და სახელმწიფოებრივი ცხოვრების ისტორიიდან. [Giorgi Merchule, k'art'veli mdserali meat'e saukunisa. Narkvevi dzveli Sak'art'velos literaturis, kulturis da sakhelmdsip'oebrivi tskhovrebis istoriidan. Giorgi Merchule, a Georgian writer of the 10th century. A study in the history of the literature, culture and political life of ancient Georgia. Edit. by V. Dondua.] pp. 888, 0125. თბილისი [*Tiflis,*] 1954. 8⁰. **17076. i. 10**

—— Шота Руставели и его поэма. pp. 87–92. *Москва, Ленинград,* 1938. 8⁰. [*Известия Академии Наук СССР. Classe des Sciences Sociales.* no. 3.] **Ac. 1125/44. (9.)**

INGUSH FOLK-TALES. [For 'Textes populaires Inguš':] *See* JABAGI (M.)

INGUSH TRIBE. [For 'В горной Ингушетии':] *See* BOROZDIN (I. N.)

—— [For 'Из культурного прошлого ингушей':] *See* GENKO (A. N.)

—— [For 'Ингуши':] *See* YAKOVLEV (N. F.)

INSTITUT. Черкесский научно-исследовательский институт. *See* CHERKESSK.—*Cherkessky Nauchno-Issledovatel'sky Institut.*

—— Лазаревскій Институтъ Восточныхъ Языковъ. *See* MOSCOW.—*Lazarevsky,* afterwards *Tsentral'ny, Institut Vostochnykh Yazykov,* afterwards *Institut Vostokovedeniya.*

—— Институт по Изучению СССР. *See* MUNICH.

—— Кабардино-балкарский научно-исследовательский институт. *See* NAL'CHIK. — *Кабардино-балкарский научно-исследовательский институт.*

—— Institut d'Ethnologie. *See* PARIS.—*Université de Paris.—Institut d'Ethnologie.*

—— Ленинградский Институт Живых Восточных Языков. *See* SAINT PETERSBURG.

—— Институт антропологии и этнографии. *See* SAINT PETERSBURG.—*Academia Scientiarum Imperialis.*

—— Институт этнографии им. Н. Н. Миклухо-Маклая. *See* SAINT PETERSBURG.—*Academia Scientiarum Imperialis.*

—— Институт Истории Материальной Культуры. *See* SAINT PETERSBURG.—*Academia Scientiarum Imperialis.*

—— Институт Востоковедения. *See* SAINT PETERSBURG.—*Academia Scientiarum Imperialis.*

—— Институт Языкознания. *See* SAINT PETERSBURG.—*Academia Scientiarum Imperialis.*

—— Яфетический Институт, afterwards Институт языка и мышления. *See* SAINT PETERSBURG.—*Academia Scientiarum Imperialis.*

—— Абхазский Институт Языка, Литературы и Истории имени Д. И. Гулиа. *See* SUKHUMI.—*Abkhazian Linguistic, Literary and Historical Institute.*

—— Институт Экономики. *See* TIFLIS.—*Academy of Sciences of the Georgian S.S.R.*

—— Институт Истории Грузинского Искусства. *See* TIFLIS.—*Academy of Sciences of the Georgian S.S.R.—Institute of the History of Georgian Art.*

—— Институт Рукописей. *See* TIFLIS.—*Academy of Sciences of the Georgian S.S.R.—Institute of Manuscripts.*

—— Институт Защиты Растений. *See* TIFLIS.—*Academy of Sciences of the Georgian S.S.R.—Institute of Plant Protection.*

INSTITUT *(cont.)*

—— Институт Зоологии. *See* Tiflis.—*Academy of Sciences of the Georgian S.S.R.—Institute of Zoology.*

—— Институт Истории им. И. А. Джавахишвили. *See* Tiflis.—*Academy of Sciences of the Georgian S.S.R.—I. A. Javakhishvili Historical Institute.*

—— Институт грузинской литературы им. Руставели. *See* Tiflis.—*Academy of Sciences of the Georgian S.S.R.—Rust'aveli Literary Institute.*

—— Тбилисский Ботанический Институт. *See* Tiflis. —*Academy of Sciences of the Georgian S.S.R.— Tiflis Botanical Institute.*

—— Кавказский Историко-Археологический Институт. *See* Tiflis.—*Kavkazsky Istoriko-Arkheologichesky Institut.*

—— Институт языка, истории и материальной культуры им. Н. Я. Марра. *See* Tiflis.—*Marr Language Institute,* afterwards *Institute of Linguistics.*

—— Akad. Iv. Beritashvilis sakhelobis p'iziologiis instituti. *See* Tiflis.—*Tiflis State University.*

—— Горский Институт Народного Образования. *See* Vladikavkaz.—*Gorsky Institut Narodnogo Obrazovaniya.*

IOANN GIORGIEVICH, *Tsarevich. See* John, *Prince of Georgia.*

IODASAF, *Saint and Hermit.* [For the Georgian versions of the legend of Barlaam and Josaphat, or Iodasaf:] *See* Barlaam, *Saint, of India.*

IORDANISHVILI (Solomon). [Joint reviser of Marjory Wardrop's translation of 'The Knight in the Tiger's Skin'.] *See* Rust'aveli (Shot'a).

——[Edit. 'Sabavshvo mot'khrobebi'.] *See* Vazha-P'shavela, *pseud.*

IOSEB, *T'bileli. See* Joseph [Ioseb Saakadze], *Bishop of Tiflis.*

IOSELIANI (Anna Nikolozis-asuli). [Joint edit. of the Book of the Living Pillar, *etc.*] *See* Nicholas I, *Catholicos of Georgia.*

IOSELIANI (Avt'andil Pavles-dze). საქართ-ველო საბჭოთა კავშირის დიდ სამამულო ომში, 1941–1945. [Sak'art'velo sabtchot'a kavshiris did samamulo omshi, 1941–1945. Georgia in the Soviet Union's Great Patriotic War, 1941–45.] pp. 532. თბილისი [*Tiflis,*] 1958. 8⁰.   **17075. e. 43**

IOSELIANI (Platon Egnates-dze). [*Biography.*] *See* Tchitchinadze (Z. E.)

—— A short history of the Georgian Church, translated from the Russian and edited with additional notes by S. C. Malan. pp. xiii. 208. *London,* 1866. 8⁰.   **4532. aaa. 14**

IOSSELIAN (Platon Ignat'evich). *See* Ioseliani (Platon Egnates-dze).

IPPOLIT, *Saint. See* Hippolytus, *Saint, of Rome.*

IRAKLI II, *King of Georgia. See* Erekle II.

IRBAK'I-CHOLAQASHVILI (Nikip'ore), *Monk of the Order of St. Basil.* [For 'Alphabetum Ibericum', attributed in part to the Monk Nicephorus, i. e. Nikoloz, otherwise Nikip'ore Irbak'i-Cholaqashvili:] *See* Iberian Alphabet.

IRUBAK'IDZE-CHOLOQASHVILI (Nikoloz). *See* Iberian Alphabet.

ISAAC, *the Patriarch.* [For 'Sur les bénédictions d'Isaac, de Jacob et de Moïse'. Greek, Armenian and Georgian texts, with French translation:] *See* Hippolytus, *Saint, of Rome.*

ISARLISHVILI (Luka). კათოლიკენი საქართვე-ლოში. [Kat'olikeni Sak'art'veloshi. Catholics in Georgia. Translated from the Russian.] pp. 61–92. ტფილისი [*Tiflis,*] 1897. 8⁰. [*Moambe.* tom. 4. no. 12.]   **17089. b. 1**

IT'ONISHVILI (Valerian Jambulis-dze). კორ-წინების ზოგიერთი წეს-ჩვეულება ძველ თბილო-

სძი. [K'ordsinebis zogiert'i dscs-chveuleba dzvel T'bilisshi. Some marriage customs of old Tiflis.] pp. 48. თბილისი [*Tiflis,*] 1959. 8⁰.   **17078. e. 2**

IVIRON MONASTERY. *See* ATHOS, *Mount.*

IVNEV (RYURIK). [Trans. 'Георгий Шестой. Поэма'.] *See* ABASHIDZE (G. G.)

JABAGI (M.). Textes populaires Inguš recueillis par M. Jabagi, traduits.... par G. Dumézil. pp. 74. *Paris,* 1935. 8⁰. *Lithographed from the Ms.*
    12976. t. 8

JACOB, *the Patriarch.* Des heiligen Hippolyt Abhandlung über die Segnungen Jakobs, wie er die zwölf Patriarchen segnete. *See* HIPPOLYTUS, *Saint, of Rome.* Drei georgisch erhaltene Schriften von H., herausgegeben von G. Nath. Bonwetsch. 1904. 8⁰.   **3628. d. 1/26**

—— [For 'Sur les bénédictions d'Isaac, de Jacob et de Moïse'. Greek, Armenian and Georgian texts, with French translation:] *See* HIPPOLYTUS, *Saint, of Rome.*

JAFAROV (ABŪ MUSLIM). Тайна Дюрка. Поэма. [Trans. from the Tabasaran language by G. Gornostaev.] pp. 121. *Москва,* 1959. 12⁰.   **17075. d. 47**

JAKOBIA (GIORGI PAVLES-DZE). [Joint author of manual of Georgian literature.] *See* BARAMIDZE (G. R.) and JAKOBIA (G. P.)

JALAGHANIA (IRINE LEVANIS-ASULI). Из истории монетного дела в Грузии XIII века. [With a map.] pp. 126. 6 *plates. Тбилиси,* 1958. 8⁰.   **17078. a. 3**

—— [Another copy.] *Dept. of Coins and Medals.*

JAMBAKURIAN-ORBELIANI (ALEK'SANDRE VAKHTANGIS-DZE). *See* ORBELIANI (A. V. JAMBAKURIAN–).

JAMES, *the Priest, of Tsurtavi.* [For 'Sainte Šušanik, martyre en Arméno-Géorgie', a study incorporating a trans. into Latin of the Georgian Vita of the saint composed by James the Priest:] *See* PEETERS (P.)

JAMES, *Saint and Apostle, called the Less, pseud.* [For the Georgian version of the Protevangelium Jacobi:] *See* BIBLE.—New Testament.—*Apocrypha.*

—— [For the Georgian version of the Liturgy of St. James, edit. with Latin trans. by M. T'arkhnishvili in 'Liturgiae Ibericae Antiquiores':] *See* LITURGIES.—Greek Rite.—*Leitourgikon I.*

—— [For 'The Georgian Version of the Liturgy of St. James', translated by F. C. Conybeare and O. Wardrop:] *See* LITURGIES.—Greek Rite.— *Leitourgikon I.*

—— [For 'Eine neue georgische Jakobosliturgie', trans. from the Graz manuscript by M. T'arkhnishvili:] *See* LITURGIES.—Greek Rite.—*Leitourgikon I.*

JANASHIA (NIKOLOZ SIMONIS-DZE). Абхазскій культъ и бытъ, в предѣлахъ Абжу. pp. 157–208. *Петроградъ,* 1917. 4⁰. [*Христіанскій Востокъ.* томъ 5. вып. 3.]   **Ac. 1125/105**

—— The Religious Beliefs of the Abkhazians. [A translation of the article originally published in Russian in "Христіанскій Востокъ", 1915.] pp. 117–53. *London,* 1937. 8⁰. [*Georgica.* vol. 1. nos. 4–5.]   **Ac. 8821. e**

—— Религіозныя вѣрованія абхазовъ. pp. 72–112. *Петроградъ,* 1915. 4⁰. [*Христіанскій Востокъ.* томъ 4. вып. 1.]   **Ac. 1125/105**

JANASHIA (SIMON NIKOLOZIS-DZE). [Edit. 'Ornement populaire géorgien'.] *See* BARDAVELIDZE (V. V.) and CHITAIA (G. S.)

—— [Edit. 'Tchanur-megrul-k'art'uli shedarebit'i lek'sikoni'.] *See* CHIK'OBAVA (A. S.)

—— [Joint edit. of Catalogue of Georgian Manuscripts in the Georgian State Museum.] *See* TIFLIS.—*Museum of Georgia.*

—— Сборник Руставели. К 750-летию ,,Вепхисткаосани". (რუსთაველის კრებული, ,,ვეფხისტყა-

ოსნის" 750 წლისთავისადმი მიძღვნილი. [Rustʻa-
velis krebuli, "Vepʻkhistqaosnis" 750 dslistʻavisad-
mi midzghvnili.] Recueil Rousthavéli. À l'occasion
du 750ᵐᵉ anniversaire de "Vephkhistkaossani".)
[A collection of articles in Russian, edited by S. N.
Janashia.] pp. xii. 222. *Тбилиси,* 1938. 8⁰.

17080. d. 7

JANASHVILI (MOSE GIORGIS-DZE). [Edit. and
trans. geographical description of Georgia.] *See*
VAKHUSHTI, *Prince of Georgia.*

—— მწერლობა მე-IX-X საუკუნისა. [Mdserloba
me-IX–X saukunisa. Literature of the ninth-tenth
centuries. Containing fragments of Old Georgian
medical and pedagogical treatises, with historical
introduction.] pp. xii. 49. ტფილისი [*Tiflis,*] 1891.
8⁰. **17076. g. 3**

—— მეფე ერეკლეს სახსოვარი, 1798–1898.
[Mepʻe Erekles sakhsovari, 1798–1898. In commemoration of the centenary of the death of King
Erekle. A collection of poems and essays by various hands, edit. with introduction by M. G. Janashvili.] pp. 47. [*Tiflis,*] 1898. 8⁰. **17075. e. 4. (5)**

—— საქართველოს დედა-ქალაქი ტფილისი.
[Sakʻartʻvelos deda-kʻalakʻi Tpʻilisi. Tiflis, mother-
city of Georgia. A historical survey.] 9 pt. ქუთაისი
[*Kʻutʻaisi,*] 1899–1900. 8⁰. [*Krebuli.* tom. 2. no. 2,
3, 4, 5, 6, 8, 10, 11, 12.] **17089. b. 4**

JAPʻARIDZE (VAKHTANG VARLAMIS-DZE). [Joint
compiler of Report of First and Second Gudarekhi
Archaeological Campaigns.] *See* MUSKHELISHVILI
(L. V.) *and others.*

—— კერამიკული წარმოება XI-XIII სს. საქართველოში, არქეოლოგიური მასალების მიხედვით.
[Keramikuli dsarmoeba XI–XIII ss. Sakʻartʻveloshi, arkʻeologiuri masalebis mikhedvitʻ. Ceramic
production in Georgia in the 11th–13th centuries,
according to the archaeological evidence. With a
summary in Russian, and illustrations in the text.]
pp. *73, 7. 72 plates.* თბილისი [*Tiflis,*] 1956. 4⁰.

17080. g. 2

JAVAKHISHVILI (IVANE ALEKʻSANDRES-DZE).

[Trans. 'Мудрость Балавара':] *See* BARLAAM, *Saint,
of India.* [The Legend of Barlaam and Josaphat.—
Georgian].

—— [Trans. 'Das Martyrium des heiligen Eustatius von Mzchetha':] *See* EUSTACE, *Saint and Martyr, of Mtskhetʻa.*

—— [For critical study of Javakhishvili's work on
Georgian palimpsests:] *See* GENKO (A. N.)

—— არილი. . . . პროფესორ ივანე ჯავახიშვი-
ლისადმი . . . მიძღვნილი კრებული. [Arili. . . .
Propʻesor Ivane Javakhishvilisadmi. . . midzghvnili krebuli. A *Festschrift,* containing essays on
Georgian language, literature, history and art.]
(Arili. Festschrift Prof. Dr. Iwane Dschawachischwili, Rektor der Universität zu Tiflis, zum
25-jährigen Jubiläum seiner wissenschaftlichen
Tätigkeit, 1900–25, dargebracht.) pp. 232. 8 *plates.*
ტფილისი [*Tiflis,*] 1925. 8⁰. **17089. c. 1**

—— Государственный строй древней Грузіи и древней Арменіи. томъ I. pp. iii. 148. *С.-Петербургъ,* 1905.
8⁰. *No more published.* [*Тексты и разысканія по
армяно-грузинской филологіи.* кн. 8.] **14005. f. 5**

—— Исторія церковнаго разрыва между Грузіей и
Арменіей въ началѣ VII вѣка. 2 pt. pp. 433–46; 511–
36. *С.-Петербургъ,* 1908. 8⁰. [*Извѣстія Акад. Наукъ.*
VI серія. томъ 2.] **Ac. 1125/44**

—— Къ исторіи церковныхъ реформъ въ древней Грузіи.—Георгій Аѳонскій. pp. 358–72. *С.-Петербургъ,*
1904. 8⁰. [*Журналъ Министерства Народнаго Просвѣщенія.* часть 351. отд. 2.] **P. P. 1213**

—— Къ вопросу о времени построенія грузинскаго
храма въ Атенѣ, *etc.* pp. 277–97. 2 *plates. С.-Петер-
бургъ,* 1912. 4⁰. [*Христіанскій Востокъ.* томъ I. вып.
I.] **Ac. 1125/105**

—— ქართული ენისა და მწერლობის ისტორიის
საკითხები. [Kʻartʻuli enisa da mdserlobis istoriis sakitʻkhebi. Collected essays on Georgian
language and literary history. Edited by Ilia Abuladze and A. G. Baramidze.] pp. 222, 1. თბილისი
[*Tiflis,*] 1956. 8⁰. **17076. i. 13**

JAVAKHISHVILI *(cont.)*

—— ქართველი ერის ისტორია. [K'art'veli eris istoria. History of the Georgian People. With plates, genealogical tables and illustrations.] bk. 1, 2. ტფილისი [*Tiflis*,] 1928, 1948. 8⁰. *Bk. 1 is of the third, bk. 2 of the second edition; bk. 1 lacks title-page.*   **17075. e. 30**

—— Матеріалы для исторіи грузинской патристической литературы. pp. 6–29. *С.-Петербургъ*, 1912. 4⁰. [*Христіанскій Востокъ*. томъ I. вып. I.]   **Ac. 1125/105**

—— Народныя переписи въ Грузіи. [Enumerates ancient statistical sources for the population census of mediaeval Georgia.] pp. 01–014. *С.-Петербургъ*, 1902. 8⁰. [*Записки Восточнаго Отдѣленія Имп. Русскаго Археологическаго Общества*. томъ 14.]   **Ac. 5584**

—— Объ одномъ анонимномъ грузинскомъ историкѣ XIV вѣка. pp. 1483–86. *Петроградъ*, 1917. 8⁰. [*Извѣстія Акад. Наукъ*. VI серия. томъ II.]   **Ac. 1125/44**

—— Обзоръ теорій и литературы о происхожденіи грузинскаго языка. pp. 241–58. *С.-Петербургъ*, 1908. 8⁰. [*Журналъ Министерства Народнаго Просвѣщенія*. Новая серія. часть 16. отд. 2.]   **P. P. 1213**

—— Проповѣдническая дѣятельность ап. Андрея и св. Нины въ Грузіи. pp. 77–113. *С.-Петербургъ*, 1901. 8⁰. [*Журналъ Министерства Народнаго Просвѣщенія*. часть 333. отд. 2.]   **P. P. 1213**

—— საქართველოს საზღვრები ისტორიულად და თანამედროვე თვალსაზრისით განხილული. [Sak'art'velos sazghvrebi istoriulad da t'anamedrove t'valsazrisit' gankhiluli. The frontiers of Georgia viewed historically and from a contemporary viewpoint.] pp. 56. ტფილისი [*Tiflis*,] 1919. 8⁰. *Imperfect; lacking the map.*   **17075. e. 29**

—— შოთა რუსთაველის ეპოქის მატერიალური კულტურა. [Shot'a Rust'avelis epok'is materialuri kultura.] (Материальная культура эпохи Шота Руставели.) [Articles in Georgian and Russian by various hands on material and economic life and culture in Georgia at the time of Shot'a

Rust'aveli, edited by I. A. Javakhishvili.] pp. viii. 468. 19 *plates*. თბილისი [*Tiflis*,] 1938. 4⁰.   **17075. ee. 4**

JAVAKHISHVILI (MIKHEIL SABAS-DZE). Арсен из Марабды. Роман. [A historical novel based on the life of the Georgian bandit and adventurer Arsena of Marabda. Trans. into Russian by the author in collaboration with B. I. Korneev. Edit. with notes by V. V. Gol'tsev. Third edition.] pp. 503. *Москва*, 1935. 8⁰.   **17076. a. 2**

—— არსენა მარაბდელი. [Arsena Marabdeli. A historical novel based on the life of the Georgian bandit and adventurer Arsena of Marabda. With a commentary and notes by S. E. Tchilaia.] pp. 582, 4. 1 *plate*. თბილისი [*Tiflis*,] 1955. 8⁰.   **17076. b. 43**

JAVRISHVILI (DAVIT' LAVRENTIS-DZE). Грузинские народные танцы. [With diagrams and musical illustrations.] pp. 277, 3. 5 *plates*. *Тбилиси*, 1958. 8⁰.   **17078. a. 1**

JEDLIČKA (JAROMÍR). [Trans. the epic, 'The Man in the Panther's Skin'.] *See* RUST'AVELI (SHOT'A).

—— Kamenité cesty Gruzie. Povídky gruzínských klasiků. [Four short novels, by D. Tchonk'adze, Ilia Tchavtchavadze, and A. Qazbegi, translated into Czech with introduction and notes, by J. Jedlička.] pp. 325, 6. *Praha*, 1958. 12⁰.   **17076. b. 44**

—— Das Studium der altgeorgischen Sprache in Georgien. Bibliographische Übersicht. pp. 299–328. *Louvain*, 1958. 8⁰. [*Le Muséon*. tom. 71.]   **P. P. 4453**

JEREMIAS, *Bishop of Georgia*. [For 'Jérémie, évêque de l'Ibérie perse':] *See* PEETERS (P.)

JERUSALEM. [For 'Плѣненіе Іерусалима персами въ 614 г.':] *See* ANTIOCHUS, *Laurae S. Sabae Monachus*.

—— [For the Metropolitan Timothy's travels to Jerusalem and other Holy Places:] *See* GABASHVILI (T.) *Metropolitan of K'ut'aisi*.

JERUSALEM (*cont.*)

—— [For 'Die Weihnachtsfeier Jerusalems im siebten Jahrhundert':] *See* Liturgies.—Greek Rite.—*Euchologion.*

—— [For 'Le grand lectionnaire de l'Église de Jérusalem':] *See* Liturgies.—Greek Rite.— *Lectionaries.*

—— [For 'Oster- und Pfingstfeier Jerusalems im siebten Jahrhundert':] *See* Liturgies.—Greek Rite.—*Pentekostarion.*

—— [For 'Quadragesima und Karwoche Jerusalems im siebten Jahrhundert:'] *See* Liturgies.— Greek Rite.—*Triodion.*

—— *Georgian Monastery of the Cross.* [For 'Житіе Прохора, *etc.*', being lives of the founder of the Georgian monastery of the Cross and of two Georgian martyrs connected with that monastery:] *See* Qip'shidze (D. A.).

—— *Greek Patriarchal Library.* Catalogue des manuscrits géorgiens de la Bibliothèque Patriarcale Grecque à Jerusalem, par R. P. Blake. 4 pt. *Paris*, 1922–26. 8°. [*Revue de l'Orient Chrétien.* tom. 3 (23)—5 (25).] **P. P. 37. ck**

JESUS CHRIST. [For 'О фрагментѣ грузинской версіи "Дѣтства Христа":] *See* Marr (N. Y.)

—— Фрагментъ грузинской версіи "Дѣтства Христа". [Edit. by L. M. Melik'set'-Begi.] pp. 315–20. *Петроградъ*, 1922. 4°. [*Христіанскій Востокъ.* томъ 6. вып. 3.] **Ac. 1125/105**

JIBLADZE (Giorgi Nikolozis-dze). [Edit. selected works of Byelinsky.] *See* Byelinsky (V. G.)

—— [Edit. collected poems of I. G. Grishashvili.] *See* Grishashvili (I. G.)

—— ქართული ლიტერატურა. სახელმძღვანელო საშუალო სკოლის XI კლასისათვის. [K'art'uli literatura. Sakhelmdzghvanelo sashualo skolis XI klasisat'vis. A manual of modern Georgian literature, composed by various hands and edited by G. Jibladze for use in the 11th form of Georgian State Schools. Illustrated.] pp. 406. თბილისი [*Tiflis*,] 1955. 8°.   **17076. f. 13**

JIBUTI (Nadezhda Makaris-asuli). [Joint author of 'Atcharis A.S.S.R'.] *See* Nizharadze (N. I.) and Jibuti (N. M.)

JIK'IA (Sergi Simonis-dze). გურჯისტანის ვილაიეთის დიდი დავთარი. [Gurjistanis vilaiet'is didi davt'ari. A Turkish census return and cadastral survey of the provinces of Georgia occupied by the Ottomans in the 16th century. Turkish text published with Georgian trans. and historical commentary, by S. S. Jik'ia.] (Пространный реестр гюрджюстанского вилайета.) bk. 1 [containing Turkish text]; bk. 3 [commentary and notes.] თბილისი [*Tiflis*,] 1947, 58. 8°. *Wants bk. 2.*   **14448. c. 32**

JOHN, *Chrysostom, Saint, Patriarch of Constantinople.* [For the Georgian version of the Liturgy of St. John Chrysostom, edit. with Latin trans. by M. T'arkhnishvili in 'Liturgiae Ibericae Antiquiores':] *See* Liturgies.—Greek Rite.—*Leitourgikon I.*

JOHN, *of Damascus, Saint.* [For the Passion of St. Peter of Capitolias, the Greek original of which was formerly attributed to St. John of Damascus:] *See* Peter, *Saint and Martyr, of Capitolias.*

JOHN, *of Mt'a-dsminda, Saint.* [*Life.*] *See* Peeters (P.). Histoires monastiques géorgiennes. 1917–19. 8°.   **2002. f**

JOHN, *Petridsi.* [For 'Іоаннъ Петрицкій, грузинскій неоплатоникъ XI–XII вѣка':] *See* Marr (N. Y.)

JOHN, *Prince of Georgia.* Калмасоба, или хожденіе по сбору Іоанна Хелашвили, иподіакона. ['Kalmasoba', or account of a tour undertaken for the collection of alms by the monk Iona Khelashvili, including a narrative of his adventures and didactic homilies on various themes. Trans. into Russian and abridged by V. Dondua.] pp. xxxii. 236. 1 *plate.* Тбилиси, 1945. 8°.   **17076. g. 8**

JOHN, *Saint and Evangelist. See* BIBLE.—New Testament.—*John.*

JOHN, *Saint, Bishop of Colonia in Armenia.* [For 'La mort de S. Jean l'Hésychaste d'après un texte géorgien inédit':] *See* GARITTE (G.)

JORDANIA (NOAH). *See* ZHORDANIA (N. N.) *President of Georgia.*

JORJADZE (ARCHIL). ძველი და ახალი. [Dzveli da akhali. The old and the new. A political tract.] pp. 109. ტფილისი [*Tiflis,*] 1906. 8⁰.
                     17075. f. 2. (1.)

—— თხზულებანი. წიგნი მესამე.—ნაახრევი. [T'khzulebani. Dsigni mesame.—Naazrevi. Works. Book 3.—Belles lettres. Essays on art, religion, philosophy, music and the theatre.] pp. vii. 216. ტფილისი [*Tiflis,*], 1911. 8⁰.   **17075. e. 7. (2.)**

JORJADZE (DAVIT' GIORGIS-DZE). [Editor of newspaper 'Sakhalkho p'urtseli'.] *See* PERIODICAL PUBLICATIONS.—*Tiflis.*

JOSAPHAT, *Saint and Hermit.* [For the Georgian versions of the legend of Barlaam and Josaphat:] *See* BARLAAM, *Saint, of India.*

JOSEPH, *of Arimathea.* [For 'Eine Benutzung des Testamentum Domini nostri Jesu Christi', being a study of one of the sources of the apocryphal legend of Joseph of Arimathea:] *See* SCHMIDT (C.)

—— Die apokryphe Erzählung des Joseph von Arimathäa über den Bau der ersten christlichen Kirche in Lydda. Aus dem Georgischen übersetzt von Dr. Theodor Kluge. pp. 24–38. *Leipzig,* 1915. 8⁰. [*Oriens Christianus.* Neue Serie. Bd. 4.]
                     Ac. 2002. b

—— Ein in georgischer Sprache überliefertes Apokryphon des Joseph von Arimathia. [Translated, on the basis of the Russian version by N. Y. Marr,] von Adolf Harnack. pp. 920–31. *Berlin,* 1901. 4⁰. [*Sitzungsberichte der K. Preussischen Akademie der Wissenschaften.* 1901, Juli-Dec. No. 39.]   **Ac. 855**

—— Сказаніе о построеніи первой церкви въ городѣ Лиддѣ. Грузинскій текстъ ... изслѣдовалъ, издалъ и перевелъ Н. Марръ. pp. 72. 2 *plates.* С.-Петербургъ, 1900. 8⁰. [*Тексты и разысканія по армяно-грузинской филологіи.* кн. 2.]   **14005. f. 5**

JOSEPH [IOSEB SAAKADZE], *Bishop of Tiflis.* Великий Моурави. Поэма XVII века о Георгии Саакадзе. [A historical poem describing the life and adventures of Giorgi Saakadze. Trans. into Russian by G. Tsagareli from the original poem, known as 'Didmouraviani', and edit. by S. Shervinsky.] pp. 81. Москва, 1945. 8⁰. **17075. d. 21. (4.)**

—— [Another copy.]   **11588. aa. 41**

JRUTCHI. [For 'Eine georgische Miniaturenfolge zum Matthäusevangelium', being a description of miniatures in the Jrutchi Gospel codex:] *See* BAUMSTARK (A.)

JUANSHERIANI (JUANSHER). [For a French trans. of Juansher's life of King Vakhtang Gorgasali, incorporated in 'Histoire de la Géorgie':] *See* BROSSET (M.-F.)

—— [For Juansher's life of King Vakhtang Gorgasali, incorporated in 'K'art'lis tskhovreba':] *See* BROSSET (M.-F.) and CHUBINOV (D. I.); GEORGIAN ANNALS.

JUGHASHVILI (IOSEB). *See* STALIN (I. V.)

JULIAN, *Saint and Martyr, of Emesa.* La Passion de S. Julien d'Émèse [trans. into Latin from the Georgian version, with introduction, by P. Peeters.] pp. 44–76. *Bruxelles,* 1929. 8⁰. [*Analecta Bollandiana.* tom. 47.]   **2002. f**

JULIAN, *Saint and Martyr, of Pella.* [For 'La Passion géorgienne des SS. Théodore, Julien, etc.':] *See* THEODORE, *Saint and Martyr, of Pella.*

JUNKER (HEINRICH F. J.). Das Awestaalphabet und der Ursprung der armenischen und georgischen Schrift. 2 pt. fasc. 2. pp. 1–82; fasc. 3. pp. 82–139. 5 *plates. Leipzig,* 1925–26. 8⁰. [*Caucasica.* fasc. 2, 3.]   **P. P. 3803. eba**

KABARDIAN LANGUAGE. *See* Circassian and Related Languages.

KAKABADZE (Ivane Konstantines-dze). ქართული ენა. სახელმძღვანელო არაქართული სკოლების X კლასისათვის. [K'art'uli ena. Sakhelmdzghvanelo arak'art'uli skolebis X klasisat'vis. The Georgian language. Manual for the 10th class of non-Georgian schools. Illustrated.] pp. 111. თბილისი [*Tiflis,*] 1958. 8⁰.   **17076. h. 15**

KAKABADZE (Polikarpe Malkhazis-dze). რჩეული თხზულებანი : პიესები. [Rcheuli t'khzulebani: piesebi. Selected writings: plays. Edit. by I. Khoshtaria.] pp. 359,2. სახელგამო [*State Publishing House: Tiflis,*] 1954. 8⁰.   **17076. b. 7**

—— *and others.* Грузинская советская драматургия. [Containing plays by P. M. Kakabadze, Sh. N. Dadiani and others, trans. into Russian by various hands, and edited by B. D. Zhghenti and others.] pp. 562, 2. Москва, 1958. 8⁰.   **17076. d. 16**

KAKABADZE (Sargis Nestoris-dze). [Edit. of 'Vep'khis tqaosani'.] *See* Rust'aveli (Shot'a).

—— The Date of the Building of the Cathedral "The Living Pillar". [With an appendix by D. Gordeev.] pp. 78–91. *London,* 1936. 8⁰. [*Georgica.* vol. 1. no. 2–3.]   **Ac. 8821. e**

—— საქართველოს მოკლე ისტორია. ახალი საუკუნეების ეპოკა. [Sak'art'velos mokle istoria. Akhali saukuneebis epok'a. Short history of Georgia. Modern period, comprising 15ᵗʰ–20ᵗʰ centuries.] pp. ii. 228. 1 *map.* ტფილისი [*Tiflis,*] 1920. 8⁰.   **17075. ee. 8**

KAKABADZE (Vasili Mikheilis-dze). ქართული ლიტერატურა. ქრესტომათია არაქართული სკოლების XI კლასისათვის. [K'art'uli literatura. K'restomat'ia arak'art'uli skolebis XI klasisat'vis. Georgian literature. Chrestomathy for the 11ᵗʰ form of non-Georgian schools. Includes specimens of prose and verse, with biographical sketches and portraits of the authors.] pp. 222. თბილისი [*Tiflis,*] 1954. 8⁰.   **17076. g. 11**

KAKHET'I. [For 'Кахетинские революционные песни':] *See* Chkhaidze (M. P.)

—— For 'Ambokheba Kakhet'isa, 1812 ds. Istoriuli ambavi':] *See* P'roneli (A.) *pseud.*

KAKHET'IAN FOLK-TALES. *See* Razikashvili (T'. P.)

KAKHIDZE (Medea Ilias-asuli). [Trans. stories by Shio Aragvispireli.] *See* Aragvispireli (Sh.) *pseud.*

—— [Joint trans. of novel 'Лицом к лицу'.] *See* K'ut'at'eli (A. N.)

—— [Trans. of tales by N. I. Lomouri.] *See* Lomouri (N. I.)

KAKUSHADZE (Noe Vasilis-dze). დიდი სიცოცხლე. მოთხრობები. [Didi sitsotskhle. Mot'khrobebi. A great life. Collected stories.] pp. 151. თბილისი [*Tiflis,*] 1958. 8⁰.   **17076. b. 37**

—— წიგნის სასახლე. მოთხრობები. მეომრის დღიურიდან. [Dsignis sasakhle. Mot'khrobebi. Meomris dghiuridan. The Book Palace. Short stories. From the diary of a Warrior. A collection of novels and tales.] pp. 379. თბილისი [*Tiflis,*] 1955. 8⁰.   **17076. b. 8**

KALADZE (Karlo Razhdenis-dze). ერთტომეული. (რჩეული ლექსები, ბალადები და სიმღერები.) [Ert'tomeuli. (Rcheuli lek'sebi, baladebi da simgherebi.) Selected verses, ballads and songs, in one volume.] pp. 311. 1 *plate.* სახელგამო [*State Publishing House: Tiflis,*] 1954. 8⁰.   **17075. c. 16**

—— Стихи, песни, баллады в переводах, *etc.* pp. 71. *Тбилиси,* 1945. 8⁰.   **11587. b. 43**

KAMBIEV (Khamat Pitovich). Къэбэрдей литературэ. Курыт школым и 10-нэ классым папщ1э хрестоматие. [Kabardian literature. Anthology for the 10th class of Middle Schools. Second edition.] pp. 288, 2. *Нальчик,* 1957. 8⁰.   **17076. h. 4**

KANCHELI (Aleksandr Ivanovich). *See* Qancheli (A. I.)

KANDELAKI (Konstantine). ეკონომიური კრიზისი. [Ekonomiuri krizisi. Essays on the Depression and its attendant economic crisis.] pp. 77. პარიზი [*Paris,*] 1932. 8⁰.   **17075. f. 9. (1)**

—— The Georgian Question before the Free World. Acts—documents—evidence. Translated from the French. pp. 217. *Paris,* 1953. 8⁰.
     8092. dd. 50

—— რას ამბობენ ფაქტები: საქართველოს ეკო-ნომიურ ცხოვრებიდან. [Ras amboben p'ak'tebi: Sak'art'velos ekonomiur tskhovrebidan. What the facts tell: From the economic life of Georgia. A pamphlet.] pp. 50. პარიზი [*Paris,*] 1927. 8⁰.
     17075. f. 26

—— საქართველოს ეროვნული მეურნეობა. წიგნი პირველი : ტერიტორია და მოსახლეობა. [Sak'art'velos erovnuli meurneoba. Dsigni pirveli: teritoria da mosakhleoba.] (Économie nationale de la Géorgie. Livre premier: Territoire et population.) [With a map.] pp. v. 188. პარიზი [*Paris,*] 1935. 8⁰.   **17075. f. 32**

KANDELAKI (Nikoloz). ქართული მჭევრმეტყველება. [K'art'uli mtchevrmetqveleba. Georgian oratory and rhetoric. An anthology of notable Georgian speeches and discourses from classical times until the early 20th century, compiled and edited by N. Kandelaki.] (Грузинское красноречие.) pp. 377. თბილისი [*Tiflis,*] 1958. 8⁰.   **17075. e. 47**

KANDELAKI (Simon). ავადმყოფობა Pappataci და კოღო Phlebotomus'ი საქართველოსა და მის მეზობელ ქვეყნებში. [Avadmqop'oba Pappataci da kogho Phlebotomus'i Sak'art'velosa da mis mezobel k'veqnebshi.] (La fièvre Pappataci et Phlebotomus en Géorgie et dans les pays voisins.) [Georgian text with French summary.] pp. 48. 3 *plates.* თფილისი [*Tiflis,*] 1920. 8⁰. [*Sak'art'velos muzeumis shromebi.* no. 1.]   **17080. b. 1**

KAPANADZE (Davit' Giorgis-dze). Грузинская нумизматика. [A treatise on Georgian numismatics, trans. from the original Georgian edition. Edit. by L. P. Kharko. Illustrated.] pp. 184. 16 *plates.* Москва, 1955. 4⁰.   **17080. f. 4**

KAPIEV, *Efendi.* [Edit. of 'Избранные песни и стихи'.] *See* Stal'sky (S.)

KAPIEVA (Nataliya Vladimirovna). [Introduction and notes to poems by G. Tsadasa.] *See* Tsadasa (G.)

KARBELASHVILI (Davit' Polievk'tis-dzè). К фонетике удинского языка. pp. 259–76. Москва, Ленинград, 1935. 8⁰. [*Язык и мышление.* вып. 3–4.]   **Ac. 1125. t/2**

KARBELASHVILI (Polievk'ti Grigolis-dze). *See* Tskhviloeli (P.) *pseud.*

KARBELASHVILI (Vasili Grigolis-dze). [Joint edit. of the Book of the Living Pillar, *etc.*] *See* Nicholas I, *Catholicos of Georgia.*

KARDANOV (Buba Matsikovich). [Edit. 'Кабар-динско-русский словарь'.] *See* Apazhev (M. L.) *and others.*

—— and **BICHOEV** (Aslan T.). Русско-кабардинско-черкесский словарь... с приложением краткого грамматического очерка кабардинского языка Б. М. Карданова. (Урыс-къэбэрдей-шэрджэс словарь. [Urys-keberdei-sherdzhes slovar'. Russian-Kabardo-Circassian dictionary.]) [Edit. by A. O. Shogentsukov.] pp. 1054. 1 *folding table.* Москва, 1955. 8⁰.   **17076. f. 10**

KARITCHASHVILI (Davit' Giorgis-dze). სვი-მონ მეფე, 1557–1600. [Svimon mep'e, 1557–1600. A biography of King Simon of K'art'li. Edit. by Z. E. Tchitchinadze.] pp. 50. ტფილისი [*Tiflis,*] 1894. 8⁰.   **17075. e. 4. (4)**

KARST (Josef). [Edit. and trans. 'Le Code de Vakhtang VI, *etc.*'.] *See* Georgia.—*Laws.*

—— Grundzüge einer vergleichenden Grammatik des Ibero-Kaukasischen. Bd. 1. pp. liii. 323, 3. *Strassburg,* 1932. 8⁰. *No more published.*
     O12904. p. 9

—— Littérature géorgienne chrétienne. pp. 177. [*Paris,* 1934.] 8⁰.   **11856. aa. 13**

KARST *(cont.)*

—— Précis de numismatique géorgienne. Avec 12 planches et un appendice sur la métrologie des Géorgiens. pp. 92. *Paris*; *Anvers* [printed], 1938. 8⁰. [*Publications de la Faculté des Lettres de l'Université de Strasbourg.* fasc. 81.]   **Ac. 2633. e**

K'ART'LIAN FOLK-TALES. *See* RAZIKASH-VILI (T'. P.)

K'ASHAKASHVILI (NIKOLOZ VASILIS-DZE) and **GHAMBASHIDZE** (ROGNEDA BIDZINAS-ASULI). მეტალურგიის ტერმინოლოგია. [Metalurgiis terminologia. A dictionary of metallurgical terminology, Russian-Georgian and Georgian-Russian.] (Металлургическая терминология.) pp. 324. თბილისი [*Tiflis,*] 1959. 8⁰.   **17076. h. 20**

KASRADZE (DAVIT' ILARIONIS-DZE). [Joint trans. of the novel 'Medrosheni'.] *See* HONCHAR (O. T.)

KASRADZE (NADIA). [Joint compiler of Catalogue of Georgian manuscripts in the Georgian State Museum.] *See* TIFLIS.—*Museum of Georgia.*

KATCHARAVA (IURI MIKHEILIS-DZE). სოცია-ლურ-პოლიტიკური ცხოვრების განსაკუთრებუ-ლი პირობები და გლეხთა რევოლუციური მოძრაო-ბის თავისებურებანი საქართველოში 1905–1907 წწ. [Sotsialur-politikuri tskhovrebis gansakut'rebuli pirobebi da glekht'a revolutsiuri modzraobis t'aviseburebani Sak'art'veloshi, 1905–1907 dsds. The special circumstances of the social and political life of the country and the particular features of the revolutionary movement among the Georgian peasantry, 1905–1907. With a summary in Russian.] pp. 136. თბილისი [*Tiflis,*] 1959. 8⁰.   **17075. e. 45**

KAUTSKY (CARL JOHANN). ინტერნაციონალი და საბჭოთა რუსეთი. [Internationali da sabtchot'a Ruset'i. Georgian trans. by R. A. of 'Die Internationale und Sowjetrussland'.] pp. 48. [*Paris; Arpajon printed,*] 1925. 8⁰.   **17075. f. 31**

K'AVZHARADZE (IRODION). [Trans. drama 'Achrdilebi'.] *See* GULIA (D. I.)

KAZBEGI (ALEKSANDR). *See* QAZBEGI (A. M.)

KEKELIDZE (KORNELI SAMSONIS-DZE). [Edit. and trans. of Passion of Agathangelus of Damascus.] *See* AGATHANGELUS, *Saint and Martyr, of Damascus.*

—— [Joint editor of Georgian version of the Shāhnāmeh.] *See* ḤASAN (ABU'L-ḲĀSIM) called FIRDAUSĪ, *Ṭūsī.*

—— [Edit. Catalogue of Georgian manuscripts in the K'ut'aisi State Historical Museum.] *See* K'UT'AISI.—*K'ut'aisi State Historical Museum.*

—— [For 'Die Weihnachtsfeier Jerusalems im siebten Jahrhundert', trans. from Kekelidze's edition of the Georgian text:] *See* LITURGIES.—Greek Rite.—*Euchologion.*

—— [For 'Oster- und Pfingstfeier Jerusalems im siebten Jahrhundert', trans. from Kekelidze's edition of the Georgian text:] *See* LITURGIES.—Greek Rite.—*Pentekostarion.*

—— [For 'Quadragesima and Karwoche Jerusalems im siebten Jahrhundert', trans. from Kekelidze's edition of the Georgian text:] *See* LITURGIES.—Greek Rite.—*Triodion.*

—— [For 'Die alt-christliche Literatur in der georgischen Überlieferung', being a revised translation of K. S. Kekelidze's bibliographical study:] *See* P'ERADZE (G.)

—— [Edit. with Russian trans. of the Georgian version of the Passion of St. Peter of Capitolias.] *See* PETER, *Saint and Martyr, of Capitolias.*

—— [Edit. 'Dzveli k'art'uli literaturis k'restomat'ia'.] *See* QUBANEISHVILI (S. I.)

—— [Joint edit. of 'Vep'khis tqaosani'.] *See* RUST'AVELI (SHOT'A).

—— [For German adaptation of the history of Georgian ecclesiastical literature by K. S. Kekelidze:] *See* T'ARKHNISHVILI (M.)

KEKELIDZE *(cont.)*

—— [Joint edit. of Catalogue of Georgian manuscripts in the Georgian State Museum.] *See* TIFLIS.—*Museum of Georgia.*

—— ეტიუდები ძველი ქართული ლიტერატურის ისტორიიდან. [Etiudebi dzveli k'art'uli literaturis istoriidan. Studies in the history of ancient Georgian literature.] tom. 1–7, *etc.* თბილისი [*Tiflis,*] 1945– 8⁰. *In progress.*   **17076. f. 19**

—— Іоаннъ Ксифилинъ, продолжатель Симеона Метафраста. pp. 325–47. С.-Петербургъ, 1912. 4⁰. [*Христіанскій Востокъ.* томъ 1. вып. 3.]   **Ac. 1125/105**

—— Историко-агіографическіе отрывки.[Containing extracts from the lives of Daniel the Stylite and Simeon of Mons Admirabilis.] pp. 187–98. С.-Петербургъ, 1913. 4⁰. [*Христіанскій Востокъ.* томъ 2. вып. 2.]   **Ac. 1125/105**

—— ქართული ლიტერატურის ისტორია. ძველი ლიტერატურა. [K'art'uli literaturis istoria. Dzveli literatura. History of Georgian literature. Ancient literature. Fourth edition, revised and enlarged. Edited by L. V. Menabde.] tom. 2. pp. iv. 747,4. თბილისი [*Tiflis,*] 1958. 8⁰.   **17076. f. 20**

—— Конспективный курс истории древне-грузинской литературы. pp. 117. Тбилиси, 1939. 8⁰.   **11864. b. 24**

—— Литургическіе грузинскіе памятники въ отечественныхъ книгохранилищахъ и ихъ научное значеніе, *etc.* pp. xxxi. 515. xiii. Тифлисъ, 1908. 4⁰.   **3475. e. 29**

—— Объ изданіи грузинскихъ агіографическихъ памятниковъ. pp. 925–32. Петроградъ, 1915. 8⁰. [*Извѣстія Акад. Наукъ.* VI серія. томъ 9.]   **Ac. 1125/44**

—— საიუბილეო კრებული . . . კორნელი სამსონის ძე კეკელიძეს დაბადების 80 წლისთავის აღსანიშნავად. [Saiubileo krebuli . . . Korneli Samsonis dze Kekelidzes dabadebis 80 dslist'avis aghsanishnavad. A jubilee symposium of essays in honour of K. S. Kekelidze's 80th birthday. Edit. by A. G.

Baramidze and others. With a portrait.] pp. 492. თბილისი [*Tiflis,*] 1959. 8⁰.   **17076. f. 30**

—— and **BARAMIDZE** (ALEK'SANDRE GIORGIS-DZE). ძველი ქართული ლიტერატურა : V–XVIII სს. [Dzveli k'art'uli literatura: V–XVIII ss. Ancient Georgian literature: 5ᵗʰ–18ᵗʰ centuries. Edit. by a committee consisting of G. Abzianidze and others.] pp. 521, 2. თბილისი [*Tiflis,*] 1954. 8⁰. [*K'art'uli literaturis istoria.* tom. 1.]   **17080. e. 5**

KEKELIDZE (PROKLE LEVARSIS-DZE). [Joint compiler of chrestomathy of 20ᵗʰ century Georgian literature.] *See* RADIANI (S. D.) and KEKELIDZE (P. L.)

KERESELIDZE (GIORGI). Le destin d'un peuple : la Géorgie. pp. 61. *Paris,* 1953. 8⁰.   **17075. f. 38**

KESHOKOV (ALIM PSHEMAKHOVICH). Стихи, перевод с кабардинского. [Collected poems, translated from the Kabardian by A. Potapova and others.] pp. 158, 1. Москва, 1951. 12⁰.   **17075. d. 38**

—— [Another copy.]   **11588. f. 14**

K'ET'EVAN, *Queen of Georgia.* [For 'T'eimuraz I and his Poem "The Martyrdom of Queen K'et'evan"':] *See* AVALISHVILI (Z. D.)

KETSKHOVELI (LADO ZAK'ARIAS-DZE). [For 'Кецховели. Роман':] *See* LISASHVILI (I.)

KETSKHOVELI (NIKOLOZ NIKOLOZIS-DZE). თოვლიან მთებში. იალბუზი. [T'ovlian mt'ebshi. Ialbuzi. In the snowy mountains. Mt. Elbruz. Illustrated.] bk. 1. pp. 119. ტფილისი [*Tiflis,*] 1927. 8⁰.   **17075. e. 38**

——*and others.* სოფლის მეურნეობის ტერმინოლოგია. [Sop'lis meurneobis terminologia. A dictionary of agricultural terms, Russian-Georgian and Georgian-Russian.] (Терминология сельского хозяйства.) pp. 621, 5. თბილისი [*Tiflis,*] 1959. 8⁰.   **17076. h. 19**

KHAIDAKOV (SAID MAGOMEDOVICH). Балхарский

диалект лакского языка. pp. 258–62. *Москва,* 1954. 8⁰. [*Труды Института Языкознания.* том 3.]

Ac. 1125. sf

KHAKHANASHVILI (Alekʻsandre). *See* Kha-khanov (A. S.)

KHAKHANOV (Aleksandr Solomonovich). [Edit. Georgian version of the legend of Barlaam and Josaphat.] *See* Barlaam, *Saint, of India.*

—— [Edit. Georgian version of life of St. Pancras of Taormina.] *See* Evagrius, *Bishop of Taormina.*

—— Экспедиціи на Кавказъ 1892, 1893 и 1895 г. [Includes a number of historical inscriptions from Georgian churches]. pp. 1–68. *7 plates. Москва,* 1898. 4⁰. [*Матеріалы по Археологіи Кавказа.* вып. 7.]

Ac. 5575/3

—— Грузинская повѣсть объ Александрѣ Македон-скомъ и сербская Александрія. pp. 239–52. *С.-Петер-бургъ,* 1893. 8⁰. [*Журналъ Министерства Народнаго Просвѣщенія.* часть 289. отд. 2.]

P. P. 1213

—— Грузинскій поэтъ XII вѣка Ш. Руставелли и его поэма „Барсова кожа‟. pp. 200–23. *С.-Петер-бургъ,* 1895. 8⁰. [*Журналъ Министерства Народнаго Просвѣщенія.* часть 302. отд. 2.]

P. P. 1213

—— Изъ исторіи сношеній Грузіи съ Россіею въ XVIII вѣкѣ. pp. 102–12. *С.-Петербургъ,* 1899. 8⁰. [*Журналъ Министерства Народнаго Просвѣщенія.* часть 323. отд. 2.]

P. P. 1213

—— ქართველთა მეფეთა ტიტული, კურთხევა და რეგალიები. [Kʻartʻveltʻ mepʻetʻa tituli, kurtʻkheva da regaliebi. The title, coronation ceremony and regalia of the Kings of Georgia.] pp. 75–88. ტფილისი [*Tiflis,*] 1895. 8⁰. [*Moambe.* tom. 2. no. 7.]

17089. b. 1

—— Очерки по исторіи грузинской словесности. вып. I. pp. iv. 366. *Москва,* 1895. 8⁰.

11826. k. 42

—— Памятники грузинской отреченной литературы. pp. 35–49. *С.-Петербургъ,* 1894. 8⁰. [*Журналъ Ми-*

нистерства Народнаго Просвѣщенія. часть 296. отд. 2.]

P. P. 1213

—— Составъ и источники начальной грузинской лѣтописи. pp. 153–60. *С.-Петербургъ,* 1892. 8⁰. [*Журналъ Министерства Народнаго Просвѣщенія.* часть 283. отд. 2.]

P. P. 1213

—— Сванетскія рукописныя евангелія. [Descrip-tion of ancient Georgian Gospel manuscripts pre-served in Svanetʻi]. pp. 1–40. *Москва,* 1904. 4⁰. [*Матеріалы по Археологіи Кавказа.* вып. 10.]

Ac. 5575/3

—— *and others.* Христіанскіе памятники. Изслѣдо-ванія. [Christian Monuments. Researches. Including historical inscriptions from Georgian churches and ancient buildings.] pp. 142. *23 plates. Москва,* 1898. 4⁰. [*Матеріалы по Археологіи Кавказа.* вып. 7.]

Ac. 5575/3

KHANDZTʻELI (Grigol) *Saint. See* Gregory, *Saint, of Khandztʻa.*

KHARKO (Lev Petrovich). [Edit. of ‘Грузинская нумизматика’.] *See* Kapanadze (D. G.)

KHATCHAPURIDZE (Giorgi Basilis-dze). საქართველო XIX საუკუნის პირველ ნახევარში. ისტორიული ნარკვევი. [Sakʻartʻvelo XIX sau-kunis pirvel nakhevarshi. Istoriuli narkvevi. Ge-orgia in the first half of the 19th century. A his-torical study. Edit. by A. I. Kikvidze.] pp. 379. თბილისი [*Tiflis,*] 1958. 8⁰. [*Shromebi,* tom. 2.]

17075. b. 6

—— შრომები. [Shromebi. Collected historical writings.] Труды. tom. 2— თბილისი [*Tiflis,*] 1958– 8⁰. *In progress.*

17075. b. 6

KHEISIN (M. L.). 50 წელიწადი სამომხმარებლო კოოპერაციისა რუსეთში. [Ormotsdaatʻi dselidsadi samomkhmareblo kooperatsiisa Rusetʻshi. 50 years of the Consumers Cooperative Movement in Russia. Trans. from the Russian by I. Gabilaia.] pp. 84. ქუთაისი [*Kʻutʻaisi,*] 1917. 8⁰.

17075. ee. 5

KHELASHVILI (Iona) *the Monk.* [For ʻКалмасоба, или хождение по сбору Иоанна Хелашвили, ипо-диакона':] *See* JOHN, *Prince of Georgia.*

KHERKHEULIDZE (OMAN). [For a French trans. of the life of King Erekle II by Oman Kherkheulidze, incorporated in 'Histoire de la Géorgie':] *See* BROSSET (M.-F.)

—— [For the life of King Erekle II by Oman Kherkheulidze, incorporated as a continuation to 'K'art'lis tskhovreba':] *See* BROSSET (M.-F.) and CHUBINOV (D. I.)

KHEVSURS. [For 'Хевсуры':] *See* GURKO-KRYAZHIN (V. A.)

—— [For 'P'shav-Khevsuruli poezia':] *See* KHORNAULI (I. G.)

KHIDASHELI (SHALVA VASILIS-DZE). [Joint compiler of Report of First and Second Gudarekhi Archaeological Campaigns.] *See* MUSKHELISHVILI (L. V.) *and others.*

—— ქართული საზოგადოებრივი და ფილოსოფიური აზრის ისტორიიდან. [K'art'uli sazogadoebrivi da p'ilosop'iuri azris istoriidan. From the history of Georgian social and philosophical thought. Essays based on 4th–6th century Byzantine and Georgian sources.] pp. 86. თბილისი [*Tiflis,*] 1954. 8⁰.   **17073. a. 4**

—— [Another copy].   **17073. a. 4***

KHIMSHIASHVILI (ḤASAN TAḤSĪN). [Edit. 'Samuslimano Sak'art'velo'.] *See* PERIODICAL PUBLICATIONS.—*Batum.*

KHIZANASHVILI (DAVIT'). ფშავური ლექსები. [P'shavuri lek'sebi. P'shav verses, collected by D. Khizanashvili.] pp. 262. ტფილისი [*Tiflis,*] 1887. 12⁰.   **17075. d. 5. (2.)**

KHIZANASHVILI (NIKO). *See* URBNELI (N.) *pseud.*

KHODZKO (IOSIF IVANOVICH) *General.* [For 'Lettres de M. Bartholomaei...; envoi de M. le colonel Khodzko, *etc.*':] *See* BROSSET (M.-F.)

KHONELI (MOSE). *See* MOSES, *of Khoni.*

KHORNAULI (IVANE G.). ფშავ-ხევსურული პოეზია. [P'shav-Khevsuruli poezia. A chrestomathy of P'shav and Khevsur popular poetry, compiled by I. G. Khornauli, with an introduction by K'. Sikharulidze.] pp. 315. თბილისი [*Tiflis,*] 1949. 8⁰.   **17075. c. 25**

KHOSHTARIA (DIMITRI). *See* MEGRELI (D.) *pseud.*

KHOSHTARIA (ILIA). [Edit. prose writings of R. M. Gvetadze.] *See* GVETADZE (R. M.)

—— [Edit. plays by P. M. Kakabadze.] *See* KAKABADZE (P. M.)

—— ლექსები. პოემა. [Lek'sebi. Poema. Verses, followed by a narrative poem entitled 'Dat'a Landia'.] pp. 153. 1 *plate.* თბილისი [*Tiflis,*] 1955. 8⁰.   **17075. c. 7**

KHUKHASHVILI (GIORGI). [Introduction to 'Грузинская весна'.] *See* AKOBIA (SH.) *and others.*

KHUNDADZE (SILOVAN T'OMAS-DZE). ქართული ზმნები. [K'art'uli zmnebi. Georgian verbs.] pp. 102. ქუთაისი [*K'ut'aisi,*] 1891. 8⁰.   **17076. g. 4**

KHURODZE (VARLAM). [Edit. poems by I. S. Davit'ashvili.] *See* DAVIT'ASHVILI (I. S.)

—— ქართული ლიტერატურის თემატიურად განხილვა, მე-XIX საუკუნიდან თებერვლის რევოლუციამდე. [K'art'uli literaturis t'ematiurad gankhilva, me-XIX saukunidan t'ebervlis revolutsiamde. Thematic survey of Georgian literature, from the 19th century until the February revolution.] pp. 222,xiii. ტფილისი [*Tiflis,*] 1927. 8⁰.   **17075. c. 24**

KHURYUGSKY (TAIR). Мой аул. Стихи. [Trans. from Lezghian by various hands.] pp. 66. *Москва,* 1959. 12⁰.   **17075. d. 48**

KHUTSISHVILI (IASON GIORGIS-DZE) *and others.* 1905–1907 წლების რევოლუცია საქართველოში,

50 წელი, 1905–1955. სტატიების კრებული. [1905–1907 dslebis revolutsia Sak'art'veloshi. 50 dseli, 1905–1955. Statiebis krebuli. The revolution of 1905–1907 in Georgia. 50th anniversary, 1905–55. A collection of essays, edited by I. G. Khutsishvili and a committee of scholars.] (Революция 1905–1907 годов в Грузии, 50 лет, 1905–1955. Сборник статей.) pp. viii. 584, 1. 2 *plates.* თბილისი [*Tiflis,*] 1955. 8⁰.   **17076. i. 14**

KHUTSISHVILI (MIKHEIL). [Publ. treatise 'Eri da katsobrioba'.] *See* TSERET'ELI (M. G.)

K'IACHELI (LEO) *pseud.* [i.e. LEON MIKHEILIS-DZE SHENGELAIA]. Человек гор. Роман. Перевод ... Э. Ананиашвили. pp. 186. [*Ленинград,*] 1949. 8⁰.   **12594. bbb. 27**

—— Гвади Бигва. Роман. (Перевела с грузинского Е. Д. Гогоберидзе.) pp. 16–191. *Москва,* 1939. 8⁰. [*Дружба народов, etc.* кн. 3. 1939.]   **P.P. 4842. dck**

—— [Гвади Бигва.] Gvadi Bigva. Translated from the Russian version of the original Georgian by Stephen Garry. pp. 192. *London,* [1945]. 8⁰.   **012591. ccc. 97**

—— Избранное. Перевод ... под редакцией В. В. Гольцева. [Novels and stories, trans. from Georgian by various hands. With a portrait.] pp. 374. *Москва,* 1948. 8⁰.   **012593. eee. 22**

KIASASHVILI. *See* QIASASHVILI.

KIKNADZE (GRIGOL) and **CHACHIBAIA** (ARCHIL). ქართული ლიტერატურა, ქრესტომა-თია. XIX საუკუნე. XI კლასისათვის. [K'art'uli literatura, k'restomat'ia. XIX saukune. XI klasis-at'vis. A chrestomathy of 19th century Georgian literature for use in the 11th Form of Georgian State Schools. Illustrated.] pp. 279. თბილისი [*Tiflis,*] 1955. 8⁰.   **17076. f. 11**

K'IK'ODZE (GERONTI). [Joint trans. of selected novels and comedies by Mérimée.] *See* MÉRIMÉE (P.)

—— [Edit. collected writings of E. Ninoshvili.] *See* NINOSHVILI (E.) *pseud.*

—— [Edit. 'Sak'art'velo. Qoveldghiuri sapolitiko, saekonomio da saliteraturo gazet'i'.] *See* PERIODICAL PUBLICATIONS.—*Tiflis.*

—— [Contributor to symposium 'Niko P'iros-manishvili'.] *See* TABIDZE (T. I.) *and others.*

K'IK'ODZE (PLATON). [Preface to 'Dionisos ghimili. Romani'.] *See* GAMSAKHURDIA (K. S.)

—— ლიტერატურული საქართველო. წიგნი მეორე. კრიტიკული წერილების კრებული 1927–33 წწ. [Literaturuli Sak'art'velo. Dsigni meore. Kritikuli dserilebis krebuli 1927–33 ds. ds. The Georgian literary world. Bk. 2. Collected critical articles, 1927–33.] (Литературная Грузия. Книга вторая. Сборник критических статей 1927–33 г.-г.) pp. 365, 3. თბილისი [*Tiflis,*] 1934. 8⁰.   **17075. f. 41**

KIKVIDZE (ABEL IASONIS-DZE). [Edit. 'Sak'art'-velo XIX saukunis pirvel nakhevarshi'.] *See* KHATCHAPURIDZE (G. B.)

—— საქართველოს ისტორია, XIX საუკუნე. [Sak'art'velos istoria, XIX saukune. History of Georgia in the 19th century. Edit. by Sh. A. Meskhia.] bk. 1, 2. თბილისი [*Tiflis,*] 1954–59. 8⁰.   **17075. ee. 7**

KIPIANI (GEORGES). *See* QIP'IANI (GIORGI).

KIPSHIDZE. [For this surname:] *See* QIP'SHIDZE.

KIURI LANGUAGE. [For 'Ausführlicher Bericht über Baron P. v. Uslar's Kürinische Studien':] *See* SCHIEFNER (F. A. von).

KLAPROTH (HEINRICH JULIUS von). [For 'Élé-ments de la langue géorgienne', incorporating an unfinished grammar by H. J. von Klaproth:] *See* BROSSET (M.-F.)

—— [For 'Extraits d'une Topographie de la Géorgie, (traduits) par M. Klaproth':] *See* GEORGIA.—*Descriptions and Travels.*

—— [Edit. 'Reisen nach Georgien und Imerethi':] *See* GUELDENSTAEDT (J. A.)

KLAPROTH *(cont.)*

—— Détails sur le dialecte géorgien usité en Mingrélie. pp. 154–61. *Paris*, 1829. 8⁰. [*Nouveau Journal Asiatique.* tom. 3.]   **R. Ac. 8808**

—— Histoirĕ de la Géorgie. [Being a summary of the first portion of the Georgian annals.] 2 pt. tom. 12. pp. 518–47; tom. 13. pp. 21–56. *Paris*, 1833–34. 8⁰. [*Nouveau Journal Asiatique.* tom. 12–13.] *No more published.*   **R. Ac. 8808**

—— Vocabulaire et grammaire de la langue géorgienne. Première partie, contenant le vocabulaire géorgien-français et français-géorgien. pp. 232. *Paris*, 1827. 8⁰. *No more published.*   **15007. h. 13**

—— [Another copy.] *Dept. of Oriental Printed Books & MSS. Reference Library.*

—— [Another copy.]   **17076. f. 4**

KLDIASHVILI (DAVITʻ SAMSONIS-DZE). ირინეს ბედნიერება. [Irines bedniereba. Irene's good fortune. A tableau of Georgian country life, in 2 acts.] pp. 58–100. ტფილისი [*Tiflis,*] 1897. 8⁰. [*Moambe.* tom. 4. no. 12.]   **17089. b. 1**

—— Избранные произведения. Перевод с грузинского под редакцией С. Д. Клдиашвили. [Translations, mostly by Nata Chkheidze.] pp. 219. *Москва*, 1947. 8⁰.   **12263. aa. 10**

—— Мачеха Саманишвили. Свиньи Бакула. Соломон Морбеладзе. Ростом Манвелидзе. (Перевод А. Неймана. Отв. редактор Б. Буачидзе.) pp. xi. 149. *Тифлис*, 1935. 8⁰.   **12593. l. 15**

—— შერისხვა: მსხვერპლი. [Sheriskhva; mskhverpli. The curse; the victim. Two tales.] pp. 56. თბილისი [*Tiflis,*] 1955. 8⁰.   **17076. b. 15**

—— თხზულებანი ორ ტომად. [Tʻkhzulebani or tomad.] (Сочинения в двух томах.) [Collected stories and plays, translated into Russian by N. Chkheidze under the editorship of A. M. Drozdov.] tom. 1. pp. xvi. 379. 1 *plate.* თბილისი [*Tiflis,*] 1950. 8⁰.   **17076. c. 7**

KLDIASHVILI (SERGO DAVITʻIS-DZE). [Edit. writings of D. S. Kldiashvili.] *See* KLDIASHVILI (D. S.)

—— Грузинские новеллы. Перевод Н. Чхеидзе. Редакция В. В. Гольцева. pp. 165. *Москва*, 1941. 8⁰.   **012593. bb. 14**

KLUGE (THEODOR). [Trans. 'Die apokryphe Erzählung des Joseph von Arimathäa über den Bau der ersten christlichen Kirche in Lydda.'] *See* JOSEPH, *of Arimathea.*

—— [Trans. 'Oster- und Pfingstfeier Jerusalems im siebten Jahrhundert ... nach Kekelidze, Iерусалимскій канонарь VII вѣка. Tiflis 1912.'] *See* LITURGIES.—Greek Rite.—*Pentekostarion.*

—— [Trans. 'Quadragesima und Karwoche Jerusalems im siebten Jahrhundert .... nach Kekelidze, Iерусалимскій канонарь VII вѣка. Tiflis 1912'.] *See* LITURGIES.—Greek Rite.—*Triodion.*

—— Georgisch-deutsches Wörterbuch. pp. 1–80. *Leipzig*, 1919, 20. 4⁰. *No more published.*   **012904. k. 60**

KLYUCHAREV (IVAN). [For a report on the diplomatic mission of Prince Myshetsky and I. Klyucharev to Kakhetʻi:] *See* POLIEVKTOV (M. A.)

KOBAKHIDZE (APOLON). [*Biography.*] *See* KOBAKHIDZE (I.)

KOBAKHIDZE (GIVI ALEKʻSANDRES-DZE). [Edit. 'Krebuli.'] *See* PERIODICAL PUBLICATIONS.—*New York.*

KOBAKHIDZE (IULIA). აპოლონ კობახიძე. [Apolon Kobakhidze. A memorial volume, containing biographical studies of Apolon Kobakhidze, letters, obituary notices, and selected literary writings. Illustrated.] pp. 158. პარიზი [*Paris,*] 1957. 8⁰.   **17075. e. 39**

KʻOBULADZE (SERGO SOLOMONIS-DZE). [Illustrator of K. Tchitchinadze's rendering of 'Цыгане' and 'Полтава'.] *See* PUSHKIN (A. S.)

K'OBULADZE *(cont.)*
—— [Joint illustrator of 'The Man in the Panther's Skin'.] *See* Rust'aveli (Shot'a).

KOCH (Karl Heinrich Emil). [For 'Quelques remarques sur un livre intitulé: *Reise durch Russland nach dem kaukasischen Isthmus* ..., von K. Koch':] *See* Brosset (M.-F.)

KOCHETKOV (A. S.). [Joint trans. of novel 'Кецховели':] *See* Lisashvili (I.)

—— [Joint trans. of novel 'Дело'.] *See* Tcheishvili (A. N.)

KOLA.—*Nine Children of.* [For Georgian text and Russian trans. of the Martyrdom of the Nine Children of Kola:] *See* Marr (N. Y.). Критика и мелкія статьи. 1903. 8⁰.   **14005. f. 5**

KOLOSOV (Mark Borisovich). Сборник произведений молодых писателей Советской Социалистической Республики Грузии. (Молодая Грузия. Редактор М. Колосов.) [Illustrated.] pp. 253. *Москва*, 1935. 8⁰.   **012264. aa. 14**

KONDAKOV (Nikodim Pavlovich). Опись памятниковъ древности въ нѣкоторыхъ храмахъ и монастыряхъ Грузіи ... Грузинскія надписи прочтены и истолкованы Д. Бакрадзе. [Illustrated.] pp. ii. 179. *С.-Петербургъ*, 1890. fol.   **7701. g. 25**

KONSTANTINOV (N. A.). [Edit. selected works of Iakob Gogebashvili in Russian trans.] *See* Gogebashvili (I. S.)

K'ORIDZE (Domenti Leonides-dze). თბილისის არქეოლოგიური ძეგლები. [T'bilisis ark'eologiuri dzeglebi. The archaeological monuments of Tiflis. With plates, illustrations in the text, and a summary in Russian.] 2 pt. თბილისი [*Tiflis*,] 1955–58. 8⁰.   **17080. d. 21**

KORNEEV (Boris Ivanovich). [Trans. stories by R. M. Gvetadze.] *See* Gvetadze (R. M.)

—— [Joint translator of romance 'Арсен из Марабды'.] *See* Javakhishvili (M. S.)

—— [Joint trans. of novel 'Лицом к лицу'.] *See* K'ut'at'eli (A. N.)

—— [Joint trans. of stories by K. Lort'k'ip'anidze.] *See* Lort'k'ip'anidze (K. A.)

KOSVEN (Mark Osipovich). [Edit. 'Кавказский этнографический сборникъ'.] *See* St. Petersburg.—*Academia Scientiarum Imperialis.*—*Институт Этнографии им. Н. Н. Миклухо-Маклая.*

—— Очерки по этнографии Кавказа. pp. 109–44. *Москва, Ленинград*, 1946. 8⁰. [*Советская Этнография.* no. 2.]   **Ac. 1125. nd**

KOTETISHVILI (Vakhtang Ilias-dze). [Introduction to tales by Niko Lomouri.] *See* Lomouri (N. I.)

KRACHKOVSKAYA (Vera Aleksandrovna). [Edit. 'Эпиграфика Востока'.] *See* St. Petersburg.—*Academia Scientiarum Imperialis.*

KRAVCHENKO (Aleksandr Vladimirovich) and **QARALASHVILI** (Nunu Ivanes-asuli). ქართული ორნამენტი. [K'art'uli ornamenti.] (Грузинский орнамент.) [An album of coloured plates, with explanatory text in Georgian and Russian, showing specimens of Georgian decorative art taken from illuminated manuscripts, frescoes, sculpture and wood carving. Edited by B. V. Lort'k'ip'anidze.] pp. 27, l. 70 *plates.* თბილისი [*Tiflis*,] 1958. fol.   **17080. g. 12**

KRONGAUZ (Anisim). [Trans. 'Говорит Селим. Сказание о Чечне'.] *See* Muzaev (N.)

KRUPNOV (Evgeny Ignatievich). Грузинский храм "Тхаба-ерды" на северном Кавказе. [With plans and facsimiles.] pp. 116–25. *Москва, Ленинград*, 1947. 8⁰. [*Краткие Сообщения Института Истории материальной Культуры.* вып. 15.]   **Ac. 1125. gd**

KRUZHKOV (Vladimir Semenovich). [Joint author of short biography of Stalin.] *See* Aleksandrov (G. F.) *and others.*

KUBACHI. [For 'Die jetzigen Kubätschi':] *See*
DORN (B.)

—— [For 'Über . . . die Kubetschi':] *See* FRAEHN
(C. M.)

—— [For 'Кубачинский котел из археологического
собрания Музея антропологии и этнографии':] *See*
GRACH (A. D.)

KUDRYAVSKY (DMITRY NIKOLAEVICH). როგორ
ცხოვრობდენ ადამიანები ძველათ. [Rogor tskhovrobden adamianebi dzvelat'. How men lived in
ancient times. Translated from the Russian by
I. Kvitsaridze.] pp. 140. თფილისი[*Tiflis,*] 1906. 8⁰.
17075. ee. 6

KUIPERS (AERT HENDRIK). [Joint author of
'Peoples and languages of the Caucasus'.] *See*
GEIGER (B.) *and others.*

—— Phoneme and Morpheme in Kabardian,
Eastern Adyghe. [With a bibliography.] pp. 124.
The Hague, 1960. 8⁰. [*Janua Linguarum.* no. 8.]
17076. f. 36

KURDIAN (HARUTIUN). The newly discovered
alphabet of the Caucasian Albanians. pp. 81–83.
1 *plate. London,* 1956. 8⁰. [*Journal of the Royal
Asiatic Society.* 1956.] **R. Ac. 8820/3**

K'URDIANI (IOSEB). ელჭექი და სეტყვიანობა
კახეთში. [Eltchek'i da setqvianoba Kakhet'shi.]
(Orages et grêle en Kakhétie.) pp. 44, 4. 1 *map.*
თფილისი[*Tiflis,*] 1935. 8⁰. **17080. b. 5**

K'URTSIKIDZE (TSIALA IVANES-ASULI). [Edit.
Georgian versions of apocryphal writings on the
Apostles.] *See* BIBLE.—New Testament.—*Apo-
crypha.*

K'UT'AISI—*K'ut'aisi State Historical Museum.*
ხელნაწერთა აღწერილობა. [Khelnadsert'a aghdseriloba. Descriptive catalogue of the Georgian
manuscripts in the Museum collection. Compiled
by E. B. Nikoladze and edit. by K. S. Kekelidze.]
tom. I— თბილისი[*Tiflis,*]1953— 8⁰. *In progress.*
17077. b. 1

KUT'AT'ELADZE (LILI). [Joint compiler of catalogue of Georgian manuscripts in the Georgian
State Museum.] *See* TIFLIS.—*Museum of Georgia.*

K'UT'AT'ELI (ALEK'SANDRE NIKOLOZIS-DZE).
Лицом к лицу. Роман. . . Перевод . . . М. Кахидзе и
Б. Корнеева. том I— *Тбилиси,* 1948-. 8⁰. **W. P. 3628**

KVAKHADZE (B.). ახალი ცხოვრებისაკენ. და-
ძმა. [Akhali tskhovrebisaken. Da-dzma. Towards
a new life. Brother and sister. A story.] pp. 94.
ტფილისი [*Tiflis,*] 1930. 8⁰. **17076. b. 35**

K'VARIANI (SVIMON ALEK'SIS-DZE). ქართველი
ერის ტრაგედია მე-17-ტე საუკუნეში. გიორგი
სააკაძე და მისი დრო. [K'art'veli eris tragedia
me-17-te saukuneshi. Giorgi Saakadze da misi dro.
The tragic history of the Georgian people in the
17th century. Giorgi Saakadze and his epoch.] pp.
iii. 135, iii. 1 *plate.* ქუთაისი [*K'ut'aisi,*] 1912. 8⁰.
17075. e. 5. (2.)

KVESELAVA (MIKHEIL). [Edit. 'Anthology of
Georgian Poetry'.] *See* URUSHADZE (V.)

KVITSARIDZE (ISIDORE). [Trans. 'Rogor tskhovrobden adamianebi dzvelat'.] *See* KUDRYAVSKY
(D. N.)

LACH (ROBERT). Gesänge russischer Kriegsgefangener. III Band: Kaukasusvölker. 1. Abteilung:
Georgische Gesänge. Transkription und Übersetzung der georgischen Texte von A. Dirr. (2. Abteilung: Mingrelische, abchasische, svanische und
ossetische Gesänge. Transkription und Übersetzung der Texte von Robert Bleichsteiner.) 2 Hft.
pp. 254, 63. *Wien, Leipzig,* 1928, 30. 8⁰. [*Akademie
der Wissenschaften in Wien, phil.-hist. Klasse.
Sitzungsberichte.* Bd. 204-5.] **Ac. 810/6**

LADYZHENSKY (ALEKSANDR M.). Обычное
семейное право черкес. pp. 224-39. *Москва,* 1928.
8⁰. [*Новый восток.* кн. 22.] **Ac. 1096. b/5**

LAK LANGUAGE. [For 'Lakkische Studien':]
See BOUDA (K.)

—— [For 'Фиалки на скалах. (Перевод с лакского)':]
See RAMAZANOV (B.)

LAK LANGUAGE *(cont.)*

—— [For 'Ausführlicher Bericht über Baron P. v. Uslar's Kasikumükische Studien':] *See* SCHIEFNER (F. A. von).

—— [For 'Лакский язык':] *See* ZHIRKOV (L. I.)

LAKERBAI (MIKHEIL ALEK'SANDRES-DZE). Абхазские новеллы. Перевод с абхазского С. Трегуба. pp. 135, 1. *Москва*, 1957. 8⁰.   **17076. b. 31**

LANG (DAVID MARSHALL). [For 'Le roman de Balahvar et sa traduction anglaise', containing a discussion of D. M. Lang's trans. of the shorter Georgian version of the legend of Barlaam and Josaphat:] *See* T'ARKHNISHVILI (M.)

—— Georgian Relations with France during the reign of Wakhtang VI, 1711–24. pp. 114–26. *London*, 1950. 8⁰. [*Journal of the Royal Asiatic Society*, 1950].   **R. Ac. 8820/3**

—— [Another copy, being an offprint.]   **17075. e. 15**

—— Georgian Studies in Oxford. [Including a handlist of the principal Georgian manuscripts in the Bodleian Library.] pp. 115–43. *Oxford*, 1955. 8⁰. [*Oxford Slavonic Papers*. vol. 6.]   **W. P. 11221**

—— The last years of the Georgian monarchy, 1658–1832. [With plates and a bibliography.] pp. xvi. 333. *New York*, 1957. 8⁰. [*Studies of the Russian Institute, Columbia University*.]   **R. Ac. 2688. ġa. (12.)**

—— *The life of the Blessed Iodasaph*: a new Oriental Christian version of the Barlaam and Ioasaph romance. — Jerusalem, Greek Patriarchal Library: Georgian MS 140. pp. 389–407. *London*, 1957. 8⁰. [*Bulletin of the School of Oriental and African Studies*. vol. 20.]   **Ac. 8820. d**

—— Lives and Legends of the Georgian Saints, selected and translated from the original texts by D. M. Lang. [With a map.] pp. 180. *London, New York*, 1956. 8⁰. [*Ethical and Religious Classics of East and West*. no. 15.]   **17075. e. 25**

—— [Another copy.]   **W. P. 5206/15**

—— Notes on Caucasian Numismatics. Part 1. pp. 137–46. 1 *plate*. *London*, 1957. 8⁰. [*The Numismatic Chronicle*. ser. 6. vol. 17.]   **Ac. 5885/2**

—— [Another copy.]   *Dept. of Coins and Medals.*

—— Recent work on the Georgian New Testament. pp. 82–93. *London*, 1957. 8⁰. [*Bulletin of the School of Oriental and African Studies*. vol. 19. pt. 1.]   **Ac. 8820. d**

—— St. Euthymius the Georgian and the Barlaam and Ioasaph Romance. pp. 306–25. *London*, 1955. 8⁰. [*Bulletin of the School of Oriental and African Studies*. vol. 17. pt. 2.]   **Ac. 8820. d**

—— Studies in the numismatic history of Georgia in Transcaucasia. pp. xii. 138. 16 *plates*. *New York*, 1955. 8⁰. [*Numismatic Notes and Monographs*. no. 130.]   *Dept. of Coins and Medals.*

—— 'Wisdom and lies': variations on a Georgian literary theme. [A study of the 'Book of Wisdom and Lies' by Sulkhan-Saba Orbeliani.] pp. 436–48. *London*, 1956. 8⁰. [*Bulletin of the School of Oriental and African Studies*. vol. 18. pt. 3.]   **Ac. 8820. d**

—— The Wisdom of Balahvar. A Christian legend of the Buddha. [With the text of 'The Wisdom of Balahvar', translated from the Old Georgian version of 'The Legend of Barlaam and Josaphat' contained in MS. 36 of the Georgian collection in the Greek Patriarchal Library at Jerusalem.] pp. 135. 1 *plate*. *London, New York*, 1957 [1958]. 8⁰. [*Ethical and Religious Classics of East and West*. no. 20.]   **W. P. 5206/20**

—— and **MEREDITH-OWENS** (GLYN MUNRO). *Amiran-Darejaniani*: a Georgian romance and its English rendering. pp. 454–90. *London*, 1959. 8⁰. [*Bulletin of the School of Oriental and African Studies*. vol. 22. pt. 3.]   **Ac. 8820. d**

LANGLOIS (VICTOR). [For 'À propos du livre intitulé: "Essai de classification des suites monétaires

LANGLOIS *(cont.)*
de la Géorgie'', par M. Victor Langlois':] *See* Brosset (M.-F.)

—— Essai de classification des suites monétaires
de la Géorgie, depuis l'antiquité jusqu'à nos jours.
pp. viii. 139. 10 *plates. Paris*, 1860. 4⁰. **7755. dd. 10**

—— Notice sur le couvent ibérien du Mont Athos.
[With a list of the Georgian manuscripts in the
Iviron Monastery, compiled by the Priest Hilarion.]
pp. 331–51. *Paris*, 1867. 8⁰. [*Journal Asiatique*. sér.
6. tom. 9.]   **R. Ac. 8808**

LANSERE (Evgeny Evgen'evich). [Illustrator
of 'Пещерные монастыри Давид-Гареджи'.] *See*
Chubinashvili (G. N.)

LANTSCHOOT (Arnoldus van). Le ms. Borgia
géorgien 4. [A description of a 12th century pa-
tristic and hagiographical miscellany in the Vatican
Library.] pp. 75–88. *Louvain*, 1948. 8⁰. [*Le Muséon*.
tom. 61.]   **P. P. 4453**

LASHK'ARADZE (Davit' Besarionis-dze).
[Edit. 'Prak'tikis shesakheb':] *See* Mao (Tse-Tung).

LATVIAN TALES. ლატვიური ზღაპრები. [Lat-
viuri zghaprebi. Latvian tales. Trans. by N. Samu-
kashvili. Illustrated.] pp. 226. თბილისი [*Tiflis*,]
1951. 8⁰.   **17077. a. 16**

LAVROV (Leonid Ivanovich). Рутульцы. [Illus-
trated.] pp. 30–40. *Москва*, 1953. 8⁰. [*Советская
Этнография*. no. 4.]   **Ac. 1125. nd**

LAZ LANGUAGE. [For 'Tchanur-megrul-
k'art'uli shedarebit'i lek'sikoni:'] *See* Chik'obava
(A. S.)

—— [For 'Tchanuri tek'stebi':] *See* Chik'obava
(A. S.)

—— [For 'Contes lazes':] *See* Dumézil (G.)

—— [*Grammar*.] *See* Marr (N. Y.)

—— [For 'Изъ поѣздки въ турецкій Лазистанъ':]
See Marr (N. Y.)

—— [For 'Original Vocabularies of Five West
Caucasian Languages', including Laz:] *See* Peacock (D. R.)

—— [For 'Дополнительныя свѣдѣнія о ч'анскомъ
языкѣ':] *See* Qip'shidze (I. A.)

—— [For 'Tchanur-megrulis p'onetika':] *See*
Zhghenti (S. M.)

**LAZAREVSKY INSTITUT VOSTOCHNYKH
YAZYKOV.** *See* Moscow.

LE FUR (Louis). საქართველო და საერთაშორისო
უფლება. [Sak'art'velo da saert'ashoriso up'leba.
Georgia and international law. Trans. from the
French.] pp. 32. პარიზი [*Paris*,] 1933. 8⁰. [*Damou-
kidebeli Sak'art'velos gamotsema*. no. 3.] **17075. f. 40**

LEIST (Arthur). [Translator of the tale 'Eliso' by
Qazbegi.] *See* Qazbegi (A. M.)

—— [Translator of the epic 'The Man in the Panther's Skin'.] *See* Rust'aveli (Shot'a).

—— Georgische Dichter. Verdeutscht von A. L.
pp. x. 150. *Leipzig*, 1887. 8⁰.   **11586. b. 15**

—— Georgische Dichter. Übersetzt von A. Leist.
Neue, vielfach vermehrte Ausgabe. [Includes translations of poems by G. Orbeliani, Alek'sandre and
Ilia Tchavtchavadze, N. Barat'ashvili, A. Tsere-
t'eli, *etc.*] pp. xxxi. 173. vii. *Dresden und Leipzig*,
1900. 8⁰.   **17077. a. 1**

—— Das georgische Volk. [With illustrations.] pp.
328. *Dresden*, [1903.] 8⁰.   **010077. k. 5**

LEKIASHVILI (Alek'si Simonis-dze). არაბული
ზმნის ფორმათა პარადიგმები. [Arabuli zmnis
p'ormat'a paradigmebi. Paradigms of Arabic verbal
forms. Edit. with an introduction by G. V. Tseret'eli. Georgian and Russian texts.] (Парадигмы
глагольных форм литературного арабского языка.)
pp. 015. III. თბილისი [*Tiflis*,] 1953. 8⁰.
       17076. f. 21

LEMM (Oscar von). Iberica. [Containing Coptic and other materials on the history of the Georgian Church.] pp. vi. 39. 2 *plates. St.-Pétersbourg*, 1906. 4⁰. [*Записки Императорской Академіи Наукъ.* ser. 8. *Classe Historico-Philologique.* vol. 7. no. 6.]
Ac. 1125/3

LENIN (Vladimir Il'ich). ნაბიჯი წინ, ორი ნა-ბიჯი უკან — კრიზისი ჩვენს პარტიაში. [Nabiji dsin, ori nabiji ukan—krizisi chvens partiashi. One step forward, two steps back—the crisis in our Party. Trans. from the 4th ed. of the works of Lenin, tom. 7.] pp. 289. [თბილისი. *Tiflis,*] 1952. 8⁰.
17075. f. 13

—— რა ვაკეთოთ? ჩვენი მოძრაობის საჩირ-ბოროტო საკითხები. [Ra vaket'ot'? Chveni mo-dzraobis satchirboroto sakit'khebi. What are we to do? Pressing problems of our movement. Trans. from the 4th ed. of the works of Lenin, tom. 5.] pp. 250. [თბილისი. *Tiflis,*] 1951. 8⁰.
17075. f. 8 (1)

LENINGRAD. *See* Saint Petersburg.

—— *Государственная Публичная Библиотека имени М. Е. Салтыкова-Щедрина. See* Saint Petersburg.
— *Императорская Публичная Библіотека.*

LEONIDZE (Giorgi Nikolozis-dze). [Edit. poems by S. N. Ap'khaidze.] *See* Ap'khaidze (S. N.)

—— [Edit. literary works of N. M. Barat'ashvili.] *See* Barat'ashvili (N. M.) *Prince.*

—— [*Life.*] *See* Gol'tsev (V. V.)

—— [Edit. 'Tskhovreba Ivane Machablisa'.] *See* Tchelidze (V.)

—— [Edit. anthology of verses trans. into Russian by G. Tsagareli.] *See* Tsagareli (G. K.)

—— Сталин. Детство и отрочество. Эпопея. Книга первая. Перевод с грузинского Н. Тихонова. pp. 140, 4. *Москва*, 1947. fol.
W. P. 12376

—— Стихотворения и поэмы. [Poems, translated

from Georgian into Russian by various hands. Edit. by V. V. Gol'tsev.] pp. 318. 1 *plate. Москва,* 1951. 8⁰.
17075. d. 8

LEONTI, *Archbishop of Ruisi.* [For a French trans. of the chronicle of Leonti Mroveli, included in 'Histoire de la Géorgie':] *See* Brosset (M.-F.)

—— [For the chronicle of Leonti Mroveli, included in Brosset and Chubinov's edition of 'K'art'lis tskhovreba':] *See* Brosset (M.-F.) and Chubinov (D. I.)

—— [For the chronicle of Leonti Mroveli, included in Qaukhchishvili's edition of 'K'art'lis tskho-vreba':] *See* Georgian Annals.

L'HUILIER (Léon). [For 'Rapport sur un ouvrage manuscrit intitulé: "Словарь Русско-черкесскій"', compiled by L. L'Huilier:] *See* Sjoegren (A. J.)

LINI (L.). [Edit., with introduction, of 'Chveni simgherebi'.] *See* Georgia.—*Georgian Legion.*

LIPKIN (Semen I.). [Trans. poems by Shogent-sukov.] *See* Shogentsukov ('Ali A.)

LISASHVILI (Iakint'e). Кецховели. Роман. [Trans. into Russian by N. Chkheidze and A. S. Kochetkov.] pp. 290. *Тбилиси*, 1951. 8⁰. **17077. a. 9**

LITURGIES.—Georgian Rite. [For liturgical books in the vernacular used by the Georgian Church, an autocephalous body within the Greek Orthodox Communion:] *See* Liturgies.—Greek Rite.

—— Greek Rite. [For 'Les monuments liturgiques prébyzantins en langue géorgienne':] *See* P'eradze (G.)

—— [For 'Zur vorbyzantinischen Liturgie Geor-giens':] *See* P'eradze (G.)

—— *Calendar.* Le calendrier palestino-géorgien du Sinaiticus 34, Xᵉ siècle. Édité, traduit et com-menté par Gérard Garitte. pp. 485. *Bruxelles*, 1958. 8⁰. [*Subsidia Hagiographica.* no. 30.] **17071. d. 3.**

LITURGIES *(cont.)*

—— [Another copy.]   **Ac. 2021**

—— *Euchologion.* Die Weihnachtsfeier Jerusalems im siebten Jahrhundert. Übersetzung nach Kekelidze, Іерусалимскій Канонарь VII. Вѣка. Tiflis 1912. S. 43–49 von Dr. Gregor Peradze, mit Einleitung und Anmerkungen von Prof. Anton Baumstark. pp. 310–18. *Leipzig*, 1927. 8⁰. [*Oriens Christianus.* Dritte Serie. Bd. 1.]   **Ac. 2002. b**

—— *Lectionaries.* Le grand lectionnaire de l'Église de Jérusalem, Vᵉ–VIIIᵉ siècle, édité (traduit [into Latin]) par † Michel Tarchnischvili. 2 tom. *Louvain*, 1959. 8⁰. [*Corpus Scriptorum Christianorum Orientalium.* vol. 188–89. = *Scriptores Iberici.* tom 9–10.] *In progress.*   **14005. a**

—— სინური მრავალთავი 864 წლისა. [Sinuri mravalt'avi 864 dslisa. The Sinai polycephalon of A.D. 864. Edit. under the supervision of A. G. Shanidze.] (Синайский многоглав 864–го года.) pp. 019. 338, 4. 11 *plates.* თბილისი [*Tiflis*,] 1959. 4⁰. [*Dzveli k'art'uli enis kat'edris shromebi.* no. 5.]   **17076. h. 13**

—— *Leitourgikon I.* The Georgian Version of the Liturgy of St. James, [translated from the edition by K. S. Kekelidze] by F. C. Conybeare and O. Wardrop. 2 pt. tom 8 (18). pp. 396–410; tom. 9 (19). pp. 155–73. *Paris*, 1913–14. 8⁰. [*Revue de l'Orient Chrétien.* tom. 8 (18), 9 (19).]   **P. P. 37. ck**

—— Die georgische "Petrusliturgie". Ins Lateinische zurückübersetzt und mit vorläufigen Bemerkungen begleitet von Dr. Heinrich Goussen. pp. 1–15. *Leipzig*, 1913. 8⁰. [*Oriens Christianus.* Neue Serie. Bd. 3.]   **Ac. 2002. b**

—— Liturgiae Ibericae Antiquiores, edidit (interpretatus est) Michael Tarchnišvili. [Containing the Liturgy of St. James in two redactions; the Liturgy of St. John Chrysostom; the Liturgy of St. Peter; the Liturgy of the Presanctified.] 2 tom. *Lovanii*, 1950. 8⁰. [*Corpus Scriptorum Christianorum Orientalium.* vol. 122–23 = *Scriptores Iberici.* ser. 1. tom. 1.]   **14005. a**

—— The Liturgy of Saint Peter. By H. W. Codrington. With a preface and introduction by Dom Placid de Meester. [With various texts, including that of the Georgian version trans. by G. P'eradze.] pp. viii. 223. *Münster i. W.*, 1936. 8⁰. [*Liturgiegeschichtliche Quellen und Forschungen.* Hft. 30.]   **03366. k. 6/8**

—— Eine neue georgische Jakobosliturgie. [Translated from the Sinai version, preserved in the Graz manuscript, by M. T'arkhnishvili.] pp. 49–82. *Città del Vaticano*, 1948. 8⁰. [*Ephemerides Liturgicae.* vol. 62.]   **P. P. 22. b**

—— *Menaia.* [For 'О древнемъ іерусалимскомъ спискѣ грузинской минеи-четьей':] *See* BENESHEVICH (V. N.)

—— *Pentekostarion.* Oster- und Pfingstfeier Jerusalems im siebten Jahrhundert. Übersetzung nach Kekelidze, Іерусалимскій канонарь VII вѣка. Tiflis 1912, S. 94–110 von Dr. Theodor Kluge, mit Einleitung und Anmerkungen von Dr. Anton Baumstark. pp. 223–39. *Leipzig*, 1916. 8⁰. [*Oriens Christianus.* Neue Folge. Bd. 6.]   **Ac. 2002. b**

—— *Synaxarion.* Le Synaxaire géorgien, rédaction ancienne de l'union arméno-géorgienne. Publié et traduit [into French] d'après le manuscrit du couvent Iviron du Mont Athos par N. Marr. pt. 1. pp. 625–741. *Paris*, 1926. 4⁰. [*Patrologia Orientalis.* tom. 19. fasc. 5.] *No more published.*   **14005. c**

—— [Another copy.]   **2002. d**

—— *Triodion.* Quadragesima und Karwoche Jerusalems im siebten Jahrhundert. Übersetzung nach Kekelidze, Іерусалимскій канонарь VII вѣка. Tiflis 1912, S. 56–88, von Dr. Theodor Kluge, mit Einleitung und Anmerkungen von Dr. Anton Baumstark. 2 pt. pp. 201–33; 359–63. *Leipzig*, 1915. 8⁰. [*Oriens Christianus.* Neue Serie. Bd. 5.]   **Ac. 2002. b**

—— *Tupikon.* [For the Typicon of the Georgian monastery at Petritzos in Bulgaria:] *See* BAKURIANI (GRIGOL).

LITURGIES *(cont.)*

—— [For 'Typikon de Grégoire Pacourianos, *etc.*':] *See* Bakuriani (Grigol).

LOLADZE (Vakhtang). დავით რონდელი. [Davit' Rondeli. A study of the life and work of this Georgian film producer.] pp. 33. 8 *plates.* თბილისი [*Tiflis*,] 1954. 8⁰. [*Sabtchot'a kinos ostatebi. Masters of the Soviet Cinema.*]　　　　**17076. g. 9**

LOLASHVILI (Ivane Alek'sandres-dze). სულ-ხან-საბა ორბელიანის ლიტერატურული მოღვა-წეობიდან, 1698–1713 წწ. [Sulkhan-Saba Orbelianis literaturuli moghvadseobidan, 1698–1713 dsds. Aspects of the literary activity of Sulkhan-Saba Orbeliani, 1698–1713. With facsimiles of manuscripts.] pp. 131. 8 *plates.* თბილისი [*Tiflis*,] 1959. 8⁰.　　　　　**17076. f. 34. (2.)**

LOMIDZE (Andro). მოთხრობები. [Mot'khrobebi. Short stories. Edited by D. G. Maisuradze.] pp. 225, 1. თბილისი [*Tiflis*,] 1953. 8⁰.　**17076. b. 24**

LOMOURI (Nikoloz Iosebis-dze). მოთხრობები. [Mot'khrobebi. Tales. With an introduction by V. I. Kotetishvili.] pp. xxiii. 505, 3. 1 *plate.* ტფილისი [*Tiflis*,] 1926. 8⁰.　　　**17076. b. 33**

—— Рассказы. Перевод с грузинского М. Кахидзе. [With a biographical essay by L. Asat'iani.] pp. 292, 4. 1 *plate.* Тбилиси, 1952. 8⁰.　　**17077. a. 10**

LOMT'AT'IDZE (Giorgi Alek'sandres-dze). Археологические раскопки в древнегрузинской столице Мцхета. pp. 113. 21 *plates.* Тбилиси, 1955. 8⁰.　　　**Ac. 1140/2. (1.)**

—— კლდეეთის სამაროვანი ახალი წელთაღრი-ცხვის II საუკუნისა. [Kldeet'is samarovani akhali dselt'aghritskhvis II saukunisa. The burial ground of the second century A.D. at Kldeet'i. With figures in the text, two tables, and a summary in Russian.] pp. 223, 3. 22 *plates.* თბილისი [*Tiflis*,] 1957. 8⁰　　　**17080. f. 15**

LOMT'AT'IDZE (K'et'evan Besarionis-asuli). აფხაზური დიალექტი და მისი ადგილი სხვა

აფხაზურ-აბაზურ დიალექტთა შორის, ტექსტ-ებითურთ. [Ashkharuli dialek'ti da misi adgili skhva ap'khazur-abazur dialek'tt'a shoris, tek'ste-bit'urt'. The Ashkharian dialect and its place among the other Abkhazo-Abazinian dialects, together with texts, and Russian summary. Edit. by A. S. Chik'obava.] (Ашхарский диалект и его место среди других абхазско-абазинских диалектов, с текстами.) pp. xii. 232, 106, 12. თბილისი [*Tiflis*,] 1954. 8⁰.　　　**17076. i. 7**

LOMT'AT'IDZE (Tchola). В тюрьме. Повести и рассказы. [In Prison. Stories and tales, translated from the Georgian by A. Qancheli.] pp. vii. 209. *Тифлис*, 1935. 8⁰.　　　**17076. c. 2**

LONDON. – *British Museum.* A Catalogue of the Armenian Manuscripts in the British Museum. By F. C. Conybeare... To which is appended a Catalogue of Georgian Manuscripts in the British Museum. By J. Oliver Wardrop. pp. viii. 410. *London*, 1913. 4⁰.　　　　　**Circ. 85. b**

—— [Another copy.] *Dept. of Oriental Printed Books & MSS. Reference Library.*

—— [Another copy.] *Oriental Students Room. Catalogue Desk.* B. 6.

—— *Georgian Historical Society.* Georgica. A journal of Georgian and Caucasian studies. [Edited by W. E. D. Allen and A. I. Gugushvili. With plates and maps.] vol. 1. no. 1–5. *London*, 1935–37. 8⁰. *No more published.*　　**Ac. 8821. e**

—— *Royal Asiatic Society of Great Britain and Ireland. See* Rust'aveli (Shot'a). The Man in the Panther's Skin, *etc.* 1912. 8⁰.　　**14003. bb. 16**

—— *See* Sargis, *of T'mogvi.* Visramiani. The Story of the Loves of Vis and Ramin, *etc.* 1914. 8⁰.　　　　　　　　　　　**14003. bb. 18**

—— The Journal of the Royal Asiatic Society, *etc.* 20 vols. *London*, 1834–63. 8⁰.

—— New Series. vols. 1–21. *London*, 1864–89. 8⁰.

LONDON *(cont.)*

—— 1890, *etc. London*, 1890, *etc.* 8⁰.   **R. Ac. 8820/3**

—— *University of London.—School of Oriental and African Studies.* Bulletin of the School of Oriental Studies (of the School of Oriental and African Studies). vol. 1— *London*, 1917–. 8⁰.
           Ac. 8820. d

LOPATINSKY (Lev Grigor'evich). Кабардин- ское сказание "Красавица Елена и Богатырь- женщина". pp. 176–96. *Баку*, 1921. 8⁰. [*Известия Бакинского гос. Университета. Гуманитарные науки.* no. 1. pt. 2.]   **Ac. 1109**

LORIA (Parmen Onisimes-dze). [Joint edit. of 'Литературная Аджария':] *See* Atchara.—*Soyuz Sovetskikh Pisatelei.—Adzharskoe Otdelenie.*

—— მაღაროებში. რომანი. [Magharoebshi. Ro- mani. In the mines. A novel.] pp. 363. ბათუმი [*Batum*,] 1954. 8⁰.   **17077. a. 17**

LORT'K'IP'ANIDZE (Bezhan Vladimeris-dze). [Edit. 'Portalebi k'art'ul ark'itek'turashi'.] *See* Gabashvili (Ts. R.)

—— [Edit. 'K'art'uli ornamenti'.] *See* Krav- chenko (A. V.) and Qaralashvili (N. I.)

LORT'K'IP'ANIDZE (K'et'evan Iovelis-asu- li). [Edit. Georgian versions of the Catholic Epistles.] *See* Bible.—New Testament.—*Epistles.*

LORT'K'IP'ANIDZE (Konstantine Alek'san- dres-dze). რჩეული ნაწერები ორ ტომად. [Rcheuli nadserebi or tomad. Selected writings in two volumes. tom. 1: Comprising the novel 'Kolkhet'is tsiskari': 'The Dawn of Colchis'. tom. 2: Containing shorter stories and novels. Illustrated.] 2 tom. თბილისი [*Tiflis*,] 1955–56. 8⁰.
           17076. b. 18

—— უკვდავება. [Ukvdaveba. Immortality. A collection of short stories.] pp. 209. 1 *plate.* თბილისი [*Tiflis*,] 1954. 8⁰.   **17076. b. 10**

—— Заря Колхиды. Роман. Рассказы... Перевод

с грузинского. [Trans. by E. Ananiashvili and B. I. Korneev.] pp. 366. *Москва*, 1951. 8⁰.   **012593. b. 38**

—— Заря Колхиды. Роман. Рассказы ... Перевод' *etc.* [With plates, including a portrait.] pp. 485. *Тбилиси*, 1953. 8⁰.   **12596. de. 11**

LORT'K'IP'ANIDZE (Margarita Nikolozis- asuli). *See* Tiflis.—*Museum of Georgia.* საქართ- ველოს სახელმწიფო მუზეუმის გემები. [Sak'art'- velos sakhelmdsip'o muzeumis gemebi. A catalogue of the engraved gems in the Georgian State Mu- seum. Compiled by M. N. Lort'k'ip'anidze.] tom. 1, 2, *etc.* 1954–. 8⁰. *In progress.*   **17080. e. 4**

LORT'K'IP'ANIDZE (Niko Merabis-dze). Гроз- ный властелин. Повести и рассказы. Перевод с грузинского [by various hands.] pp. 762, 5. *Тбилиси*, 1958. 8⁰.   **17076. c. 16**

—— Избранное. Перевод ... Елены Гогоберидзе. pp. xiv. 469. *Тбилиси*, 1948. 8⁰.   **012591. 1. 86**

—— თხზულებათა სრული კრებული ოთხ ტომად. [T'khzulebat'a sruli krebuli ot'kh tomad. Complete collection of works in four volumes. Edited by D. Benashvili and D. Gamezardashvili. With a portrait.] tom. 1— თბილისი [*Tiflis*,] 1958–. 8⁰. *In progress.*   **17076. c. 15**

LOUIS XIV, *King of France.* [For 'Documens originaux sur les relations diplomatiques de la Géorgie avec la France vers la fin du règne de Louis XIV':] *See* Brosset (M.-F.)

LOUVAIN.—*Academia Lovaniensis.* Corpus Scrip- torum Christianorum Orientalium.—Scriptores Ibe- rici. [Edit. by M. T'arkhnishvili.] tom. 1— *Lovanii*, 1950–. 8⁰. *In progress.*   **14005. a**

—— Revue d'Histoire Ecclésiastique. tom. 1— *Louvain*, 1900–. 8⁰.   **Ac. 2646/3**

LUKE, *Saint and Evangelist.* [For 'La version géorgienne ancienne de l'Évangile de Luc':] *See* Bible.—New Testament.—*Luke.*

LUKE, *Saint and Martyr, of Jerusalem.* [For 'Житіе Прохора, муч. Луки, *etc.*':] *See* QIPʻSHIDZE (D. A.)

LUNDBERG (EVGENY GERMANOVICH). [Introduction to selected tales by Qazbegi.] *See* QAZBEGI (A. M.)

—— [Edit. 'Пережитое':] *See* TSERETʻELI (A. R.) *Prince.*

LYONNET (STANISLAS). Les origines de la version arménienne et le diatessaron. pp. 9*. 302. *Roma*, 1950. 8⁰. [*Biblica et orientalia.* no. 13.]
3130. bb. 33

MACARIUS, *the Priest.* [Trans. Life of Peter the Iberian.] *See* ZACHARIAS, *Scholasticus, Bishop of. Mitylene.*

MACHABELI (IVANE GIORGIS-DZE) *Prince* [Trans. 'Julius Caesar'.] *See* SHAKSPERE (W.)

—— [Trans. 'The Tragedy of Richard III'.] *See* SHAKSPERE (W.)

—— [Trans. Tragedies of Shakspere.] *See* SHAKSPERE (W.)

—— [For 'Tskhovreba Ivane Machablisa', a novel based on the life of the dramatist I. G. Machabeli:] *See* TCHELIDZE (V.)

MACLER (FRÉDÉRIC). Catalogue des manuscrits arméniens et géorgiens de la Bibliothèque Nationale. pp. xxx. 203. *Paris*, 1908. 8⁰.　**11907. pp. 12**

MAGGI (FRANCESCO MARIA). Syntagmatων Linguarum Orientalium, quae in Georgiae regionibus audiuntur, liber primus, complectens Georgianae seu Ibericae vulgaris linguae Institutiones Grammaticas. (Liber secundus complectens Arabum et Turcarum orthographiam ac Turcicae Linguae Institutiones.) 2 pt. *Romae*, 1643. fol.　**621.1.1.(1.)**

—— [Another copy.]　**65. e. 15**

—— [Another edition.] 2 pt. *Romae*, 1670. fol.
621. 1. 2

—— [Another copy.]　**67. g. 8**

MAGGIO (FRANCESCO MARIA). *See* MAGGI.

MAGHLAKELIDZE (SHALVA). [Signatory of 'Debulebani moghvadseobisa da brdzolisatʻvis'.] *See* GEORGIA.—*Georgian Fascist Front.*

MAISURADZE (DAVITʻ GIORGIS-DZE). [Edit. short stories of A. Lomidze.] *See* LOMIDZE (A.)

MAISURADZE (ZAKʻARIA PETRES-DZE). Грузинская художественная керамика XI–XIII вв. Ангобированная керамика Дманиси. [An account of the Georgian town of Dmanisi and its characteristic ceramic ware. Edit. by G. N. Chubinashvili.] pp. 30, 2. 40 *plates*. Тбилиси, 1954. 4⁰. *Text in Russian, with captions of the plates in Georgian.*
17080. f. 1

—— ოზაანის კერამიკა. [Ozaanis keramika. A description of ornamental tiles laid on portion of the flooring of the ancient church at Ozaani in Kakhetʻi.] (Керамика Озаани.) [Georgian and Russian texts, with summary in German. Illustrated.] pp. 30. 4 *plates*. თბილისი [*Tiflis*,] 1959. 8⁰.　**17080. b. 12**

MAKALATʻIA (SERGI IOSEBIS-DZE). Из старого народного быта пшавов. [Illustrated.] pp. 98–117. *Москва, Ленинград*, 1938. 8⁰. [*Советская Этнография.* том I.]
Ac. 1125. nd

—— თეძმის ხეობა. ისტორიულ-ეთნოგრაფიული ნარკვევი. [Tʻedzmis kheoba. Istoriul-etʻngrapʻiuli narkvevi. The Tʻedzami valley. A historical and ethnographical study. Illustrated.] pp. 49, 3. თბილისი [*Tiflis*,] 1959. 8⁰.　**17076. f. 27**

MAŁAKʻIA, *the Monk.* [For the History of the Nation of the Archers, i.e. the Mongols, and their invasion of Georgia, formerly attributed to Małakʻia the Monk, translated from the Armenian by M.-F. Brosset, and included as an appendix to 'Histoire de la Géorgie':] *See* BROSSET (M.-F.)

MALAKʻIASHVILI (VARLAM). შოთა ბროლიძე. რომანი. [Shotʻa Brolidze. Romani. Shotʻa Brolidze. A novel. Second edition.] pp. 154. ტფილისი [*Tiflis*,] 1927. 8⁰.   **17076. b. 36**

MALAN (SALOMON CAESAR). [Trans. and edit. 'The Gospel of S. John, translated from the eleven oldest versions', *etc.*] *See* BIBLE.—New Testament.— *John.*

—— [Trans. and edit. 'A short history of the Georgian Church'.] *See* IOSELIANI (P. E.)

MALCAMON, *Saint*. [For 'La Passion géorgienne des SS. Théodore... Malcamon, *etc.*':] *See* THÉODORE, *Saint and Martyr, of Pella.*

MALENKOV (GEORGY MAKSIMILIANOVICH). საანგარიშო მოხსენება პარტიის XIX ყრილობაზე საკავშირო კ. პ. (ბ) ცენტრალური კომიტეტის მუშაობის შესახებ. [Saangarisho mokhseneba partiis XIX qrilobaze sakavshiro k. p. (b) tsentraluri komitetis mushaobis shesakheb. Report delivered at the 19th Congress of the Party on the work of the Central Committee of the Communist Party of the Soviet Union. Trans. from the Russian. With a portrait.] pp. 134. [თბილისი. *Tiflis*,] 1953. 8⁰.   **17075. f. 9 (5)**

MALEVANOV (NIKOLAI ALEKSANDROVICH). [Joint edit. of essay on Rust'aveli's poem 'Vep'-khis-tqaosani'.] *See* TSERET'ELI (A. R.) *Prince.*

MAMAKAEV (MUHAMMAD) *and others.* Поэзия Чечено-Ингушетии. [An anthology of Chechen-Ingush poetry, translated into Russian by various hands, compiled and edited by M. Mamakaev and others.] pp. 278. *Москва*, 1959. 4⁰.   **17075. dd. 9**

MAMULAISHVILI (IOSEB GRIGOLIS-DZE). *See* GRISHASHVILI (I. G.)

MANVELISHVILI (ALEK'SANDRE PETRES-DZE). [Edit. of 'Eris dideba'.] *See* PERIODICAL PUBLICATIONS.— *Paris.*

—— ქართულ-ფრანგული საუბრის თანამგზავრი. [K'art'ul-p'ranguli saubris t'anamgzavri.] Guide de conversation français-géorgien. pp. 64. პარიზი [*Paris*,] 1944. 12⁰.   **17076. f. 6**

—— ქართული მოდგმის ეროვნული ფორმაცია. [K'art'uli modgmis erovnuli p'ormatsia.] (La formation de la nation géorgienne.) pp. 61. პარიზი [*Paris*,] 1955. 8⁰.   **17075. f. 35**

—— ქრისტიანობა საქართველოში. [K'ristianoba Sak'art'veloshi. Christianity in Georgia.] pp. 32. პარიზი [*Paris*,] 1954. 8⁰.   **17071. a. 5**

—— საკუთრება; მიწის საკითხი საქართველოში. [Sakut'reba; Midsis sakit'khi Sak'art'veloshi. Property; The land question in Georgia.] pp. 84. პარიზი [*Paris*,] 1956. 8⁰.   **17075. f. 36**

MAO (TSÊ-TUNG). პრაქტიკის შესახებ : შემეც-ნების კავშირი პრაქტიკასთან — ცოდნის კავშირი მოქმედებასთან. [Prak'tikis shesakheb: shemetsnebis kavshiri prak'tikast'an — tsodnis kavshiri mok'medebast'an. Concerning practical action: The connection between theory and practice — the connection between knowledge and action. Trans. by G. Shahsevanidze, edit. by D. Lashk'aradze.] pp. 24. [თბილისი. *Tiflis*,] 1952. 8⁰.   **17075. f. 9 (2)**

MARCEL-PAON (ANIE). [Joint translator of the epic 'The Man in the Panther's Skin'.] *See* RUST'AVELI (SHOT'A).

MARGIANI (REVAZ AKAKIS-DZE). Да будет мир! Стихи. [Poems, translated into Russian by various hands.] pp. 151. *Москва*, 1952. 8⁰.   **17075. d. 13**

—— მისალმებათა ნაკადი. [Misalmebat'a nakadi. A Torrent of Greetings. Collected poems.] pp. 145. I *plate.* თბილისი [*Tiflis*,] 1952. 12⁰.   **17075. d. 33**

—— მხოლოდ ახალი. [Mkholod akhali. New things alone. A collection of poems and verses.] pp. 86, 5. თბილისი [*Tiflis*,] 1958. 12⁰.   **17075. d. 42**

MARIAM, *Queen of Georgia. [Biography.] See* PAPAVA (T'.) and (A.); ROTTIERS (B. E. A.)

MARIÈS (LOUIS). [Joint edit. of 'Sur les bénédictions d'Isaac, de Jacob et de Moïse:] *See* HIPPOLYTUS, *Saint, of Rome.*

MARK, *the Deacon*. La vie géorgienne de Saint Porphyre de Gaza [edit., with Latin trans., by P. Peeters.] pp. 65–216. *Bruxelles*, 1941. 8⁰. [*Analecta Bollandiana*. tom. 59.]   **2002. ġ**

MARK, *Saint and Evangelist. See* BIBLE.—New Testament.—*Mark*.

MARKOZASHVILI (IOANE). [Copyist of the Typikon composed by Grigol Bakuriani for the Georgian monastery in Bulgaria.] *See* NIKOLAEV (V.)

MARQUART, afterwards **MARKWART** (JOSEF). Die Bekehrung Iberiens und die beiden ältesten Dokumente der iberischen Kirche. pp. 111–67. *Leipzig*, 1931. 8⁰. [*Caucasica*. fasc. 7.]
                    P. P. 3803. eba

MARR (NIKOLAI YAKOVLEVICH). [Edit., with Russian trans., of 'Плѣненіе Іерусалима персами въ 614 г.'] *See* ANTIOCHUS, *Laurae S. Sabae Monachus*.

—— [For 'K'art'lis tskhovreba... Histoire de la Géorgie depuis l'antiquité... Réédition faite par N. Marr':] *See* BROSSET (M.-F.)

—— [Edit. 'Объ отношеніи абхазскаго языка къ яфе-тическимъ'.] *See* CHARAYA (P. G.)

—— [For 'Н. Я. Марр и грузиноведеніе':] *See* DON-DUA (K. D.)

—— [Edit. inscription of the Catholicos Epiphanius.] *See* EPIPHANIUS, *Catholicos of Georgia*.

—— [Edit. with Russian trans. of the life of St. Gregory of Khandzt'a.] *See* GIORGI, *Merchule*.

—— [Edit. and trans. of the Georgian version of St. Hippolytus's commentary on the Song of Solomon.] *See* HIPPOLYTUS, *Saint, of Rome*.

—— [For German trans. by G. N. Bonwetsch of N. Y. Marr's edition of the Georgian version of St. Hippolytus's Commentary on the Song of Solomon:] *See* HIPPOLYTUS, *Saint, of Rome*.

—— [Edit. and trans. of the Georgian text of the legend of the foundation of the first church at Lydda.] *See* JOSEPH, *of Arimathea*.

—— [For 'Ein in georgischer Sprache überliefertes Apokryphon des Joseph von Arimathia', trans., on the basis of the Russian version by N. Y. Marr, by A. von Harnack:] *See* JOSEPH, *of Arimathea*.

—— [Edit. and trans. 'Le Synaxaire géorgien'.] *See* LITURGIES.—Greek Rite.—*Synaxarion*.

—— [*Biography*.] *See* MIKHANKOVA (V. A.)

—— [Edit. and trans. of the Armenian and Georgian versions of the 'Physiologus'.] *See* PHYSIOLOGUS.

—— *See* SAINT PETERSBURG.—*Academia Scientiarum Imperialis.*—Яфетический Институт, afterwards Институт языка и мышления. Памяти академика Н. Я. Марра, 1864–1934. 1938. 8⁰.   **Ac. 1125.t/3**

—— [Edit. 'Яфетический сборник'.] *See* SAINT PETERSBURG.—*Academia Scientiarum Imperialis.*—Яфетический Институт, afterwards Институт языка и мышления.

—— [Edit. 'Язык и мышление'.] *See* SAINT PETERSBURG.—*Academia Scientiarum Imperialis.*—Яфетический Институт, afterwards Институт языка и мышления.

—— [Edit. with Russian trans. and commentary of the Acts of Saints Speusippus, Eleusippus and Meleusippus.] *See* SPEUSIPPUS, ELEUSIPPUS and MELEUSIPPUS, *Saints and Martyrs, of Cappadocia*.

—— [Edit. and trans. of the Georgian redaction of the Life of Peter the Iberian.] *See* ZACHARIAS, *Scholasticus, Bishop of Mitylene*.

—— Абхазско-русский словарь. Пособие к лекциям, *etc.* pp. lv. 159. *Ленинград*, 1926. 8⁰.   **12907. p. 8**

—— Абхазское происхожденіе грузинскаго термина родства *biđa*, дядя. pp. 143–46. *Петроградъ*, 1914. 8⁰. [*Извѣстія Императорской Академіи Наукъ*. VI серія. томъ 8.]   **Ac. 1125/44**

MARR *(cont.)*

—— Аг̇iографическiе матерiалы по грузинскимъ рукописямъ Ивера. [Hagiographical material from Georgian Mss. on Mt. Athos. 1. Description of five Mss. on parchment; 2. Life of St. Varlaam, Georgian text with Russian translation.] 2 част. С.-Петербургъ, 1901. 8⁰. [*Записки Восточнаго Отдѣленiя Имп. Русскаго Археологическаго Общества.* томъ 13.] **Ac. 5584**

—— [Another copy, being an offprint]. **17026. g. 8. (1.)**

—— Албанская надпись. [With a facsimile.] pp. 7–14. *Москва, Ленинградъ, 1947.* 8⁰. [*Краткие Сообщенiя Института Исторiи Матерiальной Культуры.* вып. 15.] **Ac. 1125. gd**

—— Армянскiя слова в грузинскихъ Дѣянiяхъ Пилата. pp. 024–029. С.-Петербургъ, 1907. 8⁰. [*Записки Восточнаго Отдѣленiя Имп. Русскаго Археологическаго Общества.* томъ 17.] **Ac. 5584**

—— Армянско-грузинскiе матерiалы для исторiи Душеполезной Повѣсти о Варлаамѣ и Iоасафѣ. pp. 49–78. 1899. 8⁰. *See* BARLAAM, *Saint, of India.* [*Записки Восточнаго Отдѣленiя Имп. Русскаго Археологическаго Общества.* томъ 11.] **Ac. 5584**

—— Боги языческой Грузiи по древнегрузинскимъ источникамъ. pp. 1–29. С.-Петербургъ, 1902. 8⁰. [*Записки Восточнаго Отдѣленiя Имп. Русскаго Археологическаго Общества.* томъ 14.] **Ac. 5584**

—— Дневникъ поѣздки въ Шавшiю и Кларджiю. *See* GIORGI, *Merchule.* Житiе св. Григорiя Хандзтʻiйскаго, *etc.* 1911. 8⁰. [*Тексты и разысканiя по армяно-грузинской филологiи.* кн. 7.] **14005. f. 5**

—— Древнегрузинскiе одописцы XII в. I. Пѣвецъ Давида Строителя. II. Пѣвецъ Тамары. Грузинскiй текстъ изслѣдовалъ, издалъ и словаремъ снабдилъ Н. Марръ. [Including the ode 'Abdulmesia' by Iovane Shavtʻeli and the eulogy of Queen Tʻamar by Chakhrukhadze.] pp. xii. 114. 170. С.-Петербургъ, 1902. 8⁰. [*Тексты и разысканiя по армяно-грузинской филологiи.* кн. 4.] **14005. f. 5**

—— Два грузинскихъ архитектурныхъ термина—"ачрдил" и "балавар". pp. 285–98. *Петроградъ,* 1922. 4⁰. [*Христiанскiй Востокъ.* томъ 6. вып. 3.] **Ac. 1125/105**

—— Гдѣ сохранилось сванское склоненiе? pp. 1199–206. С.-Петербургъ, 1911. 8⁰. [*Извѣстiя Акад. Наукъ.* VI серiя. томъ 5.] **Ac. 1125/44**

—— Готское слово гума, 'муж'. [On the Gothic word *guma* 'man', and the links between the Goths and the Caucasian peoples.] pp. 441–65. *Ленинградъ,* 1930. 8⁰. [*Извѣстiя Акад. Наукъ.* VII серiя. *Отдѣленiе Гуманитарныхъ Наукъ.*] **Ac. 1125/44 (2)**

—— Грамматика чʻанскаго (лазскаго) языка, с хрестоматiею и словаремъ. pp. xxx. 240. С.-Петербургъ, 1910. 8⁰. [*Матерiалы по яфетическому языкознанiю.* no. 2.] **17073. a. 3**

—— Грамматика древнелитературного грузинского языка. pp. xxiv. 026. 212. 3. 3 *plates. Ленинградъ, 1925.* 8⁰. [*Материалы по яфетическому языкознанию.* no. 12.] **17073. a. 3**

—— Грузинская поэма "Витязь въ барсовой шкурѣ" Шоты из Рустава и новая культурно-историческая проблема. 2 pt. pp. 415–46; 475–506. *Петроградъ,* 1917. 8⁰. [*Извѣстiя Акад. Наукъ.* VI серiя. томъ 11.] **Ac. 1125/44**

—— Грузинскiя приписки греческаго Евангелiя изъ Коридiи. pp. 211–40. 8 *plates.* С.-Петербургъ, 1911. 8⁰. [*Извѣстiя Акад. Наукъ.* VI серiя. томъ 5.] **Ac. 1125/44**

—— Iоаннъ Петрицскiй, грузинскiй неоплатоникъ XI–XII вѣка. [A study of the works of John Petridsi, a Georgian neo-Platonist of the 11th–12th centuries. With extracts from John Petridsi's translation of the 'Institutio Theologica' by Proclus Diadochus.] pp. 53–113. С.-Петербургъ, 1910. 8⁰. [*Записки Восточнаго Отдѣленiя Имп. Русскаго Археологическаго Общества.* томъ 19.] **Ac. 5584**

—— Исторiя Грузiи … По поводу слова Прот. I. Восторгова о грузинскомъ народѣ. pp. 88. С.-Петербургъ, 1906. 8⁰. *No. 1 of* "Къ грузинскому вопросу". **09009. aa. 15. (7.)**

MARR *(cont.)*

—— [Another copy.]   **9005. bbb. 25**

—— Исторія термина "абхазъ". pp. 697–706. С.-Петербургъ, 1912. 8⁰. [*Извѣстія Акад. Наукъ. VI серія.* томъ 6.]   **Ac. 1125/44**

—— Из грузино-персидских литературных связей. [A study of the Georgian versions of the Shāh Nāmeh and the romance of Vīs and Rāmīn.] pp. 111–38. Ленинград, 1925. 8⁰. [*Записки Коллегии Востоковедов.* том I.]   **Ac. 1125. qb**

—— Изъ гурійскихъ народныхъ преданій о постройкѣ Зарзмскаго монастыря съ преданіями о переселенцахъ изъ Месхіи и Абхазіи въ Гурію. pp. 347–50. Петроградъ, 1922. 4⁰. [*Христіанскій Востокъ.* томъ 6. вып. 3.]   **Ac. 1125/105**

—— Изъ книги царевича Баграта о грузинскихъ переводахъ духовныхъ сочиненій и героической повести "Дареджаніани". [Extracts from a 16th manuscript work on the history of Georgian literature.] pp. 233–46. St.-Pétersbourg. 1899. 4⁰. [*Извѣстія Императорской Академіи Наукъ. V серія.* томъ 10.]   **Ac. 1125/44**

—— Изъ лингвистической поѣздки въ Абхазію. pp. 303–34. 2 *plates.* С.-Петербургъ, 1913. 8⁰. [*Извѣстія Акад. Наук. VI серія.* томъ 7.]   **Ac. 1125/44**

—— Изъ поѣздки на Афонъ. О грузинскихъ рукописяхъ Ивера.—О св. Варлаамѣ.—О древне-грузинскихъ переводахъ съ армянскаго. pp. 1–24. С.-Петербургъ, 1899. 8⁰. [*Журналъ Министерства Народнаго Просвѣщенія.* часть 322. отд. 2.]   **P. P. 1213**

—— Изъ поѣздки въ турецкій Лазистанъ. 2 pt. pp. 547–70; 607–32. С.-Петербургъ, 1910. 8⁰. [*Извѣстія Акад. Наукъ. VI серія.* томъ 4.]   **Ac. 1125/44**

—— Изъ поѣздокъ въ Сванію лѣтомъ 1911 и 1912 г. pp. 1–36. С.-Петербургъ, 1913. 4⁰. [*Христіанскій Востокъ.* томъ 2. вып. I.]   **Ac. 1125/105**

—— Der japhetitische Kaukasus und das dritte ethnische Element im Bildungsprozess der mittelländischen Kultur... Aus dem Russischen übersetzt von F. Braun. pp. 76. *Leipzig,* 1923. 8⁰. [*Japhetitische Studien zur Sprache und Kultur Eurasiens.* no. 2.]   **7711. aaa. 1**

—— Къ датѣ эмиграціи Мосоховъ изъ Арменіи въ Сванію. pp. 1689–92. Петроградъ, 1916. 8⁰. [*Извѣстія Акад. Наукъ. VI серія.* томъ 10.]   **Ac. 1125/44**

—— Къ грузинскимъ надписямъ из Месхіи. [Containing emendations to readings by E. S. Tʻaqaishvili of Georgian inscriptions from Samtskhe.] pp. 228–32. Ленинградъ, 1925. 8⁰. [*Записки Коллегии Востоковедов.* том I.]   **Ac. 1125. qb**

—— Къ исторіи передвиженія яфетическихъ народовъ съ юга на сѣверъ Кавказа. pp. 1379–1408. Петроградъ, 1916. 8⁰. [*Извѣстія Акад. Наукъ. VI серія.* томъ 10.]   **Ac. 1125/44**

—— К опредѣленію племенного происхожденія Георгія, сына Тамары. pp. 473–78. Ленинградъ, 1926. 8⁰. [*Известия Акад. Наук. VI серия.* том 20.]   **Ac. 1125/44**

—— К Rusthaveliana. [Discussion of textual difficulties in Rustʻaveli's poem 'The Man in the Panther's Skin'.] pp. 361–68. Ленинградъ, 1927. 8⁰. [*Известия Акад. Наук. VI серия.* том 21.]   **Ac. 1125/44**

—— Къ столѣтію дня рожденія М. И. Броссе. [Including an appreciation of M.-F. Brosset's contribution to Georgian studies.] pp. 073–078. С.-Петербургъ, 1902. 8⁰. [*Записки Восточнаго Отдѣленія Имп. Русскаго Археологическаго Общества.* томъ 14.]   **Ac. 5584**

—— Къ вопросу о ближайшемъ сродствѣ армянскаго языка съ иверскимъ. pp. 069–072. С.-Петербургъ, 1910. 8⁰. [*Записки Восточнаго Отдѣленія Имп. Русскаго Археологическаго Общества.* томъ 19.]   **Ac. 5584**

—— Къ вопросу о положеніи абхазскаго языка среди яфетическихъ. pp. ii. 51. С.-Петербургъ, 1912. 8.⁰ [*Матеріалы по яфетическому языкознанію.* no. 5.]   **17073. a. 3**

MARR *(cont.)*

—— Къ вопросу о вліяніи персидской литературы на грузинскую. pp. 223–37. *С.-Петербургъ*, 1897. 8⁰. [*Журналъ Министерства Народнаго Просвѣщенія.* часть 310. отд. 2.]   **P. P. 1213**

—— Кавказъ и памятники духовной культуры. pp. 69–82. *С.-Петербургъ*, 1912. 8⁰. [*Извѣстія Акад. Наукъ.* VI серія. томъ 6.]   **Ac. 1125/44**

—— Кавказовѣдѣніе и абхазскій языкъ. pp. 1–27. *Петроградъ*, 1916. 8⁰. [*Журналъ Министерства Народнаго Просвѣщенія. Новая серія.* часть 63.]   **P. P. 1213**

—— Кавказскій культурный міръ и Арменія. pp. 280–330. *Петроградъ*, 1915. 8⁰. [*Журналъ Министерства Народнаго Просвѣщенія. Новая серія.* часть 57.]   **P. P. 1213**

—— Краткій каталогъ собранія грузинскихъ рукописей пріобрѣтеннаго Императорскою Публичною Библіотекою въ 1896 году. pp. 13. 1900. 8⁰. *See* SAINT PETERSBURG. — *Императорская Публичная Библіотека.*   **17031. d. 6**

—— Крещеніе армянъ, грузинъ, абхазовъ и алановъ святымъ Григоріемъ. Арабская версія. [Arabic text, with Russian translation and commentary by N. Y. Marr.] pp. 63–211. 3 *plates. С.-Петербургъ*, 1906. 8⁰. [*Записки Восточнаго Отдѣленія Имп. Русскаго Археологическаго Общества.* томъ 16.]   **Ac. 5584**

——Критика и мелкія статьи. [Including an edition, with Russian trans., of the Georgian text of the Martyrdom of the Nine Children of Kola.] pp. iii. 73. *С.-Петербургъ*, 1903. 8⁰. [*Тексты и разысканія по армяно-грузинской филологіи.* кн. 5.]   **14005. f. 5**

—— Культъ женщины и рыцарство въ поэмѣ 'Витязь въ барсовой кожѣ'. *See* RUST'AVELI (SHOT'A). Вступительныя и заключительныя строфы Витязя въ барсовой кожѣ, *etc.* 1910. 8⁰. [*Тексты и разысканія по армяно-грузинской филологіи.* кн. 12.]   **14005. f. 5**

—— La langue géorgienne. pp. 3–21. *Paris*, 1927–

28. 8⁰. [*Revue de l'Orient Chrétien.* tom. 6 (26).]   **P. P. 37. ck**

—— Матеріалы по яфетическому языкознанію. [A series edited by N. Y. Marr.] no. 1–6, 11–13. *С.-Петербургъ*, 1910–27. 8⁰.   **17073. a. 3**

—— "Мудрость Балавара", грузинская версія "Душеполезной исторіи о Варлаамѣ и Іоасафѣ." pp. 223–60. 1889. 8⁰. *See* BARLAAM, *Saint, of India.* [*Записки Восточнаго Отдѣленія Имп. Русскаго Археологическаго Общества.* томъ 3.]   **Ac. 5584**

—— Непочатый источникъ исторіи кавказскаго міра. pp. 307–38. *Петроградъ*, 1917. 8⁰. [*Извѣстія Акад. Наукъ.* VI серія. томъ 11.]   **Ac. 1125/44**

—— О фрагментѣ грузинской версіи "Дѣтства Христа". pp. 343–47. *Петроградъ*, 1922. 4⁰. [*Христіанскій Востокъ.* томъ 6. вып. 3.]   **Ac. 1125/105**

—— О кавказской версіи Библіи въ грузинскихъ палимпсестныхъ фрагментахъ. pp. 50–65. *Ленинградъ*, 1925. 4⁰. [*Тексты и разысканія по кавказской филологіи.* том 1.]   **Ac. 1125/228**

—— О Кавказскомъ Университетѣ въ Тифлисѣ. pp. 1496–1516. *Петроградъ*, 1918. 8⁰. [*Mélanges Asiatiques de l'Académie des Sciences.* Nouvelle série.]   **Ac. 1125/11**

—— О полигеніи семантики. pp. 781–86. *Ленинградъ*, 1926. 8⁰. [*Известия Акад. Наук.* VI серия. том 20.]   **Ac. 1125/44**

—— О религіозныхъ вѣрованіяхъ абхазовъ. pp. 113–40. *Петроградъ*, 1915. 4⁰. [*Христіанскій Востокъ.* томъ 4. вып. 1.]   **Ac. 1125/105**

—— Об яфетической теоріи. pp. 303–39. *Москва*, 1924. 8⁰. [*Новый Востокъ.* кн. 5.]   **Ac. 1096. b/5**

—— On the Religious Beliefs of the Abkhazians. [A translation of the article originally published in Russian in "Христіанскій Востокъ", 1915.] pp. 157–80. *London*, 1937. 8⁰. [*Georgica.* vol. 1. nos. 4–5.]   **Ac. 8821. e**

MARR *(cont.)*

—— Описание грузинских рукописей синайского монастыря. pp. xii. 276. 1940. 8⁰. *See* CATHARINE, *Saint, of Alexandria.*—Convent of, on Mount Sinai.

11916. k. 16

—— Описаніе персидскаго рукописнаго Четвероевангелія [in Georgian transcription.] pp. 377–81. 1889. 8⁰. *See* BIBLE.—Gospels.—*Appendix.* [*Записки Восточнаго Отдѣленія Имп. Русскаго Археологическаго Общества.* томъ 3.]   **Ac. 5584**

—— Основныя таблицы къ грамматикѣ древне-грузинскаго языка, съ предварительнымъ сообщеніемъ о родствѣ грузинскаго языка съ семитическими. pp. vi. 16. 20 *tables.* С.-Петербургъ, 1908. 4⁰.

12976. v. 1

—— Ossetica-Japhetica. 2 pt. *Петроградъ (Ленинградъ),* 1918–27. 4⁰. [*Извѣстія Россійской Академіи Наукъ.* VI серія. томъ 12, 21.]   **Ac. 1125/44**

—— Отчет о третьей лингвистической поездке заграницу; Отчет по весенней командировке въ Абхазію. pp. 531–49. Ленинград, 1928. 8⁰. [*Известия Акад. Наук.* VII серия. *Отделение Гуманитарныхъ Наукъ.*]

Ac. 1125/44. (2.)

—— Персидская національная тенденція въ грузинскомъ романѣ "Амирандареджаніани". pp. 352–65. *С.-Петербургъ,* 1895. 8⁰. [*Журналъ Министерства Народнаго Просвѣщенія.* часть 299. отд. 2.]

P. P. 1213

—— Пособие для изучения живого грузинского языка. вып. 1. pp. viii. 99. *Ленинград,* 1926. 8⁰. [*Изданія Ленинградскаго Института Живыхъ Восточныхъ Языков.* no. 8. *Труды Яфетическаго Семинарія.* no. 2.] *No more published.*   **Ac. 1096. d. (8.)**

—— Происхожденіе изъ охотничьяго быта двухъ грузинскихъ терминовъ уголовнаго права : გერში *gershi* и სანახშირო *sanaqshiro.* [Origin of the Georgian legal terms 'gershi' and 'sanakhshiro'.] pp. 0168–71. *С.-Петербургъ,* 1908. 8⁰. [*Записки Восточнаго Отдѣленія Имп. Русскаго Археологическаго Общества.* томъ 18.]   **Ac. 5584**

—— Разложимость мнимых примитивов, простыхъ слов, и термины для понятия 'рыба'. pp. 385–92. *Ленинградъ,* 1926. 8⁰. [*Извѣстія Акад. Наукъ.* VI серія. томъ 20.]   **Ac. 1125/44**

—— Тексты и разысканія по армяно-грузинской филологіи. [A series edited by N. Y. Marr.] кн. 1–12. *С.-Петербургъ,* 1900–11. 8⁰. [*Изданія Факультета Восточныхъ Языковъ, etc.* no. 5.]   **14005. f. 5**

—— Ѳрако-армянскій Sabadios-aswat и сванское божество охоты. pp. 827–30. *С.-Петербургъ,* 1912. 8⁰. [*Извѣстія Акад. Наукъ.* VI серія. томъ 6.]

Ac. 1125/44

—— Тристан и Исольда. Отъ героини любви феодальной Европы до богини матриархальной Афревразии. [With parallels from Georgian and Caucasian folk literature. A series of articles by various hands, edited by N. Y. Marr.] pp. iv. 286. *Ленинградъ,* 1932. 8⁰. [*Труды Института Языка и Мышления.* no. 2.]

Ac. 1125. fd (1)

—— Тубал-кайнскій вкладъ въ сванскомъ. pp. 1093–98. *С.-Петербургъ,* 1912. 8⁰. [*Извѣстія Акад. Наукъ.* VI серія. томъ 6.]   **Ac. 1125/44**

—— Возникновеніе и расцвѣтъ древне-грузинской свѣтской литературы. pp. 223–52. *С.-Петербургъ,* 1899. 8⁰. [*Журналъ Министерства Народнаго Просвѣщенія.* часть 326. отд. 2.]   **P. P. 1213**

—— Яфетическія элементы въ языкахъ Арменіи. pt. 1–11. *С.-Петербургъ,* 1911–19. 8⁰. [*Извѣстія Акад. Наукъ.* VI серія. Continued in: *Mélanges Asiatiques. Nouvelle série.*]   **Ac. 1125/44. Ac. 1125/11**

—— Яфетическія названія деревьевъ и растеній. 3 pt. pp. 769–80; 821–52; 937–50. *Петроградъ,* 1915. 8⁰. [*Извѣстія Акад. Наукъ.* VI серія. томъ 9.]

Ac. 1125/44

—— Яфетическое происхожденіе абхазскихъ терминовъ родства. pp. 423–32. *С.-Петербургъ,* 1912. 8⁰. [*Извѣстія Акад. Наукъ.* VI серія. томъ 6.]

Ac. 1125/44

MARR *(cont.)*

—— Яфетическій Кавказъ и третій этническій элемент в созидании средиземноморской культуры. pp. 54. *Лейпциг*, 1920. 8⁰. [*Матерiалы по яфетическому языкознанию.* no. II.]   **17073. a. 3**

—— Заимствованіе числительныхъ въ яфетическихъ языкахъ. pp. 789–90. *С.-Петербургъ*, 1913. 8⁰. [*Извѣстія Акад. Наукъ.* VI серія. томъ 7.]   **Ac. 1125/44**

—— Замѣтки по текстамъ св. Писанія у древнихъ армянъ и грузинъ. 2 pt. томъ 2. вып. 2. pp. 163–74; томъ 4. вып. 3. pp. 229–45. *С.-Петербургъ*, 1913–16. 4⁰. [*Христіанскій Востокъ.* томъ 2, 4.]   **Ac. 1125/105**

—— Записка объ ученыхъ трудахъ профессора Н. Я. Марра. pp. 721–32. *С.-Петербургъ*, 1909. 8⁰. [*Извѣстія Акад. Наукъ.* VI серія. томъ 3.]   **Ac. 1125/44**

—— 'Зима' ‖ 'смерть', из палеонтологии речи. pp. 325–32. 2 *plates*. *Ленинградъ*, 1927. 8⁰. [*Известия Акад. Наук.* VI серия. том 21.]   **Ac. 1125/44**

—— and **BRIÈRE** (MAURICE). La langue géorgienne. [With maps.] pp. xvi. 858. *Paris*, 1931. 8⁰.   **2272. g. 26**

MARR LANGUAGE INSTITUTE. *See* TIFLIS. — *Marr Language Institute,* afterwards *Institute of Linguistics.*

MARTIROSOV (ARAM GEORGIEVICH) and **IMNAISHVILI** (GRIGOL MOSES-DZE). ქართული ენის კახური დიალექტი. გამოკვლევა და ტექსტები ლექსიკონითურთ. [Kʻartʻuli enis kakhuri dialekʻti. Gamokvleva da tekʻstebi lekʻsikonitʻurtʻ. The Kakhian dialect of Georgian. A study, with texts and a glossary.] (Кахетинский диалект грузинского языка.) [Georgian text with summary in Russian. Edited by V.T.Tʻopʻuria.] pp. viii. 192, I. თბილისი [*Tiflis,*] 1956. 8⁰. [*Kʻartʻuli dialekʻtologia.* tom. I.]   **17080. f. 11**

MARTYRIUS, *the Monk. See* SĀHDŌNĀ, *Bishop of Māḥōzē dh-Arēwān in Bēth Garmai.*

MARY, *the Blessed Virgin.*—CHURCHES AND INSTITUTIONS.— *Athos.—Monastery of Iviron. See* ATHOS, *Mount.*

MATCHAVARIANI (ALEKʻSI DAVITʻIS-DZE). [For a study of A. D. Matchavariani's ballet on the theme of Othello:] *See* ORJONIKIDZE (G. S.)

MATCHAVARIANI (IVANE NIKOLOZIS-DZE). [Trans. Defrémery's article on Arabic and Persian writings concerning Georgia.] *See* DEFRÉMERY (C. F.)

—— and **GVARJALADZE** (ISIDORE SILOVANIS-DZE). ფრანგულ-ქართული ლექსიკონი. [Pʻrangul-kʻartʻuli lekʻsikoni.] (Dictionnaire français-géorgien. Deuxième édition.) [Revised by E. Mtʻvralashvili.] pp. 412. თბილისი [*Tiflis,*] 1955. 8⁰.   **17076. i. 11**

MATCHAVARIANI (TʻAMAR PETRES-ASULI). [Compiler of the catalogue of the N. Nikoladze archive.) *See* NIKOLADZE (N. I.)

MATTHEW, *Saint and Evangelist. See* BIBLE.— New Testament.—*Matthew.*

MAXIMUS, *Saint, Abbot and Confessor.* [For 'О мѣстѣ кончины и погребенія св. Максима Исповѣдника':] *See* BRILLIANTOV (A. I.)

MECKELEIN (RICHARD). გერმანულ-ქართული სიტყვარი. [Germanul-kʻartʻuli sitqvari.] Deutsch-georgisches Wörterbuch. Bd. I. pp. lviii. 569. *Berlin & Leipzig*, 1937. 8⁰. [*Lehrbücher des Seminars für Orientalische Sprachen zu Berlin.* Bd. 37.]   **12907. t. 1/37. i**

—— ქართულ-გერმანული სიტყვარი. [Kʻartʻul-germanuli sitqvari.] Georgisch-deutsches Wörterbuch. pp. xxiii. 656. *Berlin & Leipzig*, 1928. 8⁰. [*Lehrbücher des Seminars für Orientalische Sprachen zu Berlin.* Bd. 32.]   **12907. t. 1/32**

MEGHVINETʻ-UKHUTSESI (DIMITRI). [For 'Instruction et itinéraire pour ... M. Dimitri Méghwineth-Khoutzésof':] *See* BROSSET (M.-F.)

—— [For 'Rapport sur le voyage de M. Dimitri

MEGHVINET‛-UKHUTSESI *(cont.)*
Méghwineth-Khoutzésis-Chwili':] *See* Brosset (M.-F.)

—— [For 'Rapport sur les voyages exécutés... par M. Dimitri Méghwineth-Khoutsésov':] *See* Brosset (M.-F.)

—— Inscriptions recueillies par M. Dimitri Méghwineth-Khoutzésis-Chwili. [Trans. with introduction by M.-F. Brosset.] 2 pt. pp. 164–90; 219–22. *St.-Pétersbourg*, 1849. 4⁰. [*Bulletin Historico-Philologique de l'Académie des Sciences.* tom. 6.]
Ac. 1125/7

MEGRELI (Dutu) *pseud.* [i. e. Dimitri Khoshtaria]. ვირველი ტალღები. [Pirveli talghebi. The first waves. A novel of Georgian life.] pp. 98. თბილისი [*Tiflis*,] 1894. 8⁰. **17076. a. 6**

MEGRELIDZE (Ioseb Bart‛lomes-dze). *See* Catharine, *Saint, of Alexandria.*—Convent of, on Mount Sinai. Описание грузинских рукописей синайского монастыря. [Compiled by N. Y. Marr.] (Редактор И. В. Мегрелидзе.) 1940. 8⁰. **11916. k. 16**

—— Арабская азбука с древнегрузинской транскрипцией. pp. 36–42. 1 *plate. Москва, Ленинград*, 1953. 4⁰. [*Эпиграфика Востока.* вып. 8.]
Ac. 1125. ġd/3

—— Из грузинского революционного фольклора.' [With trans. and notes in Russian.] pp. 103–11. *Москва, Ленинград*, 1939. 8⁰. [*Советский Фольклор.* no. 6.]
Ac. 1125. nba

—— Количественные числительные языков дидойской группы. pp. 91–94. *Москва, Ленинград*, 1940. 8⁰. [*Язык и мышление.* вып. 9.]
Ac. 1125. t/2

—— Лазский и мегрельский слои в гурийском. [Edit. by I. I. Meshchaninov.] pp. 247. *Москва, Ленинград*, 1938. 8⁰. [*Труды Института Языка и Мышления.* no. 12.]
Ac. 1125. fd (4.)

—— Персидская азбука в грузинской транскрипции. pp. 61–64. *Москва, Ленинград*, 1951. 4⁰. [*Эпиграфика Востока.* вып. 5.]
Ac. 1125. ġd/3

—— Революция в грузинском фольклоре. Материалы. [Georgian texts, with Russian trans. and notes.] pp. 156–89. *Ленинград*, 1934. 8⁰. [*Советский Фольклор.* вып. 1.]
Ac. 1125. nba

—— Родительный падеж фамильных имен на —დე —de в западногрузинском. pp. 118–28. *Москва, Ленинград*, 1940. 8⁰. [*Язык и мышление.* вып. 10.] **Ac. 1125. t/2**

—— Руставели и фольклор. pp. 308,4. *Тбилиси*, 1960. 8⁰. **17076. b. 51**

—— Шота Руставели и грузинский фольклор. pp. 112–46. *Москва, Ленинград*, 1940. 8⁰. [*Советское Востоковедение.* том I.] **Ac. 1125. ik/7**

—— Склонение в дидойском языке. pp. 129–56. *Москва, Ленинград*, 1940. 8⁰. [*Язык и мышление.* вып. 10.]
Ac. 1125. t/2

—— Звуковой состав цезского (дидойского) языка. [With texts.] pp. 231–50. *Москва, Ленинград*, 1936. 8⁰. [*Язык и мышление.* вып. 6–7.] **Ac. 1125. t/2**

MEILANOVA (Uneizet Azizovna). Функции эргативного падежа в лезгинском языке. pp. 250–57. *Москва*, 1954. 8⁰. [*Труды Института Языкознания.* том 3.] **Ac. 1125. sf**

MELEUSIPPUS, *Saint and Martyr, of Cappadocia.* [For Acts of St. Meleusippus:] *See* Speusippus, Eleusippus and Meleusippus, *Saints and Martyrs, of Cappadocia.*

MELIK‛ISHVILI (Giorgi Alek‛sandres-dze). К истории древней Грузии. pp. 507. 3 *maps. Тбилиси*, 1959. 8⁰. **09012. dd. 13**

MELIK‛SET‛-BEGI (Leon Melik‛set‛is-dze). [Edit. fragment of Georgian version of an apocryphon on the childhood of Christ.] *See* Jesus Christ.

—— Армазни. Историко-археологический очерк. (არმაზნი. ისტორიულ-არქეოლოგიური მიმოხილვა. [Armazni. Istoriul-ark‛eologiuri mimokhilva.]) [A study of the antiquities of Mtskhet‛a-Armazi. Illustrated.] pp. 117. *Тбилиси.* 1938. 8⁰.

MELIKʿSETʿ-BEGI *(cont.)*

[*Masalebi Sakʿartʿvelos da Kavkasiis istoriisatʿvis.*
fasc. 2.]   **17075. e. 12**

—— Эксцерпты из древней "Истории Арменіи" по
грузинской рукописи XVII вѣка. [Fragments of
the history of Moses of Khorene in Georgian translation.] pp. 135–42. *Leningrad*, 1927. 4⁰. [*Известия
Кавказского Историко-Археологического Института.*
том 2.]   **Ac. 1125. qc**

—— Гаресджийская тетралингва эпохи монголов
1352 г. pp. 56–62. 1 *plate. Москва, Ленинград,*
1953. 4⁰. [*Эпиграфика Востока.* вып. 8.]
       Ac. 1125. ġd/3

—— Грузинская версія Агаѳангелія и ея значеніе
для грузинской исторіографіи. pp. 155–70. *Петроградъ*, 1915. 4⁰. [*Христіанскій Востокъ.* томъ 4. вып.
2.]   **Ac. 1125/105**

—— Грузинскій изводъ сказанія о постѣ "араджа-
воръ". pp. 73–111. *Петроградъ*, 1917. 4⁰. [*Христіанскій Востокъ.* томъ 5. вып. 2.]   **Ac. 1125/105**

—— Къ вопросу объ устройствѣ алтаря въ древней
Грузіи. pp. 310–12. *Петроградъ*, 1916. 4⁰. [*Христіанскій Востокъ.* томъ 4. вып. 3.]   **Ac. 1125/105**

—— მეგალითური კულტურა საქართველოში.
[Megalitʿuri kultura Sakʿartʿveloshi. Megalithic
culture in Georgia. Georgian text with Russian summary.] pp. 140, iii. 61 *plates.* თბილისი [*Tiflis,*]
1938. 8⁰.   **17080. b. 2**

—— О грузинской версіи апокрифическаго Видѣнія
Саака Парфянина о судьбѣ Арменіи. [Based on a
manuscript in the Tiflis Ecclesiastical Museum.]
pp. 164–76. *Leningrad*, 1927. 4⁰. [*Известия Кавказского Историко-Археологического Института.* том 2.]
       Ac. 1125. qc

—— Обзор источников по истории Азербайджана.
вып. 2. Источники грузинские. pp. 27. *Баку*, 1939. 8⁰.
       Ac. 1125. ne

—— საიათნოვას ვინაობა. კრიტიკულ-ბიოგრა-
ფიული ეტიუდი. [Saiatʿnovas vinaoba. Kritikul-
biograpʿiuli etiudi. The personality of Sayeatʿ-Nōva,
being a critical and biographical study of the
eighteenth century Armeno-Georgian poet Arutʿin
Sayeadeanc, known as Sayeatʿ-Nōva. With a supplement describing, with facsimiles, autograph documents written by Sayeatʿ-Nōva.] pp. viii. 164, 015.
თბილისი [*Tiflis,*] 1930. 8⁰.   **17075. c. 27**

MELIKSET-BEKOV (LEON MELIKSETOVICH).
See MELIKʿSETʿ-BEGI (L. M.)

MELUA (MIRIAN). [Joint author of 'Kʿartʿuli lekʿ-
sikoni'.] *See* SKAMKOCHAISHVILI (S.) and MELUA
(M.)

MENABDE (LEVAN VASILIS-DZE). [Edit. 'Kʿartʿ-
uli literaturis istoria. Dzveli literatura', tom. 2.]
See KEKELIDZE (K. S.)

MENGES (KARL HEINRICH). [Joint author of
'Peoples and languages of the Caucasus'.] *See*
GEIGER (B.) *and others.*

MEPʿARISHVILI (LUBA LAVRENTIS-ASULI).
[Joint compiler of Catalogue of Georgian manu-
scripts in the Georgian State Museum.] *See* TIF-
LIS.—*Museum of Georgia.*

MERABASHVILI (AVTʿANDIL). [Edit. 'Vepʿ-
khistqaosanis mzis metqveleba'.] *See* NOZADZE
(V.)

—— [Edit. 'Vepʿkhistqaosanis sazogadoebatʿ-
metqveleba'.] *See* NOZADZE (V.)

—— [Edit. 'Vepʿkhistqaosanis varskvlavtʿmet-
qveleba'.] *See* NOZADZE (V.)

MERCHULE (GIORGI). *See* GIORGI, *Merchule.*

MERCIER (BASILE–CHARLES). [Joint edit. of
'Sur les bénédictions d'Isaac, de Jacob et de
Moïse'.] *See* HIPPOLYTUS, *Saint, of Rome.*

MEREDITH-OWENS (GLYN MUNRO). [Joint
author of '*Amiran-Darejaniani:* a Georgian romance and its English rendering'.] *See* LANG (D.
M.) and MEREDITH-OWENS (G. M.)

MÉRIMÉE (Prosper). რჩეული ნოველები და კომედიები. [Rcheuli novelebi da komediebi. Selected novels and comedies. Trans. by G. K'ik'odze and A. L. Tsagareli.] pp. 392. თბილისი [*Tiflis,*] 1949. 8⁰.   **17077. a. 12**

MERKVILADZE (Giorgi Ivanes-dze). სოცია- ლისტური რეალიზმის შესახებ. სოციალისტური რეალიზმის განვითარება 30-ანი წლების ქართულ საბჭოთა ლიტერატურაში. [Sotsialisturi realizmis shesakheb. Sotsialisturi realizmis ganvit'areba 30-ani dslebis k'art'ul sabtchot'a literaturashi. A study of the development of Socialist Realism in Georgian Soviet literature of the 1930's.] pp. 313. თბილისი [*Tiflis,*] 1954. 8⁰.   **17076. d. 6**

MESHCHANINOV (Ivan Ivanovich). [Edit. 'Лазский и мегрельский слои в гурийском'.] *See* Megrelidze (I. B.)

—— [Edit. 'Памяти академика Н. Я. Марра.'] *See* Saint Petersburg:—*Academia Scientiarum Imperialis.*—*Яфетический Институт,* afterwards *Институт языка и мышления.*

—— [Joint edit. of 'Языки Северного Кавказа и Дагестана'.] *See* Serdyuchenko (G. P.)

—— [General editor of 'Грамматический очерк агульского языка'.] *See* Shaumyan (R. M.)

—— Серия *caucasica.* Материалы и исследования по кавказским языкам. Под редакцией акад. И. И. Ме- щанинова. 2 no. *Москва, Ленинград,* 1938,41. 8⁰. [*Академия Наук СССР. Труды Института Языка и Мышления имени Н. Я. Марра.*]   **Ac. 1125. fd. (4, 5.)**

MESKHI, *pseud. See* Gvaramadze (K.)

MESKHI (Sergei Svimonis-dze). ნაწერები. [Nadserebi. Collected political and critical articles. Edited by S. P'irtskhalava.] tom. I. pp. 533, vi. 2 *plates.* ტფილისი [*Tiflis,*] 1903. 8⁰. *No more published.*   **17075. f. 39**

MESKHIA (Shot'a Ambakos-dze). [Edit. 'P'eo-

daluri Sak'art'velos sotsialuri urt'iert'obis istorii-dan'.] *See* Gvritishvili (D. V.)

—— [Edit. history of Georgia in the 19th century.] *See* Kikvidze (A. I.)

MESKHIEVI (Konstantine I.). [Edit. biography of Shot'a Rust'aveli.] *See* Tchitchinadze (Z. E.)

METREVELI (Elene Pavles-asuli). [Joint compiler of Catalogue of Georgian manuscripts in the Georgian State Museum.] *See* Tiflis.—*Museum of Georgia.*

—— [Edit. 'Mimoslva'.] *See* Gabashvili (T.), *Metropolitan of K'ut'aisi.*

MEUNARGIA (Iona Mikheilis-dze). [Edit. N. Dadiani's 'Dastur-lama'.] *See* Dadiani (N. G.)

MGALOBLISHVILI (Sop'ron Zak'arias-dze). საყმაწვილო მოთხრობანი. [Saqmadsvilo mot'-khrobani. Children's stories. With a biographical introduction.] pp. 96. გორი [*Gori,*] 1916. 12⁰.   **17076. b. 29**

MGALOBLISHVILI (Vladimer Konstantines-dze). [Joint trans. of selected works of Byelinsky.] *See* Byelinsky (V. G.)

—— [Joint edit. of writings of Shalva Dadiani.] *See* Dadiani (Sh. N.)

MGELADZE (Vlasa). მოგონებები. წიგნი პირ-ველი. საქართველო აჯანყებამდე, 1921–1924. [Mogonebebi. Dsigni pirveli. Sak'art'velo ajanqe-bamde, 1921–1924. Reminiscences. Bk. 1. Georgia up to the insurrection, 1921–1924.] pp. 46. პარიზი [*Paris,*] 1936. 8⁰.   **17075. f. 23**

MIANSAROV (Mikhail M.). Bibliographia Caucasica et Transcaucasica. Essai d'une biblio-graphie systématique relative au Caucase, à la Transcaucasie et aux populations de ces contrées. …Опытъ справочнаго систематическаго каталога печатнымъ сочиненіямъ о Кавказѣ, *etc.* том. I. sections I, 2. St.-*Pétersbourg,* 1874–76. 8⁰. *No more published.*   **11927. f. 16**

MICHAEL, *Saint and Martyr, Laurae S. Sabae Monachus.* [*Life.*] *See* BASIL, *Laurae S. Sabae Presbyter.*

MIDSISHVILI (NIKOLO). Поэты Грузии. В переводах Б. Л. Пастернака и Н. С. Тихонова. [Edit. by N. Midsishvili.] pp. xv. 199. *Тифлис*, 1935. 8⁰.

                              O11586. p. 9

MIK'ADZE (GIVI VARLAMIS-DZE). ქართული პოეტიკის ქრესტომათია — XVIII–XIX სს. [K'art'uli poetikis k'restomat'ia—XVIII–XIX ss. Chrestomathy of writings on Georgian poetics, taken from 18th and 19th century authors.] pp. 277. თბილისი [*Tiflis*,] 1954. 8⁰.   **17075. c. 17**

MIK'ELADZE (MOSE DIANOZIS-DZE). შრიფტები ნახატებზე წარწერებისათვის. [Shrip'tebi nakhatebze dsardserebisat'vis. Scripts for captions to plans and sketches. An album of characters used in Georgian and other alphabets. Edit. by V. O. Gordon.] (Шрифты для надписей на чертежах.). pp. ii. 42. 82 *plates.* თბილისი [*Tiflis*,] 1957. 4⁰.   **17076. f. 22**

MIKHANKOVA (VERA ANDREEVNA). Николай Яковлевич Марр. Очерк его жизни и научной деятельности. [Second edition.] pp. 450. 8 *plates. Москва, Ленинград*, 1948. 8⁰. [*Академия Наук СССР. Научно-популярная серия.*]   **Ac. 1125/226 (15)**

—— [Third edition.] pp. 553. 13 *plates. Москва, Ленинград*, 1949. 8⁰. [*Академия Наук СССР. Итоги и проблемы современной науки.*]   **Ac. 1125/224 (32)**

MILTON (JOHN). დაკარგული სამოთხე. დაბრუნებული სამოთხე. [Dakarguli samot'khe. Dabrunebuli samot'khe.] (Paradise Lost. Paradise Regained. Translated into Georgian by V. Chelidze.) [Edit. by G. Gachechiladze, and with illustrations by Gustave Doré.] pp. 345. 17 *plates.* თბილისი [*Tiflis*,] 1956. 4⁰.   **17076. k. 1**

MINGRELIA. [For 'Церкви и церковные древности Мегрелии':] *See* T'AQAISHVILI (E. S.)

MINGRELIAN FOLK-SONGS. [For 'Gesänge russischer Kriegsgefangener. III Band: Kaukasus-

völker, *etc.*', including Mingrelian folk-songs:] *See* LACH (R.)

MINGRELIAN LANGUAGE. [For 'Megruli dialek'tis nat'esaobrivi damokidebuleba k'art'ult'an':] *See* CHARAYA (P. G.)

—— [For 'Tchanur-megrul-k'art'uli shedarebit'i lek'sikoni':] *See* CHIKOBAVA (A. S.)

—— [For 'Détails sur le dialecte géorgien usité en Mingrélie':] *See* KLAPROTH (H. J. von).

—— [For 'Original Vocabularies of Five West Caucasian Languages', including Mingrelian:] *See* PEACOCK (D. R.)

—— [For 'Tchanur-megrulis p'onetika':] *See* ZHGHENTI (S. M.)

MINGRELIAN STUDIES. [For 'Мингрельскіе этюды':] *See* TSAGARELI (A. A.)

MINGRELIAN TALES. [For 'Contes et légendes du Caucase', including Mingrelian tales:] *See* MOURIER (J.)

MINGRELIAN TEXTS. [For 'Kaukasische Forschungen... Erster Teil. Georgische und Mingrelische Texte':] *See* BLEICHSTEINER (R.)

MIRI, *King of Egypt.* Le Miriani, ou histoire du roi Miri, conte géorgien, traduit en français par M. Brosset jeune. [Followed by extracts from the Georgian original]. 4 pt. *Paris*, 1835–36. 8⁰. [*Nouveau Journal Asiatique.* tom. 16; *Journal Asiatique.* sér. 3, tom. I.]   **R. Ac. 8808**

—— Miriani. A Georgian romance. [An abridged rendering of the French translation by M.-F. Brosset.] 3 pt. *London*, 1836–37. 8⁰. [*The Asiatic Journal.* New series, vol. 21–22.]   **P. P. 3780**

MIRTSKHULAVA-MASHASHVILI (ALIO ANDRIAS-DZE). [Joint edit. of writings of Shalva Dadiani.] *See* DADIANI (SH. N.)

—— რჩეული. [Rcheuli. Selected poems.] pp. 379. 1 *plate.* თბილისი [*Tiflis*,] 1952. 12⁰.   **17075. d. 32**

MITIN (Mark Borisovich). [Joint author of short biography of Stalin.] *See* Aleksandrov (G. F.) *and others.*

MITSISHVILI (Nikolo). *See* Midsishvili.

MOCHALOV (V. D.). [Joint author of short biography of Stalin.] *See* Aleksandrov (G.F.) *and others.*

MOCHKHUBARIDZE (Alekʻsandre) *pseud. See* Qazbegi (A. M.)

MOCIMUS, *Saint.* [For 'La Passion géorgienne des SS. Théodore,... Mocimus, *etc.*':] *See* Theodore, *Saint and Martyr, of Pella.*

MODESTUS, *Patriarch of Jerusalem.* [For 'La sépulture de Modeste de Jérusalem':] *See* Garitte (G.)

MOLITOR (Joseph). [For 'Das Adysh-Tetra-evangelium, neu übersetzt ... von Joseph Molitor':] *See* Bible.—New Testament.—*Gospels.*

—— Altgeorgisches Glossar zu ausgewählten Bibel-texten, *etc.* pp. 294, 1. *Roma*, 1952. 4⁰. [*Monumenta Biblica et Ecclesiastica.* no. 6.]   **14005. e. 15**

—— [Another copy.]   **Ac. 2002. d. (72.)**

—— Chanmetifragmente. Ein Beitrag zur Text-geschichte der altgeorgischen Bibelübersetzung. Tl. 1 – *Wiesbaden*, 1957. 8⁰. [*Oriens Christianus.* Bd. 41 – (Vierte Serie. Bd. 5–.)] *In progress.*   **Ac. 2002. b**

—— Evangelienzitate in einem altgeorgischen Väterfragment. pp. 16–21. *Wiesbaden*, 1956, 8⁰. [*Oriens Christianus.* Bd. 40. (Vierte Serie. Bd. 4.)]   **Ac. 2002. b**

—— Die georgische Bibelübersetzung. Ihr Werde-gang und ihre Bedeutung in heutiger Sicht. pp. 23–29. *Wiesbaden*, 1953. 8⁰. [*Oriens Christianus.* Bd. 37. (Vierte Serie. Bd. 1.)]   **Ac. 2002. b**

—— Monumenta Iberica Antiquiora. Textus Chan-

meti et Haemeti ex Inscriptionibus, S. Bibliis et Patribus collegit et in linguam latinam convertit, addito Glossario, J. Molitor. [Georgian texts with Latin trans. and introduction in German.] pp. xviii. 165. *Louvain*, 1956. 8⁰. [*Corpus Scriptorum Christianorum Orientalium.* vol. 166=Subsidia. tom. 10.]   **14005. a**

MOSASHVILI (Ilo Onisimes-dze). Избранные произведения. [Poems and plays, translated into Russian by various hands.] pp. 343. *Москва*, 1953. 8⁰.   **17075. d. 11**

—— ლექსები, პოემა, პიესა. [Lekʻsebi, poema, piesa. Verses, together with a historical poem 'The Lake of Bazaletʻi', and a historical drama 'The Path of the Future'.] pp. 351. 1 *plate.* სახელგამი [*State Publishing House: Tiflis*,] 1954. 8⁰.   **17075. c. 12**

—— Потопленные камни. Драма . . . Перевод с грузинского Элисбара Ананиашвили. pp. 5–62. *Москва*, 1951. 8⁰. [*Советская драматургия.* 1950.]   **W. P. B. 49/2**

—— [Another edition.] pp. 112. *Москва*, 1952. 8⁰. *Imperfect; pp. 18–19, 22–23, 26–27, 30–31 are blank.*   **17075. d. 20**

MOSCOW. [For 'Monographie géorgienne de Mos-cou':] *See* Brosset (M.-F.)

—— *Академия Наук СССР. See* Saint Peters-burg. — *Academia Scientiarum Imperialis.*

—— *Imperatorskoe Moskovskoe Arkheologicheskoe Obshchestvo.* Матеріалы по Археологіи Кавказа .... под редакціей графини Уваровой. вып. I–II. *Москва*, 1888–1907. 4⁰.   **Ac. 5575/3**

—— *Lazarevsky, afterwards Tsentralʻny, Institut Vostochnykh Yazykov, afterwards Institut Vo-stokovedeniya.* Труды по Востоковѣдѣнію. вып. I–29, pt. 1. *Москва*, 1899–1910. 4⁰ and 8⁰. *Incom-plete; wanting* вып. *5, 6, 10, 12, 15, 16, pt. 2–3, 18, 21, 22, 24–26, 28.*   **17068. g. 1**

—— *Nauchnaya Assotsiatsiya Vostokovedeniya*

S. S. S. R. Новый Востокъ ... под редакцией М. Павловича [i. e. M. L. Velʼtman]. (Nouvel Orient, *etc.*) кн. 1–29. *Москва*, 1922–30. 8⁰. **Ac. 1096. b/5**

MOSES, *of Khoni.* [For 'Analyse du Roman géorgien 'Amiran Daredjaniani':] *See* BROSSET (M.-F.)

—— [For '*Amiran-Darejaniani:* a Georgian romance and its English rendering':] *See* LANG (D. M.) and MEREDITH-OWENS (G. M.)

—— Amiran-Darejaniani. A cycle of medieval Georgian tales traditionally ascribed to Mose Khoneli. Translated by R. H. Stevenson. pp. xxxiii. 240. *Oxford*, 1958. 8⁰. **17076. b. 42**

MOSES, *Khorenaci.* [For 'Эксцерпты из древней "Исторіи Арменіи"', containing fragments of the history of Moses of Khorene in Georgian rendering:] *See* MELIKʻSETʻ-BEGI (L. M.)

MOSES, *the Lawgiver.* [For 'Des Hippolyt Erklärung der Segnungen des Moses zu den zwölf Stämmen'.] *See* HIPPOLYTUS, *Saint, of Rome.* Drei georgisch erhaltene Schriften von H., herausgegeben von G. Nath. Bonwetsch. 1904. 8⁰. **3628. d. 1/26**

—— [For 'Sur les bénédictions d'Isaac, de Jacob et de Moïse'. Greek, Armenian and Georgian texts, with French translation:] *See* HIPPOLYTUS, *Saint, of Rome.*

—— [For 'Une page de saint Hippolyte retrouvée', being a Georgian fragment of the Benedictions of Moses, edit. and trans. by R. P. Blake:] *See* HIPPOLYTUS, *Saint, of Rome.*

MOURIER (JULES). [Trans. 'L'armée géorgienne au Moyen Âge'.] *See* DADISHKELIANI (Tʻ. Tʻ.) *Prince.*

—— Chota Rousthavéli, poète géorgien du XIIᵉ siècle. Sa vie et son oeuvre. pp. 520–30. *Paris*, 1887. 8⁰. [*Journal Asiatique.* sér. 8. tom. 9.] **R. Ac. 8808**

—— Contes et légendes du Caucase, traduits par J. Mourier. pp. 112, 3. *Paris*, 1888. 8⁰. [*Collection orientale.* no. 1.] **14003. aa. 6/1**

MROVELI (LEONTI). *See* LEONTI, *Archbishop of Ruisi.*

MSHVENIERADZE (DOMENTI MELITONIS-DZE). გამოქვაბული ნაგებობანი საქართველოში. [Gamokʻvabuli nagebobani Sakʻartʻveloshi. Cave dwellings in Georgia.] (Пещерные сооружения в Грузии.) [Edit. by R. Agababiani.] tom. 1. pp. 38. 63 *plates.* თბილისი [*Tiflis,*] 1955. 8⁰. **17080. f. 2**

—— Строительное искусство в древней Грузии. (სამშენებლო ხელოვნება ძველ საქართველოში. [Samsheneblo khelovneba dzvel Sakʻartʻveloshi. The art of building in ancient Georgia.]) pp. 127. 181 *plates.* *Тбилиси*, 1959. 4⁰. **17080. g. 8**

MTCHEDLISHVILI (JUANSHER IOSEBIS-DZE). [Joint trans. of selections from 'The Book of Wisdom and Fiction'.] *See* SAVVA, *the Monk* [*Prince* SULKHAN ORBELIANI].

MTSKHETʻA. [For 'Mtskhetʻa. Kʻartʻlis samepʻos dzveli dedakʻalakʻi':] *See* APʻAKʻIDZE (A. M.)

—— [For 'Мцхета. Итоги археологических исследований, *etc.*':] *See* APʻAKʻIDZE (A. M.) *and others.*

—— [For 'Sur une inscription géorgienne de l'église patriarchale de Mtzkhétha':] *See* BROSSET (M.-F.)

—— [For 'Mtskhetʻis udzvelesi arkʻeologiuri dzeglebi':] *See* CHUBINISHVILI (T. N.)

——[For 'Археологические раскопки в ... Мцхета':] *See* LOMTʻATʻIDZE (G. A.)

—— [For 'Армазни, *etc.*', being a study of the antiquities of Mtskhetʻa-Armazi:] *See* MELIKʻSETʻ-BEGI (L. M.)

MTʻVARADZE (SIMON). სურამის ციხე. ტრაგედია 4 მოქმედებად . . . დაწერილია დ. ჭონქაძის მოთხრობის მიხედვით. [Suramis tsikhe. Tragedia 4 mokʻmedebad ... Dadserilia D. Tchon-

MTʻVARADZE *(cont.)*
kʻadzis motʻkhrobis mikhedvitʻ. Suram castle. Tragedy in 4 acts ... adapted from the story by D. Tchonkʻadze.] pp. 92. [თბილისი. *Tiflis*,] 1954. 8⁰.   **17075. d. 30**

—— [Another copy.]   **17075. d. 30***

MTʻVARELISHVILI (NIKOLOZ). [Biographical sketch of I. S. Davitʻashvili.] *See* DAVITʻASHVILI (I. S.)

MTʻVRALASHVILI (EKATERINE). [Edit. French-Georgian Dictionary.] *See* MATCHAVARIANI (I. N.) and GVARJALADZE (I. S.)

MUḤAMMAD ẒILLĪ ibn DARVĪSH, known as EVLIYĀ CHELEBI. [For 'Die kaukasische Sprachproben in Evliya Çelebi's Seyahetname':] *See* BLEICHSTEINER (R.)

MUNICH. —Институт по Изучению СССР. Caucasian Review. *Munich*, 1955— 8⁰.   **Ac. 7357/10**

MUSEUM OF GEORGIA. *See* TIFLIS.—*Museum of Georgia.*

MUSKHELISHVILI (LEVAN VAKHTANGIS-DZE). Раскопки в Дманиси. Краткий очерк. [With a summary in French. Illustrated.] pp. 258–86. 1 *plate.* *Москва, Ленинград*, 1940. 8⁰. [*Советская Археология.* no. 6.]   **Ac. 1125. nb/2**

—— *and others.* გუდარეხის პირველი და მეორე, 1938 და 1939 წწ., არქეოლოგიური კამპანიის ანგარიში. [Gudarekhis pirveli da meore, 1938 da 1939 dsds., arkʻeologiuri kampaniis angarishi. Report of the First and Second Gudarekhi Archaeological Campaigns, 1938 and 1939.] (Отчет Гударехских первой и второй, 1938 и 1939 гг., археологических кампаний.) [Georgian text with summary in Russian. With a folder containing 4 charts. Illustrated.] pp. xi. 137. თბილისი [*Tiflis*,] 1954. 8⁰.   **17080. f. 7**

MUZAEV (NURDIN). Говорит Селим. Сказание о Чечне. Поэма. Авторизованный перевод с чеченского Анисима Кронгауза. pp. 119, 4. *Москва*, 1958. 8⁰.   **17075. d. 43**

MYESHCHANINOV. [For this Russian surname:] *See* MESHCHANINOV.

MYSHETSKY (EFIM FEDOROVICH) *Prince.* [For a report on the diplomatic mission of Prince Myshetsky and I. Klyucharev to Kakhetʻi:] *See* POLIEVKTOV (M. A.)

NADIRADZE (GIORGI ALEKʻSANDRES-DZE). რუსთაველის ესთეტიკა. [Rustʻavelis estʻetika. Studies on the poetic art of Shotʻa Rustʻaveli.] pp. 430. თბილისი [*Tiflis*,] 1958. 8⁰.   **17075. d. 41**

NADIRADZE (KʻETʻEVAN SIMONIS-ASULI). [Joint trans. of 'Bukhara: mogonebani'.] *See* ʻAINĪ (ŜADR AL-DĪN).

NAKASHIDZE (NINO). [Trans. 'A Christmas Carol'] *See* DICKENS (C.)

NALʻCHIK. — Кабардино-балкарский научно-исследовательский институт. *See* APAZHEV (M. L.) *and others.* Кабардинско-русский словарь .... под общей редакцией Б. М. Карданова. 1957. 8⁰.   **17076. f. 16**

——*See* NARTY. Нарты. Кабардинский эпос. [Second edition.] 1957. 8⁰.   **17075. c. 20**

—— Грамматика кабардино-черкесского литературного языка. [Written and compiled by M. L. Abitov, B. Kh. Balkarov, Yu. D. Desheriev and others.] pp. 239. *Москва*, 1957. 8⁰.   **17076. i. 16**

NAMITOK (AYTEK). [Joint compiler and trans. of 'Récits oubykh'.] *See* DUMÉZIL (G.) and NAMITOK (A.)

—— [Joint trans. and edit. of fables of Tsey Ibrāhim.] *See* TSEY IBRAHIM.

NANITASHVILI (BORIS GRIGOLIS-DZE). [Joint edit. of 'Kʻartʻvel dramaturgtʻa piesebi'.] *See* BERDZENISHVILI (G.) *and others.*

NAPOLI (BERNARDO MARIA DA). *See* GIOFFI (B. M.)

NARTY. Нарты. Кабардинский эпос. [An epic saga in verse and prose, trans. into Russian by V. Zvyagintseva and others. Second edition.] pp. 526, 2. 9 *plates. Москва,* 1957. 8⁰.   **17075. c. 20**

NASIDZE (MIKHEIL). დავით გურამიშვილი. [Davit' Guramishvili. A biography of the eighteenth century Georgian poet.] pp. 63. თბილისი [*Tiflis,*] 1887. 8⁰.   **17075. d. 4. (2.)**

—— Учебникъ грузинскаго языка для русскихъ. [Second edition.] pp. III. *Тифлисъ,* 1894. 8⁰.   **17076. g̱. 5**

—— ვახტანგ მეექვსე. [Vakhtang meek'vse. Vakhtang VI. A historical study of the eighteenth century Georgian king.] pp. 54. ტფილისი [*Tiflis,*] [1887]. 8⁰.   **17075. e. 4. (1.)**

NATROSHVILI (GIORGI KONSTANTINES-DZE). [Introduction to 'На южной границе'.] *See* ABASHIDZE (G. G.)

NEIMAN (ALEK'SANDRE PAVLES-DZE). [Trans. 'Мачеха Саманишвили' and other stories.] *See* KLDIASHVILI (D. S.)

NEISSER (FRIEDRICH). Studien zur georgischen Wortbildung.... Herausgegeben von Gerhard Deeters. pp. x.90. *Wiesbaden,* 1953. 8⁰. [*Abhandlungen für die Kunde des Morgenlandes.* Bd. 31. Hft. 2.]   **753. f. 39**

NERSĒS IV, KLAYEÇI, *Catholicos of Armenia,* surnamed ŠNORHALI. Preces S. Nersis Clajensis, Armeniorum Patriarchae, viginti quatuor linguis [including Georgian] editae [by Pasquale Aucher]. [With a portrait.] pp. 2, 422, 2. *Venetiis, In Insula S. Lazari,* 1823. 12⁰.   **17024. c. 12**

—— Preces Sancti Nersetis Clajensis. [Another edition.] pp. 3, 434. *Venetiis, In Insula S. Lazari,* 1837. 12⁰.   **3455. aaa. 41**

—— Preces Sancti Nersetis Clajensis... triginta sex linguis [including Georgian] editae. [With a portrait.] pp. 11, 597, 2. *Venetiis, in Insula S. Lazari,* 1882. 12⁰.   **17026. b. 25**

NEW YORK.—*Metropolitan Museum of Art.* [For 'A fifteenth-century Georgian Needle Painting in the Metropolitan Museum, New York':] *See* AVALISHVILI (Z. D.)

NICEPHORUS, *the Monk.* [NIKOLOZ IRUBAK'IDZE-CHOLOQASHVILI]. *See* IBERIAN ALPHABET.

NICHOLAS, *Dvali, Saint and Martyr, of Damascus.* [For 'Житіе Прохора, муч. Луки и муч. Николая Двали':] *See* QIP'SHIDZE (D. A.)

NICHOLAS I, *Catholicos of Georgia.* საკითხავი სუეტის ცხოველისაჲ, კუართისა საუფლოჲსა და კათოლიკე ეკლესიისა. [Sakit'khavi sueytis tskhovelisay, kuart'isa saup'loysa da kat'olike eklesiisa. Book of the Living Pillar, the Tunic of Our Lord, and the Church Universal. Edit. by A. N. Ioseliani and V. G. Karbelashvili.] pp. iv. ii. 128. ტფილისი [*Tiflis,*] 1908. 8⁰.   **17071. d. 2**

NICHOLAS I, *Tsar of Russia.* უკანასკნელნი ჟამნი ცხოვრებისა იმპერატორის ნიკოლოზ პირველისა. [Ukanasknelni zhamni tskhovrebisa Imperatoris Nikolooz pirvelisa. The last hours of the life of the Emperor Nicholas I. Translated from Russian into Georgian by the priest M. Gurgenidze.] pp. 42. მოსკოვი [*Moscow,*] 1855. 8⁰.   **17075. ee. 1**

NIKOLADZE (ANNA KONSTANTINES-ASULI). Русско-грузинские литературные связи. pp. 233, 3. *Тбилиси,* 1958. 8⁰.   **17073. a. 6**

NIKOLADZE (EVSEVI BARNABIS-DZE). [Compiler of Catalogue of Georgian manuscripts in the K'ut'aisi State Historical Museum.] *See* K'UT'AISI.—*K'ut'aisi State Historical Museum.*

NIKOLADZE (NIKOLOZ IAKOBIS-DZE). [Edit. revolutionary newspaper 'Drosha'.] *See* PERIODICAL PUBLICATIONS.—*Paris.*

—— [For 'Niko Nikoladzis sotsialur-politikuri shekhedulebani':] *See* ZAK'ARIADZE (G. I.)

—— ნ. ნიკოლაძის არქივის კატალოგი. [N. Nikoladzis ark'ivis katalogi. Catalogue of the N. Niko-ladze Archive. pt. 1: 1829–1917. Compiled and prepared for publication by T'. Matchavariani.] pp. 343. 2 *plates.* თბილისი [*Tiflis,*] 1954. 8⁰. *In progress.*　　　　　　　　　　　**17080. d. 19**

NIKOLAEV (Vsevolod). La destinée du Typikon de Grégoire Bakouriani (Pakourianos) pour le monastère de Petritzos (Bačkovo) et de sa copie géorgienne de la Bibliothèque Nationale de Bulgarie. [In Bulgarian, with Russian and French summaries.] pp. 266–97. 9 *plates.* София, 1951. 8⁰. [*Известия на Института за Българска История.* no. 1–2.]　　　　　　　　　　**Ac. 1136. bf**

NIKOLSKAYA (Z. A.) *and others.* Народы Дагестана. Сборник статей. [With an introduction by A. D. Daniyalov. With a map. Illustrated.] pp. 245, 2. 2 *plates.* Москва, 1955. 8⁰. [*Академия Наук СССР. Научно-популярная серия.*]　　　　　　　　**Ac. 1125/226 (185)**

NIKORDSMINDA. [For 'Nikordsmindis reliep'e-bi':] *See* Aladashvili (N. A.)

NINO, *Saint, of Cappadocia.* [For 'Проповѣдниче-ская дѣятельность ап. Андрея и св. Нины въ Грузіи':] *See* Javakhishvili (I. A.)

——— [For 'Akhali varianti dsm. Ninos tskhovre-bisa':] *See* T'aqaishvili (E. S.)

——— Life of St. Nino. [Translated from the Geor-gian original in the 'Sak'art'velos Samot'khe', or 'Lives of Georgian Saints' and from other sources, by Marjory and J. O. Wardrop. With the Armenian version of the Life, trans. by F. C. Conybeare.] pp. 88. *Oxford,* 1900. 8⁰. [*Studia Biblica et Ec-clesiastica,* vol. 5, pt. 1.]　　　　　　**3130. h. 26**

NINOSHVILI (Egnate) *pseud.* [i.e. Egnate T'omas-dze Ingoroqva]. [*Biography.*] *See* Sakho-kia (T'. T.)

——— Избранное. [Stories. Translated by A. I. Qancheli and others.] pp. xxxi. 454. *Тифлис,* 1935. 8⁰.　　　　　　　　　　　　　　**12593. b. 4**

——— Сочинения в двух томах ... Перевод с грузин-ского Ф. Твалтвадзе. Литературная редакция Н. Чу-ковского. [With a portrait.] том 1— *Тбилиси,* 1950— 8⁰.　　　　　　　　　　　　　　**W. P. 1618**

——— თხზულებათა სრული კრებული. [T'khzule-bat'a sruli krebuli. Complete collection of writings, comprising stories, articles and letters. Edited with an introduction by G. K'ik'odze.] pp. x. 621. 1 *plate.* თბილისი [*Tiflis,*] 1954. 8⁰.　　**17076. b. 11**

——— Восстание в Гурии. Исторический роман. [Trans. into Russian by A. Starostin, with a bio-graphical sketch of the author by V. Margvela-shvili.] pp. 132, 4. *Москва,* 1959. 8⁰.　**17076. c. 18**

NIORADZE (Giorgi). კარსნის ხევის სასაფლაო. [Karsnis khevis sasap'lao.] Das Gräberfeld von Karssnis Chewi. [Georgian text with German summary. Illustrated.] pp. vi. col. 54. 3 *plates. Tiflis,* 1926. 4⁰. [*Sak'art'velos muzeumis shromebi.* no. 4.]　　　　　　　　　　　　**17080. b. 1**

——— პალეოლითის ადამიანი დევისხვრელში. [Paleolit'is adamiani Deviskhvrelshi.] Der Paläo-lithiker in der Höhle Dewiss-Chwreli. [Georgian text with German summary. Illustrated. With a plan.] pp. iv. 109. 8 *plates. Tiflis,* 1933. 8⁰. [*Sak'art'velos muzeumis shromebi.* no. 6.]

　　　　　　　　　　　　　　　　17080. b. 1

NIZHARADZE (Ivane Ivanes-dze). Русско-сванскій словарь. pp. iii. 520. [*Тифлисъ,* 1910.] 8⁰. *Title-page missing.*　　　　　　　**12976. w. 21**

NIZHARADZE (Nadim Izetis-dze) and **JIBUTI** (Nadezhda Makaris-asuli). აჭარის ასსრ. ფიზიკურ-გეოგრაფიული და ეკონომიურ-გეო-გრაფიული დახასიათება. [Atcharis A.S.S.R. P'izi-kur-geograp'iuli da ekonomiur-geograp'iuli dakha-siat'eba. The Atcharan A.S.S.R. A physico-geographical and economico-geographical descrip-tion. Illustrated.] pp. 263, 8. 6 *maps.* ბათუმი [*Batum,*] 1957. 8⁰.　　　　　　　　**17080. d. 23**

NOGMOV (Shora Bekmurzin). *See* Shora-Bekmurzin-Nogmov.

NOSADZE (Victor). *See* Nozadze (V.)

NOZADZE (Viktor). [Preface to 'Debulebani moghvadseobisa da brdzolisat'vis'.] *See* Georgia. —*Georgian Fascist Front.*

—— განკითხვანი ვეფხისტყაოსანისა. [Gankit'-khvani Vep'khistqaosanisa. Doctrines of 'The Man in the Panther's Skin'.] ვეფხისტყაოსნის ფერთამეტყველება.[Vep'khistqaosanis p'ert'ametqveleba.] The Symbolism of Colours in the Georgian romantic epic of the 12th century by Shotha Rousthaveli, 'The Knight in the Tiger's Skin'. pp. 207. ბუენოს აირეს [*Buenos Aires*,] 1953. 4⁰.
17076. d. 8

—— ვეფხისტყაოსანის მზის მეტყველება. [Vep'khistqaosanis mzis metqveleba.] La Significacion del Sol en el Epos heroico georgiano del siglo XII por Schotha Rusthaveli, "El Caballero de la Piel de Tigre". [Edited by A. Merabashvili, with a preface by G. de la Torre Botarro.] pp. xiv. 223, 1. *Santiago de Chile*, 1957. 4⁰.　**17076. d. 12. (1)**

—— [Another copy.]　　　**17076. d. 17**

—— ვეფხისტყაოსანის საზოგადოებათმეტყვე-ლება. [Vep'khistqaosanis sazogadoebat'metqveleba.] Estructura social y costumbres de la sociedad en el Epos Heroico Georgiano del Siglo XII, por Schotha Rusthaveli: "El Caballero de la Piel de Tigre". [Edited by A. Merabashvili, with a preface by G. de la Torre Botarro.] pp. vi. 311. *Santiago de Chile*, 1958. 4⁰.　**17076. d. 18**

—— ვეფხისტყაოსანის ვარსკვლავთმეტყველება. [Vep'khistqaosanis varskvlavt'metqveleba.] La Significacion de la Astronomia y Astrologia en el Epos heroico georgiano del siglo XII por Schotha Rusthaveli, "El Caballero de la Piel de Tigre". [Edited with a preface by A. Merabashvili.] pp. xvi. 263. *Santiago de Chile*, 1957. 4⁰.
17076. d. 12 (2)

NUCUBIDZE (Shalva Isakis-dze). *See* Nutsubidze.

NUTSUBIDZE (K'et'evan Shalvas-asuli).

დასავლეთ საქართველოს კვედა ცარცის ბრაქიოპოდები. [Dasavlet' Sak'art'velos k'veda tsartsis brak'iopodebi.] Les Brachiopodes du Crétacé inférieur de la Géorgie Occidentale. [Georgian text with French summary.] pp. 145–240. 4 plates. თბილისი [*Tiflis*,] 1945. 8⁰. [Offprint from *Academy of Sciences of the Georgian S.S.R.*: *Travaux de l'Institut Géologique*. tom. 2. fasc. 7. pt. 2.]
17080. d. 17

NUTSUBIDZE (Shalva Isakis-dze). [For 'Les origines du "Barlaam et Joasaph" grec. À propos de la thèse nouvelle de M. Nucubidze':] *See* Devos (P.)

—— [Trans. 'Витязь в тигровой шкуре'.] *See* Rust'aveli (Shot'a).

—— ქართული ფილოსოფიის ისტორია. [K'art'uli p'ilosop'iis istoria. History of Georgian philosophy.] (История грузинской философии.) tom. 1, 2— თბილისი [*Tiflis*,] 1956—. 8⁰. *In progress.* **17078. d. 2**

—— Творчество А. Р. Церетели. pp. 103–18. *Москва*, 1940. 8⁰. [*Известия Академии Наук СССР. Classe des Sciences Littéraires et Linguistiques.* no. 2.]
Ac. 1125/44. (11.)

OCHIAURI (T'inat'in Alek'sis-asuli). ქართ-ველთა უძველესი სარწმუნოების ისტორიიდან. [K'art'velt'a udzvelesi sardsmunoebis istoriidan. From the history of the most ancient beliefs of the Georgians. A study of fortune-telling among the Khevsurs.] pp. 145. თბილისი [*Tiflis*,] 1954. 8⁰.
17080. b. 7

ODZELASHVILI (Arsena). [For a historical novel on the life of A. Odzelashvili, or Arsena of Marabda:] *See* Javakhishvili (M. S.)

—— არსენას ლექსი. [Arsenas lek'si. Ballad of Arsena. A folk poem relating the exploits of this Georgian bandit and popular hero. Edit. by P. Umikashvili. Illustrated.] pp. 15. ტფილისი [*Tiflis*,] 1892. 8⁰.　**17075. d. 2. (3)**

OK'ROPIRIDZE (Elisabed). ქართულ-ფრანგუ-ლი ლექსიკონი. [K'art'ul-p'ranguli lek'sikoni.] Dictionnaire géorgien-français. pp. xi. 523. თბილისი [*Tiflis*,] 1953. 8⁰.   **17076. f. 8**

OKUNEV (Nikolai L.). О грузино-греческой рукописи съ миніатюрами. [Description of a composite manuscript written in Georgian and Greek and containing selections from the New Testament, prayers, etc.] pp. 43–44. *С.-Петербургъ,* 1912. 4⁰. [*Христіанскій Востокъ.* томъ I. вып. I.]
                                        Ac. 1125/105

OPIZARI. [For biography of the Georgian goldsmith Bek'a of Opiza, or Opizari:] *See* AMIRA-NASHVILI (S. I.)

ORBELI (Iosif Abgarovich). [Edit. 'Очерки по истории и культуре кавказской Албании'.] *See* TREVER (K. V.)

ORBELI (Rusudana Rubenovna). [Author of brief description of the Georgian manuscripts in the Oriental Institute of the Academy of Sciences of the U.S.S.R.] *See* St. PETERSBURG.—*Academia Scientiarum Imperialis.*—*Институт Востоковеде-ния.*

—— [Compiler of Catalogue of the Georgian manuscripts in the Oriental Institute of the Academy of Sciences of the U.S.S.R.] *See* St. PETERSBURG.—*Academia Scientiarum Imperialis.* —*Институт Востоковедения.*

ORBELIANI (Alek'sandre Vakhtangis-dze Jambakurian–). აღა-მამად-ხანის შემოსვლა ქ. ტფილსში. [Agha-Mamad-Khanis shemosvla k'. Tp'ilisshi. Āghā-Muḥammad-Khān's attack on Tiflis, a historical study. Edited by E. S. T'aqai-shvili.] pp. 117–65. ტფილისი [*Tiflis*,] 1895. 8⁰. [*Moambe.* tom. 2. no. 8.]   **17089. b. 1**

—— მეფე დავით აღმაშენებელი. [Mep'e Davit' Aghmashenebeli. King David the Builder, a historical drama in 4 acts. Edited by Z. E. Tchitchinadze.] pp. 116. თფილისი [*Tiflis*,] 1891. 8⁰.   **17075. d. 6. (2.)**

ORBELIANI (Elisabed Iraklis-asuli). [Joint reviser of Marjory Wardrop's translation of 'The

Knight in the Tiger's Skin'.] *See* RUST'AVELI (Shot'a).

ORBELIANI (Grigol Zurabis-dze) *Prince.* [For selected poems, in Russian translation:] *See* GOL'TSEV (V. V.) and CHIK'OVANI (S. I.). Поэзия Грузии. 1949. 4⁰.   **17075. dd. 1**

ORBELIANI (Papuna). [For a French trans. of the chronicle of Papuna Orbeliani, incorporated in 'Histoire de la Géorgie':] *See* BROSSET (M.-F.)

—— [For chronicle of, incorporated as a continuation to 'K'art'lis tskhovreba':] *See* BROSSET (M.-F.) and CHUBINOV (D. I.)

ORBELIANI (Sulkhan) *Prince. See* SAVVA, *the Monk.*

ORENTIUS, *Saint, of Rize.* La notice du synaxaire géorgien sur S. Orentius. [Edit., with Latin trans., by] G. Garitte. pp. 283–89. *Louvain,* 1954. 8⁰. [*Le Muséon.* tom. 67.]   **P. P. 4453**

ORJONIKIDZE (Givi Shios-dze). "Отелло" А. Мачавариани. [A study, with photographs and musical illustrations, of A. D. Matchavariani's ballet on the theme of Othello.] pp. 49. 9 *plates.* *Москва,* 1958. 8⁰.   **17076. b. 48**

OTAROVA (Nina Artemovna). Тбилиси, столица Грузинской ССР. [A historical and topographical description of Tiflis. Illustrated.] pp. 72. 2 *plates.* *Москва,* 1951. 8⁰.   **17075. f. 16**

OXFORD.—*Bodleian Library.* [For 'The Man in the Panther Skin', a study of a 17th century manuscript of the epic by Shot'a Rust'aveli, acquired by the Bodleian Library:] *See* GRAY (B.)

—— [For 'De codice Hiberico Bibliothecae Bod-leianae Oxoniensis':] *See* PEETERS (P.)

OZAANI. [For 'Ozaanis keramika':] *See* MAISU-RADZE (Z. P.)

PACURIANUS (Gregorius). *See* BAKURIANI (G.)

P'AGHAVA (AKAKI). ვასო აბაშიძე. მოკლე მიმოხილვა. [Vaso Abashidze. Mokle mimokhilva. Short biography of the Georgian actor Vaso Abashidze. Edit. by S. Ap'khaidze.] pp. 28. 4 *plates.* თბილისი [*Tiflis*,] 1954. 8⁰.   **17075. e. 22**

PAITCHADZE (NOE). [Author of biographical introduction to verses of P. Rurua.] *See* RURUA (P.)

PAKHOMOV (EVGENY ALEKSANDROVICH). Монеты Грузіи. Часть I. Домонгольскій періодъ. pp. 1–129. 10 *plates.* С.-Петербургъ, 1910. 8⁰. [*Записки Нумизматическаго Отдѣленія Имп. Русскаго Археологическаго Общества.* томъ I. вып. 4.] *No more published.*   **Ac. 5584/14**

—— [Another copy.]   *Dept. of Coins and Medals.*

—— Неизданныя грузинскія монеты XI вѣка. pp. 150–52. 1 *plate.* Тифлисъ, 1909. 8⁰. [*Извѣстія Кавказскаго Музея.* томъ 4.]   **Ac. 1127**

—— Вес и достоинство медной монеты Тифлиса XVII –XVIII в.в. pp. 88–109. 2 *plates.* Баку, 1928. 8⁰. [*Известия Восточного Факультета Азербайджанского гос. Университета. Востоковедение.* том 3.]   **Ac. 1109. c**

PALMIERI (AURELIO). La conversione ufficiale degl'Iberi al cristianesimo. 2 pt. *Rom*, 1902–1903. 8⁰. [*Oriens Christianus.* Jahrg. 2–3.]   **Ac. 2002. b**

PAL'MOV (NIKOLAI NIKOLAEVICH). Къ свѣдѣніямъ о личности архидіакона Гаіоза, впослѣдствіи архіепископа астраханскаго и ставропольскаго, † 20 февр. 1821 г. pp. 37–53. С.-Петербургъ, 1913. 4⁰. [*Христіанскій Востокъ.* томъ 2. вып. I.] **Ac. 1125/105**

PANCRAS, *Saint and Martyr, Bishop of Taormina.* [*Life.*] *See* EVAGRIUS, *Bishop of Taormina.*

PANEK (LIDIYA BORISOVNA). О терминах родства в грузинском языке. pp. 71–77. Москва, Ленинград, 1949. 8⁰. [*Сборник Музея Антропологии и Этнографии.* том 12.]   **Ac. 1126**

—— Следы родового строя у мтиулов. [With sum-mary in French.] pp. 67–87. Москва, Ленинград, 1939. 8⁰. [*Советская Этнография.* том 2.]
   Ac. 1125. nd

—— Жилище мтиулов. [Illustrated.] pp. 237–66. Ленинград, 1930. 4⁰. [*Сборник Музея Антропологии и Этнографии.* том 9.]   **Ac. 1126**

PANKURIANOS (GREGORY). *See* BAKURIANI (G.)

PANSOPHIOS, *Saint, of Alexandria.* La Passion de S. Pansophios d'Alexandrie. [The Georgian version, trans. into Latin, with introduction, by P. Peeters.] pp. 307–37. *Bruxelles*, 1929. 8⁰. [*Analecta Bollandiana.* tom. 47.]   **2002. f**

PAPAVA (AKAKI). [Joint author of biography of Queen Mariam of Georgia.] *See* PAPAVA (T'AMAR) and (AKAKI).

PAPAVA (T'AMAR). დიდი სახეები პატარა ჩარჩოებში. [Didi sakheebi patara charchoebshi. Great portraits in small frames. Character studies of eminent figures in Georgian history.] pp. 321. 1 *plate.* პარიზი [*Paris*,] 1937. 4⁰.   **17075. e. 14**

—— [Another copy.]   **17075. e. 14***

—— and (AKAKI). მარიამ, უკანასკნელი დედოფალი საქართველოსი. [Mariam, ukanaskneli dedop'ali Sak'art'velosi. Mariam, last queen of Georgia. A biographical study. Illustrated.] pp. 333. 1 *plate.* ბუენოს აირეს [*Buenos Aires*,] 1956. 8⁰.   **17075. e. 27**

PARIS.—*Bibliothèque Royale,* afterwards *Impériale,* afterwards *Nationale.* [For 'Note sur le manuscrit géorgien No. 23, de la Bibliothèque Impériale de Paris':] *See* BROSSET (M.-F.)

—— [For 'Notice du Code géorgien, manuscrit de la Bibliothèque Royale':] *See* BROSSET (M.-F.)

—— [For 'Notice sur le dictionnaire géorgien de Soulkhan Saba Orbeliani, récemment acquis par la Bibliothèque royale de Paris':] *See* BROSSET (M.-F.)

PARIS *(cont.)*

—— Catalogue des manuscrits arméniens et géorgiens de la Bibliothèque Nationale. [By] F. Macler. pp. xxx. 203. *Paris*, 1908. 8⁰.   **11907. pp. 12**

—— *Caucasian Confederation.* კავკასიის კონფედერაცია. აქტები და კომენტარიები. [Kavkasiis konpʻederatsia. Akʻtebi da komentariebi. The Caucasian Confederation. Documents and commentaries. Published by the Council of the Caucasian Federation.] pp. 48. [*Paris, Leuville* printed,] 1937. 8⁰.   **17075. f. 34**

—— *Société Asiatique.* Journal Asiatique, *etc.* [Continued as:] Nouveau Journal Asiatique. [Continued as:] Journal Asiatique... Troisième (Quatrième, *etc.*) Série. *Paris*, 1822— 8⁰. *In progress.*   **R. Ac. 8808. 2109. b** (Index only)

—— *Université de Paris.—Institut d'Ethnologie.* Travaux et mémoires de l'Institut d'Ethnologie. tom. I— *Paris*, 1926— 8⁰. *In progress.*   **Ac. 442. 1**

PARKADZE (GRIGOL). მასალები ქართლის გლეხთა რევოლუციური მოძრაობის შესახებ, 1905—1907 წწ. [Masalebi Kʻartʻlis glekhtʻa revolutsiuri modzraobis shesakheb, 1905–1907 dsds. Materials on the revolutionary movement of the Kʻartʻlian peasantry, 1905–1907.] pp. 200. თბილისი [*Tiflis,*] 1954. 8⁰.   **17075. e. 21**

PʻASHALISHVILI (SIKO). [Joint trans. of the novel 'Medrosheni'.] *See* HONCHAR (O. T.)

PʻASHVI-BERTKADZE (PʻESHANGI). [For extracts from the 'Shahnavaziani' or poetic history of King Vakhtang V, incorporated in 'Histoire de la Géorgie':] *See* BROSSET (M.-F.)

PASTERNAK (BORIS LEONIDOVICH). [Trans. poems by Baratʻashvili.] *See* BARATʻASHVILI (N. M.) *Prince.*

—— [Joint trans. of 'Поэты Грузии'.] *See* MIDSISHVILI (N.)

—— Грузинские лирики. [Translations from Georgian poets. With illustrations.] pp. 136. *Москва*, 1935. 8⁰.   **20003. d. 39**

PATARIDZE (ELISE ARKHIPES-DZE). [Edit. of political journal 'Iveria'.] *See* PERIODICAL PUBLICATIONS.—*Paris.*

—— [Edit. political journal 'Samshoblo'.] *See* PERIODICAL PUBLICATIONS.—*Paris.*

—— დემოკრატიზმი. [Demokratizmi. A treatise on the principles of democracy.] pp. 70. პარიზი [*Paris,*] 1938. 8⁰.   **17075. f. 19 (3.)**

PATKANOV (KHERÔBĒ PETROSEAN). [For 'Profesori Patkanovi da kʻartʻuli istoriis dsqaroebi':] *See* BAKʻRADZE (D. Z.)

PAVLENKO (PETR ANDREEVICH). [Preface to 'Избранные песни и стихи'.] *See* STALʻSKY (S.)

PAVLOVICH (MIKHAIL) *pseud.* [i.e. M. L. VELʻTMAN]. [Edit. 'Новый Восток'.] *See* MOSCOW.— *Nauchnaya Assotsiatsiya Vostokovedeniya S.S.S.R.*

PEACOCK (DMITRI RUDOLF). Original Vocabularies of Five West Caucasian Languages. [Comprising Georgian, Mingrelian, Laz, Svanian and Abkhazian.] pp. 145–56. *London*, 1887. 8⁰. [*Journal of the Royal Asiatic Society.* New ser. vol. 19.]   **R. Ac. 8820/3**

PEETERS (PAUL). [Trans. 'La Passion de S. Michel le Sabaïte'.] *See* BASIL, *Laurae S. Sabae Presbyter.*

—— [Trans. 'La Passion de S. Basile d'Épiphanie'.] *See* BASIL, *Saint, Bishop of Epiphania.*

—— [Edit., with Latin trans. and commentary, of the Passion of St. Constantine.] *See* CONSTANTINE, *Saint and Martyr, of Kakhetʻi.*

—— [Edit., with Latin trans., of the autobiography of Dionysius the Areopagite.] *See* DIONYSIUS, *Saint,* called *the Areopagite.*

—— [For critical study of the Latin trans. by

PEETERS *(cont.)*

P. Peeters of the biography of Gregory of Khan-dzt'a:] *See* Dondua (K. D.)

——— [For the Georgian life of Saint Hilarion, trans. into Latin by P. Peeters:] *See* Hilarion, *Saint, of Iberia.*

——— [Trans. into Latin the Passion of St. Julian of Emesa.] *See* Julian, *Saint and Martyr, of Emesa.*

——— [Edit., with Latin trans., of the Life of St. Porphyrius of Gaza.] *See* Mark, *the Deacon.*

——— [Trans. Passion of St. Pansophios.] *See* Pansophios, *Saint, of Alexandria.*

——— [Trans. into Latin the Passion of St. Razh-den.] *See* Razhden, *Saint, of Persia.*

——— [Trans. Passion of St. Romanus.] *See* Roma-nus, *Saint, of Galatia.*

——— [Joint editor and translator of the Georgian Passion of Saints Theodore, Julian, *etc.*] *See* Theodore, *Saint and Martyr, of Pella.*

——— [Edit. and trans. 'Un colophon géorgien de Thornik le Moine'.] *See* Thornicius, afterwards Johannes, *Monk at Mount Athos.*

——— Les débuts du Christianisme en Géorgie d'après les sources hagiographiques. pp. 5–58. *Bruxelles*, 1932. 8⁰. [*Analecta Bollandiana.* tom. 50.]
2002. g

——— De codice Hiberico Bibliothecae Bodleianae Oxoniensis. [Description of a Georgian Ms. in the Bodleian Library, containing lives of saints.] pp. 301–318. *Bruxelles*, 1912. 8⁰. [*Analecta Bollandiana.* tom. 31.]
2002. f

——— [Another copy, being an offprint.]
4824. df. 24

——— L'église géorgienne du Clibanion au Mont Admirable. pp. 241–86. *Bruxelles*, 1928. 8⁰. [*Analecta Bollandiana.* tom. 46.]
2002. f

——— [Another copy, being an offprint.]
4534. g. 37

——— [Hagiographical miscellanies, reprinted from the 'Analecta Bollandiana', *etc.*] 1902, *etc.* 8⁰.
4824. df. 24

——— Histoires monastiques géorgiennes. I. Vie des SS. Jean et Euthyme. II. Vie de S. Georges l'Hagiorite. III. Vie de S. Sérapion de Zarzma. IV. Vie de S. Grégoire de Khandztha. *Lat.* pp. 319. *Bruxelles*, 1917–19 [1922]. 8⁰. [*Analecta Bollandiana.* tom. 36–37.]
2002. f

——— Jérémie, évêque de l'Ibérie perse, 431. pp. 5–33. *Bruxelles*, 1933. 8⁰. [*Analecta Bollandiana.* tom. 51.]
2002. g

——— [Another copy, being an offprint.]
4824. df. 24

——— Les Khazars dans la Passion de S. Abo de Tiflis. pp. 21–56. *Bruxelles*, 1934. 8⁰. [*Analecta Bollandiana.* tom. 52.]
2002. g

——— [Another copy, being an offprint.]
4824. df. 24

——— Un manuscrit byzantin daté du pontificat du pape Jean XIX. [Historical notes on a Georgian codex, formerly MS. No. 1 of the Tiflis Ecclesiastical Museum.] pp. 373–92. *Bucarest*, 1948. 8⁰. [*Archives de l'Orient Chrétien.* tom. 1. *Mémorial Louis Petit.*]
Ac. 7941/2 (1)

——— Orient et Byzance. Le tréfonds oriental de l'hagiographie byzantine. pp. 235. *Bruxelles*, 1950. 8⁰. [*Subsidia hagiographica.* no. 26.]
Ac. 2021

——— La Passion de S. Pierre de Capitolias. [A critical analysis of the Georgian version published by K. S. Kekelidze.] pp. 299–333. *Bruxelles*, 1939. 8⁰. [*Analecta Bollandiana.* tom. 57.]
2002. g

——— Recherches d'histoire et de philologie orientales. [With a memoir of the author.] 2 tom. *Bruxelles*, 1951. 8⁰. [*Subsidia hagiographica.* no. 27.]
Ac. 2021

PEETERS *(cont.)*

—— S. Barlaam du Mont Casius. [With reference to the Georgian and other versions of the life of St. Barlaam]. pp. 805–813. *Paris, London* and *Leipzig,* 1909. 4⁰. [*Université Saint-Joseph, Beyrouth: Mélanges de la Faculté Orientale.* tom. 3. fasc. 2.]   **Ac. 8800**

—— Sainte Šoušanik, martyre en Arméno-Géorgie. [Including a Latin translation of the Vita of the Saint by James the Priest.] 2 pt. pp. 5–48; 245–307. *Bruxelles,* 1935. 8⁰. [*Analecta Bollandiana.* tom. 53.]   **2002. g**

—— Traductions et traducteurs dans l'hagiographie orientale à l'époque byzantine. pp. 241–98. *Bruxelles,* 1922. 8⁰. [*Analecta Bollandiana.* tom. 40.]   **2002. f**

—— [Another copy, being an offprint.]   **011851. dd. 76**

—— La version géorgienne de l'autobiographie de Denys l'Aréopagite. pp. 5–10. *Bruxelles,* 1912. 8⁰. [*Analecta Bollandiana.* tom. 31.]   **2002. f**

P'ERADZE (Grigol) *Archimandrite.* [Trans. apocryphal letter from Dionysius the Areopagite to Bishop Timothy of Ephesus.] *See* Dionysius, *Saint,* called *the Areopagite.*

—— [Trans. 'Die Weihnachtsfeier Jerusalems im siebten Jahrhundert .... nach Kekelidze, Іерусалимскій Канонарь VII Вѣка. Tiflis 1912'.] *See* Liturgies.—Greek Rite.—*Euchologion.*

—— [Trans. Georgian version of the Liturgy of St. Peter.] *See* Liturgies.—Greek Rite.—*Leitourgikon I.*

—— L'activité littéraire des moines géorgiens au monastère d'Iviron, au Mont Athos. pp. 530–39. *Louvain,* 1927. 8⁰. [*Revue d'Histoire Ecclésiastique.* tom. 23.]   **Ac. 2646/3**

—— Die alt-christliche Literatur in der georgischen Überlieferung. [Being a revised translation of K. S. Kekelidze's bibliographical study, publish-

ed in 'Tp'ilisis Universitetis Moambe', tom. 8, 1927.] 8 pt. *Leipzig,* 1930–33. 8⁰. [*Oriens Christianus.* Dritte Serie. Bd. 3–8.]   **Ac. 2002. b**

—— Die altgeorgische Literatur und ihre Probleme. pp. 205–22. *Leipzig,* 1927. 8⁰. [*Oriens Christianus.* Dritte Serie. Bd. 2.]   **Ac. 2002. b**

—— Georgian Manuscripts in England. pp. 80–88. *London,* 1935. 8⁰. [*Georgica.* vol. I. no. I.]   **Ac. 8821. e**

—— Les monuments liturgiques prébyzantins en langue géorgienne. pp. 255–72. *Louvain,* 1932. 8⁰. [*Le Muséon.* tom. 45.]   **P. P. 4453**

—— Die Probleme der ältesten Kirchengeschichte Georgiens. pp. 153–71. *Leipzig,* 1932. 8⁰. [*Oriens Christianus.* Dritte Serie. Bd. 7.]   **Ac. 2002. b**

—— Über die georgischen Handschriften in Österreich. pp. 219–32. *Wien,* 1940. 8⁰. [*Wiener Zeitschrift für die Kunde des Morgenlandes.* Bd. 47. Hft. 3–4.]   **P. P. 5057**

—— Zur vorbyzantinischen Liturgie Georgiens. pp. 90–99. *Louvain,* 1929. 8⁰. [*Le Muséon.* tom. 42.]   **P. P. 4453**

PEREVALENKO (B.). [For 'Lettres de M. Bartholomaei...; inscriptions d'Akhal-Kalak, par M. Pérévalenko':] *See* Brosset (M.-F.)

—— Inscriptions géorgiennes, recueillies à Gandza et à Phoca. pp. 150–64. *St.-Pétersbourg,* 1853. 8⁰. [*Mélanges Asiatiques de l'Académie des Sciences.* tom. 2.]   **Ac. 1125/11**

—— Rapport sur un voyage en Géorgie. pp. 261–268. *St.-Pétersbourg,* 1850. 8⁰. [*Mélanges Asiatiques de l'Académie des Sciences.* tom. I. livr. 2.]   **Ac. 1125/11**

PERIODICAL PUBLICATIONS. — *Batum.* სამუსლიმანო საქართველო. [Samuslimano Sak'art'velo. Organ of the Muslim Georgian Liberation Committee. Edited by Hasan Taḥsīn Khimshiashvili.] no. 6 (two copies). ბათუმი [*Batum,*] 1919. fol.   **O. P. 530.(2.)**

PERIODICAL *(cont.)*

—— *K'ut'aisi.* კოოპერაცია. [Kooperatsia.] Le journal géorgien "Cooperatzia" ("Coopération"). [The bi-weekly organ of the Georgian Co-operative Movement. Edited by I. Gabilaia.] 8th year. no. 1–4. ქუთაისი [*K'ut'aisi,*] 1918. 8⁰.   **17089. b. 10**

—— მწყემსი. [Mdsqemsi. The Shepherd. A bi-monthly religious review, edited and published by Davit' Ghambashidze.] 1900, no. 1—1904, no. 10. ქუთაისი [*K'ut'aisi*], ყვირილა [*Qvirila,*] 1900–1904. 4⁰.   **17089. b. 3**

—— ფონი. [P'oni. The Current. A weekly political and literary journal.] 1909, nos. 1, 3–17; 1910, nos. 1–5. ქუთაისი [*K'ut'aisi,*] 1909–10. fol.   **O. P. 505**

—— თვიური კრებული. [T'viuri krebuli. Monthly review. Edited by Akaki Tseret'eli.] tom. 2. ქუთაისი [*K'ut'aisi,*] 1899–1900. 8⁰.   **17089. b. 4**

—— *Leipsic.* Caucasica. Zeitschrift für die Erforschung der Sprachen und Kulturen des Kaukasus. Editor, A. Dirr. fasc. 1–11. *Lipsiae,* 1924–34. 8⁰.   **P. P. 3803. eba**

—— *Louvain.* Bibliothèque du Muséon. tom. 1— *Louvain,* 1929— 8⁰. *In progress. Tom. 4, entitled 'Le Muséon. Tables des années 1882 à 1931', is bound up with 'Le Muséon', tom. 44.*   **P. P. 1927. d**

—— Le Muséon, revue internationale publiée par la Société des Lettres et des Sciences. tom. 1–15. *Louvain,* 1882–96. [Continued as:] Le Muséon et la Revue des Religions, *etc.* tom. 16–18. *Louvain,* 1897–99. [Continued as:] Le Muséon. Études philologiques, historiques et religieuses .... Nouvelle série. tom. 1— *Louvain, Cambridge,* 1900— 8⁰.   **P. P. 4453**

—— *Munich.* The Caucasus. Der Kaukasus. Organ of independent national thought. *Eng.* 1951. no. 1 — 1952. no. 12. Aug. 1951—Dec. 1952. *Munich,* 1951, 52. 8⁰. [Continued as:] United Caucasus. Vereinigtes Kaukasien. 1953. no. 1/2, *etc.* Jan./Febr. 1953, *etc. Munich,* 1953—. 8⁰.   **P. P. 3554. ewi**

—— Свободный Кавказ. The Free Caucasus. Der freie Kaukasus. Caucase libre. Орган кавказской национально-демократической мысли. год изд. 2. no. 4 (7), *etc.* апрель 1952, *etc. München,* 1952. 4⁰.
                    P. P. 3554. ewo

—— *New York.* კრებული. ქართული ლიტერატურისა, ისტორიისა და ხელოვნების ყოველდსლიური ორგანო. [Krebuli. K'art'uli literaturisa, istoriisa da khelovnebis qoveldsliuri organo.] (Krebuly. Symposium of Georgian literature, history and art, published annually in Georgian language.) [Edited by G. A. Kobakhidze. Illustrated.] bk. 1— ნიუ იორკი [*New York,*] 1957. 8⁰.
                    17089. a. 4

—— Traditio. Studies in Ancient and Medieval History, Thought and Religion. *New York,* 1943— 8⁰.   **P. P. 3437. bl**

—— *Paris.* ბედი ქართლისა. [Bedi K'art'lisa. The Destiny of Georgia.] Le Destin de la Géorgie. Recueil Historique, Scientifique et Littéraire Géorgien. [Edited by K. Salia]. *Geo. & Fr. Paris,* 1948— 4⁰. *In progress.*   **17089. a. 2**

—— ჩვენი დროშა. ორგანო საქ. სოც.-დემ. პარტიის საზღვარ-გარეთელ ბიუროსი. [Chveni drosha. Organo Sak'. sots.-dem. partiis sazghvaret'el biurosi. Our banner. Organ of the Georgian Social-Democratic Party's Overseas Bureau. Edit. by M. Sturua.] Notre Drapeau. no. 1–9. *Paris,* 1949–51. 8⁰.   **17089. b. 12**

—— დროშა. ქართული სოციალური გაზეთი. [Drosha. K'art'uli sotsialuri gazet'i. The Banner. A revolutionary newspaper, appearing anonymously under the editorship of N. I. Nikoladze.] no. 1–3. 1 (13) April—3 (15) April, 1873. პარიჯი [*Paris,*] 1873. 4⁰. *Lithographed.*   **17089. a. 1**

—— ერის დიდება, პერიოდული ორგანო : პოლიტიკა, მეცნიერება, ხელოვნება. [Eris dideba, perioduli organo: politika, metsniereba, khelovneba.] Grandeur de la Nation, Périodique: L'Art, Science, Politique. [Edited by A. Manvelishvili.] no. 1–6. *Paris,* 1953–58. 8⁰.   **17089. b. 11**

—— La Géorgie. [A political journal, being the

PERIODICAL *(cont.)*

French counterpart of 'Sak'art'velo'.] 1 tom. *Paris,* 1903–1905. fol.   **O. P. 286. p.p**

—— La Géorgie, organe de défense nationale… Directeur: Georges Gvazava. no. 1–3. *Paris,* 1938–39. 8⁰.   **P. P. 3555. akd**

—— იბერია. ქართული ეროვნული პოლიტიკის ორგანო, პერიოდული გამოცემა. [Iveria. K'art'uli erovnuli politikis organo, perioduli gamotsema.] L'organe de la politique nationale géorgienne, "Ivéria". Directeur E. Pataridze. [Published by the Georgian National-Democratic Party.] no. 1– პარიზი [*Paris,*] 1949— 8⁰.   **17089. b. 8**

—— Кавказ. Le Caucase. Орган независимой национальной мысли. 1934. no. 2—1939. no. 7. февраль 1934 — июль 1939. *Париж,* 1934–39. 4⁰.   **P. P. 4842. dha**

—— Revue de l'Orient chrétien. Dirigée par R. Graffin. tom. 1–30. *Paris,* 1896–1946. 8⁰.   **P. P. 37. ck**

—— საქართველო. თავისუფალი ორგანო. [Sak'art'velo. T'avisup'ali organo. Georgia. An independent journal. Organ of the Georgian Socialist-Federalist Revolutionary Party.] nos. 1–6, 11–14, 17–25. *Paris,* 1903–05. 4⁰.   **17089. b. 5**

—— სამშობლო. ეროვნულ-დემოკრატიული მიმართულების ყოველთვიური ორგანო. [Samshoblo. Erovnul-demokratiuli mimart'ulebis qovelt'viuri organo.] La Patrie. L'organe de la démocratie nationale géorgienne. [Published by the Georgian National-Democratic Party and edited by E. Pataridze.] no. 1–8, 11, 12, 14, 16–17, 19–26. პარიზი *Paris,*] 1929–38. 8⁰.   **17089. b. 9**

—— *Qvirila.* [For 'Mdsqemsi', a bi-monthly religious review, published at Qvirila and at K'ut'aisi:] *See* PERIODICAL PUBLICATIONS.—*K'ut'aisi.*

—— *Saint Petersburg.* [For 'Журналъ Министерства Народнаго Просвѣщенія':] *See* RUSSIA.—*Министерство Народнаго Просвѣщенія.*

—— *Tiflis.* ახალი ნაკადი. [Akhali nakadi. The new stream. Newspaper of the Georgian Left-Wing Socialist-Federalist Party.] no. 3. თფილისი [*Tiflis,*] 1919. fol.   **O. P. 530. (1.)**

—— წიგნის მატიანე. [Dsignis matiane. The book chronicle. A bibliographical journal.] yr. 10, no. 1–6; yr. 11. no. 1–20. ტფილისი [*Tiflis,*] 1934–35. 8⁰.   **17089. b. 7**

—— ერთობა. [Ert'oba. Unity. Organ of the Georgian Social-Democratic Workers' Party.] no. 20. თფილისი [*Tiflis,*] 1919. fol.   **O. P. 530. (4)**

—— იბერია. [Iveria. A Georgian daily newspaper. Edited by I. G. Tchavtchavadze.] no. 3–12, 14–40, 43–64, 67–79, 81–100, 107–116, 127–162, 165–172, 177, 178, 182, 185–198, 201, 202, 204, 207–210, 213, 214, 217–233, 235, 237, 238, 240, 242–246, 249, 251–253, 255–259, 261–263, 265–267, 269–274, 277–283. ტფილისი [*Tiflis,*] 1895. fol.   **O. P. 202**

—— ჯეჯილი. საყმაწვილო ნახატებიანი ჟურნალი. [Jejili. Saqmadsvilo nakhatebiani zhurnali. The Meadow. An illustrated children's magazine.] tom. 13. no. 1–3. ტფილისი [*Tiflis,*] 1902. 8⁰.   **17089. b. 6**

—— კომუნისტი. [Komunisti. The Communist. A daily newspaper.] 181 pt. ტფილისი [*Tiflis,*] 1934, 52. fol.   **O. P. 558**

—— კვალი. [Kvali. The Furrow. A weekly political, scientific and literary illustrated paper.] no. 11–28, 30–36. [ტფილისი. *Tiflis,*] 1897. 4⁰.   **17089. b. 2**

—— მათრახი და სალამური. [Mat'rakhi da salamuri. The Whip and the Bagpipes. A weekly humorous journal. Edited by E. Turabelidze.] tom. 2. no. 1–4, 7, 8, 10. თფილისი [*Tiflis,*] 1910. 4⁰.   **O. P. 506**

—— მეოცნებე ნიამორები. [Meotsnebe niamorebi. The dreaming gazelles. A literary and poetic miscellany, edited by V. Gap'rindashvili.] no. 2. [ტფილისი. *Tiflis,*] 1919. 8⁰.   **17075. c. 31**

—— მნათობი. სრულიად საქართველოს საბჭოთა

PERIODICAL *(cont.)*

მწერლების კავშირის ყოველთვიური სალიტერატურო, სახელოვნო და საზოგადოებრივ-საპო-
ლიტიკო ჟურნალი. [Mnat'obi. Sruliad Sak'art'velos sabtchot'a mdserlebis kavshiris qovelt'viuri
saliteraturo, sakhelovno da sazogadoebriv-sapoliti-
ko zhurnali. The Beacon. Monthly journal of the
Georgian Soviet writers' union.] yr. II. no. I–6.
ტფილისი [*Tiflis,*] 1934. 8⁰.   **17089. a. 3**

—— მოამბე. თვიური ჟურნალი. [Moambe. T'viuri
zhurnali. The Messenger. A monthly review of
literature, history and sciences. Edited by A.
Tchqonia.] yr. I. no. I–3, 8, 10; yr. 2. no. I, 3–12;
yr. 3. no. I, 2, 4; yr. 4. no. 12; yr. 9. no. 4. ტფილისი.
[*Tiflis,*] 1894–1902. 8⁰.   **17089. b. 1**

—— მუშა. [Musha. The Worker. A daily newspaper edited by M. Diasamidze.] no. 21–30, 32,
34–36, 38–40, 42–51. თბილისი [*Tiflis,*] 1906. fol.
         O. P. 504

—— ნობათი. [Nobat'i. The Tocsin. A weekly journal. Edited by D. Erist'avi-Mdivani.] no. I–10, 12,
14. ტფილისი [*Tiflis,*] 1906. fol.   **17089. b. 13**

—— საქართველო. ყოველდღიური საპოლიტიკო,
საეკონმიო და სალიტერატურო გაზეთი. [Sa-
k'art'velo. Qoveldghiuri sapolitiko, saekonomio da
saliteraturo gazet'i. Georgia. Daily political, economic and literary paper. Edited by G. K'ik'odze.]
no. 19. თბილისი [*Tiflis,*] 1919. fol.   **O. P. 530.(5.)**

—— საქართველოს რესპუბლიკა. მთავრობის მოამბე. [Sak'art'velos respublika. Mt'avrobis moambe. The Georgian Republic. Organ of the Government.] no. 26. ტფილისი [*Tiflis,*] 1919. fol.
         O. P. 530. (3.)

—— სახალხო ფურცელი. [Sakhalkho p'urtseli.
The People's Paper. A left-wing newspaper, edited
by D. Jorjadze.] no. 885–889, 891–893, 895, 896,
898–902, 904–912, 914. ტფილისი [*Tiflis,*] 1917. fol.
         O. P. 503

—— სახალხო საქმე. [Sakhalkho sak'me. The
People's Cause. Newspaper of the Georgian Socialist-Federalist Revolutionary Party. Edited by

Samson P'irtskhalava.] no. 2, 3, 8, 10, 11, 13-16,
19, 20, 22, 23, 25, 28, 30–36, 38, 39, 41, 43–50, 52–
55, 57–65, 67–70, 72–81, 83–86, 88–92, 94–97, 99–
104, 107–134, 440. ტფილისი [*Tiflis,*] 1917–19. fol.
         O. P. 502

—— სახელგამის გამოცემათა კატალოგი. [Sa-
khelgamis gamotsemat'a katalogi. Catalogue of
the publications of the Georgian State publishing
house.] 3 pt. ტფილისი [*Tiflis,*] 1927–1930. 8⁰.
         17077. a. 8

PERSIA. [For 'Sparset'i da ik'auri k'art'velebi':]
See AGHNIASHVILI (L.)

—— [For 'Персидская національная тенденція въ
грузинскомъ романѣ "Амирандареджаніани"':] *See*
MARR (N. Y.)

—— [For a collection of Persian historical charters
relating to Georgia:] *See* P'UT'URIDZE (V. S.)

PERSIAN ALPHABET. [For 'Персидская азбука
в грузинской транскрипціи':] *See* MEGRELIDZE
(I. B.)

PERSIAN LITERATURE. [For 'Къ вопросу о
вліаніи персидской литературы на грузинскую':]
See MARR (N. Y.)

P'ESHANGI. *See* P'ASHVI-BERTKADZE (P'.)

PETER, *the Iberian, Bishop of Mayūmā. [Life.]*
See ZACHARIAS, *Scholasticus, Bishop of Mitylene.*

PETER, *Saint and Apostle.* [For the Georgian
version of the Liturgy of St. Peter, edit. with Latin
trans. by M. T'arkhnishvili in 'Liturgiae Ibericae
Antiquiores':] *See* LITURGIES.—Greek Rite.—*Leitourgikon I.*

—— [For 'Die georgische "Petrusliturgie". Ins
Lateinische zurückübersetzt':] *See* LITURGIES.—
Greek Rite.—*Leitourgikon I.*

PETER, *Saint and Martyr, of Capitolias.* [For 'La
Passion de S. Pierre de Capitolias', being a critical
study of the Georgian version:] *See* PEETERS (P.)

PETER *(cont.)*

—— Житіе Петра Новаго, мученика Капетолійскаго. [Georgian version of lost Greek text, formerly attributed to St. John Damascene, edit. with Russian trans. by K. S. Kekelidze.] pp. 1–71. *Петроградъ*, 1915. 4⁰. [*Христіанскій Востокъ.* томъ 4. вып. 1.]   **Ac. 1125/105**

PETIT (LOUIS). [Edit. 'Typikon de Grégoire Pacourianos'.] *See* BAKURIANI (GRIGOL).

PETRIDSONI MONASTERY. [For 'Typicon Gregorii Pacuriani', drawn up for the Georgian Petridsoni Monastery in Bulgaria:] *See* BAKURIANI (GRIGOL).

—— [For 'Typikon de Grégoire Pacourianos pour le monastère de Pétritzos, *etc.*':] *See* BAKURIANI (GRIGOL).

—— [For 'La destinée du Typikon de Grégoire Bakouriani (Pakourianos) pour le monastère de Petritzos':] *See* NIKOLAEV (V.)

PETROGRAD. *See* SAINT PETERSBURG.

PETROVA (IRINA VLADIMIROVNA). [Joint trans. of selections from 'The Book of Wisdom and Fiction'.] *See* SAVVA, *the Monk* [*Prince* SULKHAN ORBELIANI].

PHYSIOLOGUS. Физіологъ. Армяно-грузинскій изводъ. Грузинскій и армянскій тексты изслѣдовалъ, издалъ и перевелъ Н. Марръ. pp. lii. 130. *Санкт-петербургъ*, 1904. 8⁰. [*Тексты и разысканія по армяно-грузинской филологіи.* кн. 6.]   **14005. f. 5**

—— Der georgische Physiologos. Übersetzt von Georg Graf. [Translated from the edition by N. Y. Marr.] pp. 93–114. *Leipzig*, 1925. 8⁰. [*Caucasica.* fasc. 2.]   **P. P. 3803. eba**

PILATUS (PONTIUS). [For 'Армянскія слова въ грузинскихъ Дѣяніяхъ Пилата':] *See* MARR (N. Y.)

PILSUDSKI (JÓZEF KLEMENS) *Regent of Poland.* იანვრის აჯანყების მილიტარული ისტორიის მი-მოხილვა : 1863 წ. პოლონეთის აჯანყება. [Ianvris

ajanqebis militaruli istoriis mimokhilva: 1863 ds. Polonet'is ajanqeba. Survey of the military history of the January rebellion: the Polish rebellion of 1863. Trans. from the Polish by V. S. With a map.] pp. 91. 1 *plate.* პარიზი [*Paris,*] 1931. 8⁰.   **17075. e. 28**

P'IROSMANISHVILI (NIKO). [For collection of essays on this Georgian painter:] *See* TABIDZE (T. I.) *and others.*

P'IRTSKHALAVA (SAMSON). [Edit. collected writings of S. S. Meskhi.] *See* MESKHI (S. S.)

—— [Editor of newspaper 'Sakhalkho sak'me':] *See* PERIODICAL PUBLICATIONS.—*Tiflis.*

—— ამბავთა და საქმეთა მოლოდინში. [Ambavt'a da sak'met'a molodinshi. In expectation of news and deeds. A patriotic discourse.] pp. 68. პარიზი [*Paris,*] 1935. 8⁰.   **17075. f. 18**

—— ისტორიული ლანდები. [Istoriuli landebi. Shades from history. Evocations of characters prominent in Georgian mediaeval history.]. pp. 72. პარიზი [*Paris,*] 1934. 8⁰.   **17076. g. 10**

P'ITSKHELAURI (ALEK'SANDRE IOSEBIS-DZE). დეკორატიული კერამიკა. [Dekoratiuli keramika. Decorative ceramics. A practical handbook on making ceramic ware. Illustrated.] pp. 175. 1 *plate.* თბილისი [*Tiflis,*] 1954. 8⁰.   **17080. d. 20**

P'ITSKHELAURI (GRIGOL ZAK'ARIAS-DZE). [Joint author of 'T'bilisis ghrmad mokhutsebuli adamianebi', or essays about the oldest inhabitants of Tiflis:] *See* SHAP'IRO (I. B.) *and others.*

POLÁK (VÁCLAV). L'état actuel des études linguistiques caucasiennes. pp. 383–407. *Praha*, 1950. 8⁰. [*Archiv Orientální.* vol. 18. no. 1–2.]   **Ac. 8818. d**

—— Notules kartvéliennes. pp. 279–96. *Louvain*, 1955. 8⁰. [*Le Muséon.* tom. 68].   **P. P. 4453**

POLIEVKTOV (MIKHAIL ALEKSANDROVICH). Из истории русского академического Кавказоведения XVIII века. pp. 759–74. *Москва, Ленинград*, 1935. 8⁰.

POLIEVKTOV *(cont.)*

[*Известия Академии Наук СССР*. ser. 7. *Classe des Sciences Sociales*. 1935.] **Ac. 1125/44. (9)**

—— სტოლნიკი ტოლოჩანოვისა და დიაკი იევლე- ვის ელჩობა იმერეთში, 1650–1652. [Stolniki Tolo- chanovisa da diaki Ievlevis elchoba Imeret'shi, 1650 –1652. Embassy of the Steward Tolochanov and the Scribe Ievlev to Imeret'i, 1650–52.] Посольство стольника Толочанова и дьяка Иевлева в Имеретию, 1650–1652. [Russian text, with introduction in Georgian and Russian.] pp. viii. 046. 230, I. ტფი- ლისი [*Tiflis*,] 1926. 8⁰. [Sak'art'velos saert'ashoriso urt'iert'obani utskho k'veqnebt'an. no. I.]

17075. e. 11/1

—— [Another copy.] **17075. e. 11***

—— თავადი მიშეცკისა და დიაკი კლუჩარევის ელჩობა კახეთში, 1640–1643. [T'avadi Mishets- kisa da diaki Klucharevis elchoba Kakhet'shi, 1640–1643. Embassy of Prince Myshetsky and the Scribe Klyucharev to Kakhet'i, 1640–43.] Посоль- ство князя Мышецкого и дьяка Ключарева в Кахе- тию, 1640–1643. [Russian text, with introduction in Georgian and Russian.] pp. 021. 208, I. ტფი- ლისი [*Tiflis*,] 1928. 8⁰. [Sak'art'velos saert'ashoriso urt'iert'obani utskho k'veqnebt'an. no. 2.]

17075. e. 11/2

P'ORCHKHIDZE (Shalva). ცისფერ გზაზე. [Tsisp'er gzaze. On the Sky-blue Road. Collected verses.] pp. 141. I *plate*. თბილისი [*Tiflis*,] 1954. 8⁰.

17075. c. 15

PORFIRY [Konstantin Aleksandrovich U- spensky], *Bishop of Chigirin*. [For 'Преосвященный Порфирій о грузинскихъ древностяхъ':] *See* Tsaga- reli (A. A.)

PORPHYRIUS, *Saint, Bishop of Gaza*. [*Life*.] *See* Mark, *the Deacon*.

POSPYELOV (Petr Nikolaevich). [Joint author of short biography of Stalin.] *See* Aleksandrov (G. F.), *and others*.

POSTUPAL'SKY (Igor'). [Edit. selected poems of Grishashvili in Russian trans.] *See* Grishashvili (I. G.)

POTAPOVA (A.). [Joint trans. of poems by A. Keshokov.] *See* Keshokov (A.)

PRILEZHAEVA (M.). შენთან ამხანაგები არიან. [Shent'an amkhanagebi arian. Your comrades are with you. A story for children. Trans. by D. Dekanozishvili.] pp. 149. თბილისი. [*Tiflis*,] 1952. 8⁰. **17077. a. 15**

PROCHORUS, *Saint, of Jerusalem*. [For 'Житіе Прохора, *etc*.':] *See* Qip'shidze (D. A.)

PROCLUS, *Diadochus*. [For 'Іоаннъ Петрицкій, *etc*.', a study of the works of the Georgian neo- Platonist, with extracts from the Georgian translation of the 'Institutio Theologica':] *See* Marr (N. Y.)

PROCOPIUS, *Saint and Martyr*. [*Life*.] *See* Eusebius, *Pamphili, Bishop of Caesarea in Palestine*.

P'RONELI (Alek'sandre) *pseud*. [i.e. Alek'san- dre Qip'shidze]. ამბოხება კახეთისა, 1812 წ.: ის- ტორიული ამბავი. [Ambokheba Kakhet'isa, 1812 ds.: Istoriuli ambavi. The 1812 revolt in Kakhet'i. A historical narrative.] pp. 239, vi. ტფილისი [*Tiflis*,] 1907. 8⁰. **17075. e. 3**

P'SHAV FOLK-TALES. *See* Razikashvili (T'. P.)

P'SHAV POPULAR POETRY. [For 'P'shavuri lek'sebi':] *See* Khizanashvili (D.)

—— [For 'P'shav-Khevsuruli poezia':] *See* Khor- nauli (I.G.)

P'SHAVS. [For 'Из старого народного быта пша- вов':] *See* Makalat'ia (S. I.)

P'URTSELADZE (Anton Nikolozis-dze). თხზუ- ლებანი. [T'khzulebani. Collected dramatic works. Edited by Z. E. Tchitchinadze.] tom. 2. pp. vi. 240. თბილისი [*Tiflis*,] 1884. 8⁰.

17075. d. 6. (1)

PUSHKIN (ALEKSANDR SERGYEEVICH). ბოშები. პოლტავა. [Boshebi. Poltava. Georgian rendering by K. A. Tchitchinadze of Pushkin's poems 'Цыгане', or 'The Gipsies', and 'Полтава'. Illustrated by S. S. K'obuladze.] pp. 76. 10 *plates.* თბილისი [*Tiflis,*] 1954. 4⁰.   **17075. dd. 2**

—— მებადურისა და თევზის ზღაპარი. [Mebadurisa da t'evzis zghapari. The tale of the Fisherman and the Fish. Translated from Russian into Georgian by V. Gorgadze, with illustrations by I. Gabashvili.] pp. 8, 2. თბილისი [*Tiflis,*] 1954. 4⁰.   **17075. dd. 7**

—— რჩეული ნაწერები ოთხ ტომად. [Rcheuli nadserebi ot'kh tomad. Selected writings in four volumes. Trans. by various hands and edit. by S. Chik'ovani and K. A. Tchitchinadze, with an introductory essay by V. Shaduri.] Избранные сочинения в четырех томах. tom. I— თბილისი [*Tiflis,*] 1952— 8⁰. *In progress.*   **17075. d. 26**

P'UT'URIDZE (VLADIMER SARDIONIS-DZE). ქართულ-სპარსული ისტორიული საბუთები. [K'art'ul-sparsuli istoriuli sabut'ebi. Georgian-Persian historical charters.] (Грузино-персидские исторические документы.) [Persian and Georgian texts, with Georgian translation and notes, and facsimiles in the text.] pp. xv. 527. 8 *plates.* თბილისი [*Tiflis,*] 1955. 8⁰.   **17075. e. 35**

PYESHKOV (A. M.). *See* GOR'KY (M.) *pseud.*

QANCHELI (ALEK'SANDRE IVANES-DZE). [Trans. tales by Tchola Lomt'at'idze.] *See* LOMT'AT'IDZE (Tch.)

—— *and others.* [Trans. selected stories by E. Ninoshvili.] *See* NINOSHVILI (E.) *pseud.*

QARALASHVILI (NUNU IVANES-ASULI). [Joint author of 'K'art'uli ornamenti'.] *See* KRAVCHENKO (A. V.) and QARALASHVILI (N. I.)

QAUKHCHISHVILI (SIMON GIORGIS-DZE). [Edit. of revised, critical edition of the Georgian Annals.] *See* GEORGIAN ANNALS.

—— [Edit. 'Ort'ograp'iuli lek'sikoni'.] *See* T'OP'U-RIA (V. T.) and GIGINEISHVILI (I. M.)

QAZBEGI (ALEK'SANDRE MIKHEILIS-DZE). *See* JEDLIČKA (J.). Kamenité cesty Gruzie. Povídky gruzínských klasiků. [Including a Czech translation of the story 'Khevisberi Gocha' by A. Qazbegi.] 1958. 12⁰.   **17076. b. 44**

—— [For separate tales by, published in the journal 'Moambe':] *See* PERIODICAL PUBLICATIONS. —*Tiflis.*

—— Elissa, opowiadanie z życia Czeczeńców przez A. Moczchubarydzego [i.e. A. Qazbegi]. Przekład z gruzínskiego. [By Arthur Leist. Polish translation of A. Qazbegi's tale of Chechen life ელისო, Eliso.] pp. 20. *Warszawa,* 1887. 8⁰. [*Dodatek do numeru 1145 "Kłosów".*]   **012590. dd. 39 (4)**

—— Избранное. [Selected tales. Translated into Russian by E. D. Ghoghoberidze. With a biographical sketch by E. G. Lundberg.] pp. 271. Москва, 1949. 8⁰.   **17076. c. 5**

—— თხზულებანი. [T'khzulebani. Collected works containing novels and tales of Georgian life, *etc.*] 4 tom. თბილისი [*Tiflis,*] 1891–92. 8⁰.   **17076. c. 3**

—— თხზულებანი ორ ტომად. I : მოთხრობები და რომანები. [T'khzulebani or tomad. I: mot'khrobebi da romanebi. Works in two volumes. I: Tales and novels. Edit. by S. Chik'ovani, with a glossary compiled by Sh. Dzidziguri.] pp. 554. თბილისი [*Tiflis,*] 1955. 8⁰. *In progress.*   **17076. b. 19**

QIASASHVILI (NIKOLOZ ALEK'SANDRES-DZE). ქართული შექსპირიანა. [K'art'uli Shek'spiriana. Essays on aspects of Shakspere's dramatic art by various hands, edited with foreword and notes by N. A. Qiasashvili.] (The Georgian Shakespeariana.) tom. I. pp. 330, 6. 11 *plates.* თბილისი [*Tiflis,*] 1959. 8⁰. *In progress.*   **17076. f. 25**

—— შექსპირი. [Shek'spiri. A critical biography of Shakspere. With two fascimiles.] pp. 273. თბილისი [*Tiflis,*] 1959. 8⁰.   **17076. f. 24**

QIPʻIANI (GIORGI). ლექსთა კრებული. [Lekʻstʻa krebuli. Collected poems.] bk. I. pp. 103. პარიზი [*Paris,*] 1935. 8⁰.   **17075. d. 21. (3.)**

—— რჩეული შაირების კრებული. . . . გრიგოლ რობაქიძის წინასიტყვაობით. [Rcheuli shairebis krebuli.... Grigol Robakʻidzis dsinasitqvaobitʻ. Collection of selected poems... with a preface by Grigol Robakʻidze.] Des poèmes choisis. pp. 164. პარიზი [*Paris,*] 1951. 8⁰.   **17075. d. 22**

QIPʻSHIDZE (ALEKʻSANDRE). *See* Pʻroneli (A.) *pseud.*

QIPʻSHIDZE (DAVITʻ ALEKʻSIS-DZE). Житіе Прохора, муч. Луки и муч. Николая Двал-и. [Lives of the founder of the Georgian monastery of the Cross at Jerusalem and of two Georgian martyrs connected with that monastery. Georgian text edit. with Russian trans. and commentary by D. A. Qipʻshidze.] pp. 31–68. Ленинградъ, 1927. 4⁰. [*Извѣстія Кавказскаго Историко-Археологическаго Института.* tom. 2.]   **Ac. 1125. qc**

QIPʻSHIDZE (GRIGOL TʻEVDORES-DZE). თავადი რაფაელ ერისთავი და მისი სალიტერატურო მოღვაწეობა. [Tʻavadi Rapʻael Eristʻavi da misi saliteraturo moghvadseoba. Prince Raphael Eristʻavi and his literary career.] pp. 80–98. ტფილისი [*Tiflis,*] 1895. 8⁰. [*Moambe.* tom. 2. no. 10.]   **17089. b. 1**

QIPʻSHIDZE (IOSEB ALEKʻSIS-DZE). [Edit. with Russian trans. of Passion of St. Antony Rawaḣ.] *See* Antony, *Saint and Martyr,* called Rawaḣ.

—— Дополнительныя свѣдѣнія о ʻчанскомъ языкѣ. Изъ лингвистической экскурсіи въ русскій Лазистанъ. pp. vi. 33. С.-Петербургъ, 1911. 8⁰. [*Матеріалы по яфетическому языкознанію.* no. 3.]   **17073. a. 3**

—— Грамматика грузинскаго языка. (Курсы кавказскихъ туземныхъ языковъ для кандидатовъ на судебныя должности Министерства Юстиціи.) pp. 95. С.-Петербургъ. 1911. fol. *Lithographed from the MS.*   **Ac. 2355/2**

—— Мингрелизмы въ грузинскихъ надписяхъ изъ Мингреліи. pp. 315–17. Петроградъ, 1916. 4⁰. [*Христіанскій Востокъ.* томъ 4. вып. 3.]   **Ac. 1125/105**

QUBANEISHVILI (SOLOMON IVLIANES-DZE). [Edit. 'Vepʻkhistqaosani', together with the supplementary and interpolated passages.] *See* Rustʻaveli (Shotʻa).

—— [Joint edit. of collected works of Sulkhan-Saba Orbeliani.] *See* Savva, *the Monk* [*Prince* Sulkhan Orbeliani].

—— ძველი ქართული ლიტერატურის ქრესტომათია. [Dzveli kʻartʻuli literaturis kʻrestomatʻia.] (Chrestomatie [*sic*] de la littérature géorgienne ancienne.) 2 tom. [Edit. by K. S. Kekelidze and A. G. Baramidze.] თბილისი [*Tiflis,*] 1946–49. 4⁰.   **17076. i. 5**

—— ვეფხისტყაოსნის ხელნაწერთა სტროფული შედგენილობა. [Vepʻkhistqaosnis khelnadsertʻa stropʻuli shedgeniloba. An analytical concordance to the principal manuscripts of Rustʻaveli's epic poem, 'The Man in the Panther's Skin'.] pp. 327. 24 *plates.* თბილისი [*Tiflis,*] 1959. 8⁰. **17076. d. 19**

RACINE (JEAN). [For the tragedy 'Iphigénie' by Racine, rendered into Georgian by Prince D. Cholaqashvili:] *See* Tsagareli (A. A.). Свѣдѣнія о памятникахъ грузинской письменности. вып. 3. 1894. 8⁰.   **7708. d. 3**

—— მითრიდატი რასინისა. [Mitʻridati Rasinisa. The 'Mithridate' of Racine, trans. by G. Gvazava.] pp. 80. პარიზი [*Paris,*] 1934. 8⁰. **17075. d. 21. (1.)**

RADIANI (SHALVA DIMITRIS-DZE). [Joint author of 'Исторія грузинской литературы'.] *See* Baramidze (A. G.) *and others.*

—— and **KEKELIDZE** (PROKLE LEVARSIS-DZE). ქართული ლიტერატურის ქრესტომათია. XX საუკუნე. საშუალო სკოლის XI კლასისათვის. [Kʻartʻuli literaturis kʻrestomatʻia. XX saukune. Sashualo skolis XI klasisatʻvis. Chrestomathy of 20th century Georgian literature for use in the 11th form of Georgian State Intermediate Schools. Illustrated.] pp. 547. თბილისი [*Tiflis,*] 1955. 8⁰.   **17076. i. 9**

RAMAZANOV (Badavi). Фиалки на скалах. (Перевод с лакского.) [Poems, trans. by various hands.] pp. 78. [*Москва,*] 1959. 12⁰. **17075. c. 37**

RAMISHVILI (Noe). დემოკრატიული სოცია-ლიზმი. [Demokratiuli sotsializmi.] Le socialisme démocratique. [With a portrait, and a preface by N. N. Zhordania.] pp. 129. პარიზი [*Paris,*] 1931. 8⁰. **17075. f. 27**

RAMISHVILI (Valeriane T'omas-dze). ქართუ-ლი ენა, გრამატიკა და მართლწერა სავარჯიშოები-თურთ. III და IV კლასის სახელმძღვანელო. [K'art'uli ena, gramatika da mart'ldsera savarji-shoebit'urt'. III da IV klasis sakhelmdzghvanelo. The Georgian language, grammar and ortho-graphy, with exercises. Manual for 3rd and 4th forms. 13th edition. Illustrated.] pp. 75. თბილისი [*Tiflis,*] 1957. 8⁰. **17076. h. 5**

RASHIDOV (Rashid). Весенние гости. Стихи. [Trans. from the Dargwa language by various hands.] pp. 70. *Москва,* 1959. 12⁰. **17075. d. 46**

RATIANI (Prokopi Konstantines-dze). ილია ჭავჭავაძე : ფილოსოფიური და სოციალურ-პოლიტიკური შეხედულებანი. [Ilia Tchavtcha-vadze: p'ilosop'iuri da sotsialur-politikuri shekhe-dulebani. The philosophical and social-political ideas of Ilia Tchavtchavadze. Second edition.] pp. 401. თბილისი [*Tiflis,*] 1954. 8⁰. **17075. f. 20**

RAZHDEN, *Saint, of Persia.* S. Razden le Persan. [Latin translation by P. Peeters of the Georgian life of St. Razhden.] pp. 294–317. *Bruxelles,* 1914. 8⁰. [*Analecta Bollandiana.* tom. 33.] **2002. f**

RAZIKASHVILI (Luka Pavles-dze). *See* Vazha-P'shavela, *pseud.*

RAZIKASHVILI (Nikoloz) known as Bachana. [For selected poems, in Russian translation:] *See* Gol'tsev (V. V.) and Chik'ovani (S. I.). Поэзия Грузии. 1949. 4⁰. **17075. dd. 1**

—— დაბადება და აღზრდა ერეკლე ბატონიშვი-ლისა. ლეგენდა. [Dabadeba da aghzrda Erekle

Batonishvilisa. Legenda. The birth and upbringing of Prince Erekle. A legend about the childhood of King Erekle II of Georgia, put into verse.] pp. 31. თბილისი [*Tiflis,*] 1890. 12⁰. **17075. d. 5. (3.)**

RAZIKASHVILI (T'evdore Pavles-dze). ხალ-ხური ზღაპრები, კახეთსა და ფშავში შეკრებილი. [Khalkhuri zghaprebi, Kakhet'sa da P'shavshi shekrebili. Folk tales, collected in Kakhet'i and P'shavet'i.] pp. ii. 168, 84, 2, 2. ტფილისი [*Tiflis,*] 1909. 8⁰. **17076. a. 7. (2.)**

—— ხალხური ზღაპრები, ქართლში შეკრებილი. [Khalkhuri zghaprebi, K'art'lshi shekrebili. Folk tales, collected in K'art'li.] pp. ii. 266, 2. ტფილისი [*Tiflis,*] 1909. 8⁰. **17076. a. 7. (1.)**

REGEL (Wilhelm). [Joint edit. of 'Византійскій Временникъ'.] *See* St. Petersburg.—*Academia Scientiarum Imperialis.*

ROBAK'IDZE (Alek'si Ivanes-dze). კოლექ-ტიური ნადირობის გადმონაშთები რაჭაში. [Kolek'tiuri nadirobis gadmonasht'ebi Ratchashi.] Les survivances de la chasse collective en Ratchа. pp. 203. თბილისი [*Tiflis,*] 1941. 8⁰. [*Les formes d'organisation du travail dans l'économie sociale de l'ancienne Géorgie.* tom. 1.] **17075. e. 19**

ROBAK'IDZE (Grigol). [For 'Rcheuli shairebis krebuli', with a preface by G. Robak'idze:] *See* Qip'iani (G.)

—— [Contributor to symposium 'Niko P'iros-manishvili'.] *See* Tabidze (T. I.) *and others.*

ROBERT [Bellarmino] *Saint, Cardinal, Arch-bishop of Capua.* [For a treatise on the Seven Sacraments, based in part on the manual by Cardinal Bellarmino:] *See* Tlukaant'i (D.)

—— Dottrina Christiana breve, composta dal Cardinale Bellarmino, et tradotta dal P. Bernardo Maria da Napoli ... dalla Italiana in lingua volgare Giorgiana. (საკრისტიანო მოძღუარება სიმოკლეობით დარიგებული კარდინალ ბელარ-მინისაგან. [Sak'ristiano modzghuareba simokleo-

ROBERT *(cont.)*
bit' darigebuli Kardinal Belarminisagan.]) pp. 79.
Nella Stampa della Sac. Congr. de Prop. Fide: Roma,
1681. 8⁰.   **G. 20,004. (1.)**

—— საქრისტიანო მოძღუარება, მოკლედ დარიგებული მარტვილთათვს ზეპირად დასასწავ-
ლებლათ. [Sak'ristiano modzghuareba, mokled darigebuli martvilt'at'vis zepirad dasasdsavleblat'.
Manual of Christian doctrine, abridged for learning
by heart by children. Being a revised and amplified
edition of the Georgian version of Cardinal Bellarmino's 'Dottrina Christiana breve', published by
the Sac. Congr. de Prop. Fide for the use of
Catholic missionaries.] pp. 92. პრომის კალაკს
[*Rome,*] 1741. 8⁰.   **17073. b. 1**

ROBINS (ROBERT HENRY) and **WATERSON**
(NATALIE). Notes on the Phonetics of the Georgian
Word. pp. 55–72. *London*, 1952. 8⁰. [*Bulletin of the
School of Oriental and African Studies.* vol. 14.
pt. I.]   **Ac. 8820. d**

ROGAVA (APOLON ANDRIAS-DZE). [Edit. 'Sak'-
art'velos samart'lisa da kanont'mtsodneobis mimokhilva'.] *See* DAVID, *Prince-Regent of Georgia.*

ROMAN CATHOLIC CHURCH. [For 'Kat'olikeni Sak'art'veloshi':] *See* ISARLISHVILI (L.)

ROMANUS, *Saint, of Galatia.* S. Romain le néo-
martyr († 1ᵉʳ mai 780) d'après un document
géorgien. [Georgian version of the Passion of St.
Romanus, trans. into Latin with introduction by
P. Peeters.] pp. 393–427. *Bruxelles,* 1911. 8⁰.
[*Analecta Bollandiana.* tom. 30.]   **2002. f**

—— [Another copy, being an offprint.]
     4830. e. 4. (1.)

ROME.—*Collegium des deutschen Campo Santo.*
Oriens Christianus. Römische Halbjahrshefte für
die Kunde des christlichen Orients. [Edit. by A.
Baumstark and others.] Jahrg. I— *Rom, Leipzig*
and *Wiesbaden,* 1901— 8⁰. *In progress.* **Ac. 2002. b**

——*Pontificio Istituto per gli Studi Orientali.*

Orientalia Christiana Periodica. vol. I — *Roma*,
1935— 8⁰.   **Ac. 2002. bb/2**

RONDELI (DAVIT' EVGENIS-DZE). [For a study
of the life and work of this Georgian film producer:]
See LOLADZE (V.)

ROSEN (VICTOR) *Baron.* [Edit. 'Записки Восточнаго
Отдѣленія, *etc*'.] *See* SAINT PETERSBURG.—*Императорское Русское Археологическое Общество.*

ROTTIERS (BERNARD EUGÈNE ANTOINE). De la
religion chrétienne en Géorgie et dans les pays
circonvoisins. 2 pt. pp. 193–217; 282–98. *Paris,*
1827. 8⁰. [*Journal Asiatique.* tom. 11.] **R. Ac. 8808**

—— Notice biographique sur Marie, dernière
Reine de Géorgie. pp. 367–79. *Paris,* 1827. 8⁰.
[*Journal Asiatique.* tom. 10.]   **R. Ac. 8808**

ROUSTHAVÉLI (CHOTA). *See* RUSTAVELI (SHO-
T'A).

ROZEN (VIKTOR ROMANOVICH) *Baron. See* ROSEN
(V.)

RUDENKO (BORIS TIKHONOVICH). Дифференци-
рующая роль древнелитературных форм в семасио-
логии современного грузинского литературного
языка. pp. 39–46. *Москва, Ленинград,* 1940. 8⁰.
[*Язык и мышление.* вып. 9.]   **Ac. 1125. t/2**

—— Грамматика грузинского языка. (Ответственный
редактор А. П. Баранников.) pp. 275. *Москва, Ленинград,* 1940. 8⁰. [*Труды Института Востоковедения.*
no. 32.]   **17076. f. 3**

—— [Another copy.]   **Ac. 1125. ik**

—— [Another copy.]   **Ac. 1125. ik/2**

—— О творительном падеже личных местоимений
1-го и 2-го лица в грузинском языке. pp. 215–17.
Москва, Ленинград, 1945. 8⁰. [*Советское Востоковедение.* том 3.]   **Ac. 1125. ik/7**

RURUA (PARMEN). ერთტომეული. [Ert'tomeuli.
Collected verses in one volume. With a biography

of the author by N. Paitchadze.] pp. x. 290, vi. 1 *plate*. ბათუმ [*Batum*,] 1954. 8⁰.　　**17075. c. 13**

RURUA (PʻILIPE ISIDORES-DZE). ქართული ენა. არაქართული სკოლების VII კლასის სახელმძ-ღვანელო. [Kʻartʻuli ena. Arakʻartʻuli skolebis VII klasis sakhelmdzghvanelo. The Georgian language. Manual for the 7ᵗʰ class of non-Georgian Schools. Illustrated. Eighth edition.] pp. 93, 3. თბილისი [*Tiflis*,] 1956. 8⁰.　　**17076. h. 2**

——— [Ninth edition.] pp. 93, 3. თბილისი [*Tiflis*,] 1957. 8⁰.　　**17076. f. 17**

——— ქართული ენა. სახელმძღვანელო არაქარ--თული სკოლებისათვის, V–VI კლასი. [Kʻartʻuli ena. Sakhelmdzghvanelo arakʻartʻuli skolebisatʻ-vis, V–VI klasi. The Georgian language. Manual for the 5ᵗʰ–6ᵗʰ classes of non-Georgian schools. Illustrated. Seventh, revised edition.] pp. 190. თბილისი [*Tiflis*,] 1956. 8⁰.　　**17076. h. 2**

RUSSIA.—*Laws, etc.* საბჭოთა სოციალისტური რესპუბლიკების კავშირის კონსტიტუცია..... უმაღლესი საბჭოს I, II და III სესიების მიერ მიღებული. [Sabtchotʻa sotsialisturi respublikebis kavshiris konstitutsia... umaghlesi sabtchos I, II da III sesiebis mier mighebuli. Constitution of the U.S.S.R.,... adopted by the 1st, 2nd and 3rd Sessions of the Supreme Soviet.] pp. 34. თბილისი [*Tiflis*,] 1953. 8⁰.　　**17075. f. 9 (4)**

——— *Instructions to Ambassadors.* [For Посольство князя Мышецкого и дьяка Ключарева в Кахетию, 1640–1643':] *See* POLIEVKTOV (M. A.)

——— [For Посольство стольника Толочанова и дьяка Иевлева в Имеретию, 1650–1652':] *See* POLIEVKTOV (M. A.)

——— *Министерство Иностранныхъ Дѣлъ.* [For decrees and other historical documents of the 18ᵗʰ century relative to Georgia:] *See* TSAGARELI (A. A.)

——— *Министерство Народнаго Просвѣщенія.* Приложеніе къ таблицамъ для взаимнаго обученія чтенію и письму ... с переводомъ словъ и фразъ на Грузинскій, Армянскій и Татарскій языки. pp. 131. 20. Тифлисъ, 1855. 8⁰.　　**17073. a. 1**

——— Журналъ Министерства Народнаго Просвѣщенія. часть 1–93, 95–362. Новая серія. часть 1–71. *Санктпетербургъ*, 1834–1917. 8⁰. *Imperfect; wanting часть 94 and the latter half of Новая серія*, 1914, *часть* 53–55, *and the last volume issued, Новая серія, часть* 72.　　**P. P. 1213**

——— *Россійская Коммунистическая Партія.* [For 'Sitqva sakavshiro k.p. (b) XIX qrilobaze, *etc.*':] *See* BERIYA (L. P.)

——— [For 'Saangarisho mokhseneba partiis XIX qrilobaze, *etc.*':] *See* MALENKOV (G. M.)

——— [For 'Saangarisho mokhseneba partiis XVIII qrilobaze, *etc.*':] *See* STALIN (I. V.)

——— [For 'Sitqva partiis XIX qrilobaze, *etc.*':] *See* STALIN (I. V.)

——— პარტიის XIX ყრილობის დირექტივები .... მეხუთე ხუთწლიანი გეგმის შესახებ. [Partiis XIX qrilobis direkʻtivebi ... mekhutʻe khutʻdsliani gegmis shesakheb. Directives of the 19ᵗʰ Party Congress ... concerning the fifth 5-year Plan. Trans. from the Russian.] pp. 39. [თბილისი. *Tiflis*,] 1953. 8⁰.　　**17075. f. 9 (3.)**

——— საბჭოთა კავშირის კომუნისტური პარტია ყრილობების, კონფერენციებისა და ცენტრალური კომიტეტის პლენუმების რეზოლუციებსა და გადაწყვეტილებებში. [Sabtchotʻa kavshiris komunisturi partia qrilobebis, konpʻerentsiebisa da tsentraluri komitetis plenumebis rezolutsiebsa da gadadsqvetilebebshi. The Communist Party of the Soviet Union: Resolutions of conferences and plenary sessions. pt. 1, covering the years 1898–1924. Trans. from the 7ᵗʰ Russian edition.] pp. 1074. თბილისი [*Tiflis*,] 1954. 8⁰.　　**17075. e. 18**

——— საბჭოთა კავშირის კომუნისტური პარტიის წესდება მიღებული პარტიის XIX ყრილობის მიერ. [Sabtchotʻa kavshiris komunisturi partiis dsesdeba, mighebuli partiis XIX qrilobis mier.

RUSSIA *(cont.)*
Statutes of the Communist Party of the Soviet Union, adopted by the 19th Congress of the Party.] pp. 32. [თბილისი. *Tiflis,*] 1952. 8⁰.   **17075. f. 8 (2.)**

—— *Центральный Комитет.* საკავშირო კომუნისტური პარტიის (ბოლშევიკების) ისტორია. მოკლე კურსი. [Sakavshiro komunisturi partiis (bolshevikebis) istoria. Mokle kursi. History of the Communist Party of the Soviet Union (Bolsheviks). Short course. Trans. from the Russian by a commission of the Georgian Communist Party Central Committee.] pp. 447. [თბილისი. *Tiflis,*] 1952. 8⁰.   **17075. f. 14**

—— *Центральный Исполнительный Комитет Советов.* [For 'Новый Восток':] *See* Moscow.—*Nauchnaya Assotsiatsiya Vostokovedeniya S.S.S.R.*

—— [For 'Восточные Записки':] *See* St. Petersburg.—*Ленинградский Институт Живых Восточных Языков.*

—— *Ukrainian Soviet Socialist Republic.* საბჭოთა უკრაინას – ქართველი მწერლები. [Sabtchot'a Ukrainas – k'art'veli mdserlebi. An anthology of poems, tales, *etc.* by modern Georgian writers, dedicated to the Soviet Ukrainian Republic.] Радянській Україні – Грузинські письменники. [Edited by I. Abashidze and others.] pp. 605. თბილისი [*Tiflis,*] 1954. 4⁰.   **17075. d. 15**

RUST'AVELI (Sʜᴏᴛ'ᴀ). [For 'Rust'velis da Dantes idumali':] *See* Beliashvili (L.)

—— [For 'Sakhisa da khasiat'is problema "Vep'khistqaosanshi"', being a study of Rust'aveli's epic poem:] *See* Benashvili (D.)

—— [*Life.*] *See* Beridze (S.); Gol'tsev (V. V.); Tchitchinadze (Z. E.)

—— [For 'Шота Руставели в русской литературе':] *See* Berkov (P. N.)

—— [For 'Recherches sur la poésie géorgienne … et extraits du roman de Tariel':] *See* Brosset (M.-F.)

—— [For 'Шота Руставели и грузинская литература':] *See* Dondua (K. D.)

—— [For 'Шота Руставели и его время. Сборник статей':] *See* Gol'tsev (V. V.)

—— [For 'The Man in the Panther Skin', a study of a 17th century manuscript of the epic by Shot'a Rust'aveli, acquired by the Bodleian Library:] *See* Gray (B.) *Keeper of Oriental Antiquities, British Museum.*

—— [For 'Rust'aveli and his Poem':] *See* Gvazava (G.)

—— [For 'Rust'velologiuri literatura, 1712–1956 dslebi':] *See* Imedashvili (G.)

—— [For 'Шота Руставели и его поэма':] *See* Ingoroqva (P. I.)

—— [For 'Сборник Руставели. К 750-летию "Вепхисткаосани"':] *See* Janashia (S. N.)

—— [For 'Shot'a Rust'avelis epok'is materialuri kultura':] *See* Javakhishvili (I. A.)

—— [For 'Грузинскій поэтъ XII вѣка Ш. Руставелли':] *See* Khakhanov (A. S.)

—— [For 'Грузинская поэма "Витязь въ барсовой шкурѣ" … и новая культурно-историческая проблема':] *See* Marr (N. Y.)

—— [For 'К Rusthaveliana', being a discussion of textual difficulties in 'The Man in the Panther's Skin':] *See* Marr (N. Y.)

—— [For 'Руставели и фольклор':] *See* Megrelidze (I. B.)

—— [For 'Шота Руставели и грузинский фольклор':] *See* Megrelidze (I. B.)

—— [For 'Chota Rousthavéli, poète géorgien du XIIᵉ siècle':] *See* Mourier (J.)

—— [For 'Rust'avelis est'etika':] *See* Nadíradze (G. A.)

RUST'AVELI *(cont.)*

—— [For 'Gankit'khvani Vep'khistqaosanisa', an essay on the symbolism of colours in Rust'aveli's epic 'The Man in the Panther's Skin':] *See* NO-ZADZE (V.)

—— ['Vep'khistqaosanis mzis metqveleba':] *See* NOZADZE (V.)

—— [For 'Vep'khistqaosanis sazogadoebat'met-qveleba':] *See* NOZADZE (V.)

—— [For 'Vep'khistqaosanis varskvlavt'metqve-leba':] *See* NOZADZE (V.)

—— [For 'Vep'khistqaosnis khelnadsert'a stro-p'uli shedgeniloba':] *See* QUBANEISHVILI (S. I.)

—— [For 'Памятники эпохи Руставели':] *See* SAINT PETERSBURG. – *Императорский*, afterwards *Государственный, Эрмитажъ*.

—— [For ' "Vep'khis-tqaosnis" qalbi adgilebi', being an examination of spurious passages in the epic of Rust'aveli:] *See* SARAJISHVILI (A.)

—— [For 'Vep'khis-tqaosnis simp'onia':] *See* SHANIDZE (A. G.)

—— [For 'Шота Руставели. Несколько параллелей и аналогий':] *See* SHISHMAREV (V. F.)

—— [For 'Неопубликованная рукопись грузинского поэта А. Р. Церетели', comprising an essay on Rust'aveli's poem 'Vep'khis-tqaosani':] *See* TSERE-T'ELI (A. R.) *Prince.*

—— L'Homme à la peau de léopard. Texte français de M. Georges Gvazava et de Mme Anie Marcel-Paon. pp. 278. 1 *plate. Paris*, 1938. 8⁰.   **17076. a. 4**

—— The Knight in the Tiger's Skin. Translated by Marjory Scott Wardrop. Supplemented and revised by E. Orbelyani and S. Jordanishvili. [With an introductory essay by P. I. Ingoroqva.] pp. xlvii. 299. 21 *plates. Moscow*, 1938. 4⁰.   **17076. d. 4**

—— The Man in the Panther's Skin. A romantic epic... A close rendering from the Georgian attempted by Marjory Scott Wardrop. pp. xviii. 273. *London*, 1912. 8⁰. [*Royal Asiatic Society. Oriental Translation Fund.* New series. vol. 21.]

14003. bb. 16

—— Der Mann im Tigerfelle, von Schota Rusta-weli. Aus dem Georgischen übersetzt von A. Leist. pp. iv. 288. *Dresden & Leipzig*, [1889]. 8⁰.

17077. a. 3

—— Muž v tygří kůži. (Přeložil Jaromír Jedlička.) [A verse rendering, followed by a prose translation, of Rust'aveli's epic, 'The Man in the Panther's Skin'.] pp. 622. 1 *plate. Praha*, 1958. 8⁰.   **17075. c. 34**

—— La Peau de Léopard, d'après Chota Roustha-véli. Par A. Borin. pp. 137. *Tiflis*, 1885. 8⁰.

17076. a. 1

—— La Peau de léopard, imitée du Vepkhis Tao-xané de Rousthavéli [by Achas Borin]. *See* BORIN (A.). Contes orientaux, *etc.* 1886. 8⁰.   **17076. a. 3**

—— Première Histoire de Rostéwan, roi d'Arabie, traduite du roman géorgien intitulé "l'Homme à la peau de tigre", suivie de quelques Observations sur les dictionnaires géorgiens, par M. Brosset. pp. 277–94. *Paris*, 1828. 8⁰. [*Nouveau Journal Asiatique.* tom. 2.]   **R. Ac. 8808**

—— ვეფხის-ტყაosანი. [Vep'khvis-tqaosani. The Man in the Panther's Skin. An epic poem. Edited by Prince P. G. Dsulukidze.] pp. 183. ქუთაისი [K'ut'aisi,] 1883. 8⁰.   **17075. d. 4. (1.)**

—— [Another edition. Edited by K. T'avart'k'i-ladze.] pp. xvi. 248. 22 *plates.* ახალ-სენაკი [Akhal-Senaki,] 1896. 8⁰.   **17075. c. 5**

—— [Twenty-second edition. Edit. by Iustine Abuladze.] pp. lvii. 274. 13 *plates.* ტფილისი [Tif-lis,] 1914. 8⁰. *Pp.* 193–274 *are incorrectly numbered as* 185–266.   **17076. b. 2**

—— [Edited with introduction by S. Kakabadze. Second edition.] pp. cxlvi. 216, vi. 33 *plates.* ტფილისი [Tiflis,] 1927. 8⁰.   **17076. b. 1**

RUST'AVELI *(cont.)*

—— [Another edition.] pp. 576. ბერლინი [*Berlin,*] 1943. 12⁰.   **17075. d. 27**

—— [Edited, with notes and variant readings, by P. I. Ingoroqva.] pp. 517. თბილისი [*Tiflis,*] 1953. 8⁰.   **17075. d. 16**

—— ვეფხისტყაოსანი, ჭანართი და დანართი ტექსტებით. [Vep'khistqaosani, chanart'i da danart'i tek'stebit'. The epic poem, 'The Man in the Panther's Skin', edited, together with the supplementary and interpolated passages, by S. I. Qubaneishvili.] pp. 012. 358, 1. 1 *plate.* თბილისი [*Tiflis,*] 1956. 4⁰.   **17075. d. 36**

—— ვეფხის ტყაოსანი. (სარედაქციო კოლეგია : ალ. ბარამიძე, კ. კეკელიძე, ა. შანიძე.) [Vep'khis tqaosani. Saredak'tsio kolegia: Al. Baramidze, K. Kekelidze, A. Shanidze. The epic poem, 'The Man in the Panther's Skin', edited by A. Baramidze and others.] pp. 401. 19 *plates.* თბილისი [*Tiflis,*] 1957. 4⁰.   **17075. c. 22**

—— Витязь в тигровой шкуре. Поэма. Перевод с грузинского К. Д. Бальмонта. [Rust'aveli's epic poem 'The Man in the Panther's Skin', translated into Russian verse by K. D. Bal'mont.] pp. xxiii. 290. 22 *plates.* Москва, 1936. 8⁰.   **17076. d. 2**

—— Витязь в тигровой шкуре. Поэма в стихах. Перевод ... Шалва Нуцубидзе. [With plates.] pp. v. 252. Тбилиси, 1949. 8⁰.   **11588. cc. 51**

—— Витязь в тигровой шкуре. Перевод с грузинского Шалва Нуцубидзе. [With illustrations by M. Zichy.] pp. 370. 17 *plates.* Тбилиси, 1957. 4⁰.   **17075. dd. 6**

—— Витязь в тигровой шкуре. Перевод с грузинского Шалва Нуцубидзе. [With illustrations by M. Zichy, S. K'obuladze, and I. T'oidze.] pp. 370. 19 *plates.* Тбилиси, 1957. 4⁰.   **17076. d. 15**

—— Витязь в тигровой шкуре. Поэма. [Translated from Georgian into Russian by G. K. Tsagareli. Edited by V. V. Gol'tsev. Second, revised edition.] pp. 246. 19 *plates.* Москва, 1953. 4⁰.   **17076. d. 5**

—— Вступительныя и заключительныя строфы Витязя въ барсовой кожѣ Шоты изъ Рустава. Грузинскій текстъ, русскій переводъ и поясненія с этюдомъ 'Культъ женщины и рыцарство въ поэмѣ'. [By N. Y. Marr.] pp. lvi. 54. *Санктпетербургъ,* 1910. 8⁰. [*Тексты и разысканія по армяно-грузинской филологіи. кн. 12.*]   **14005. f. 5**

RUST'AVELI INSTITUTE OF THE HISTORY OF GEORGIAN LITERATURE. *See* Tiflis.—*Academy of Sciences of the Georgian S.S.R.—Rust'aveli Literary Institute.*

RUST'AVI. [For an archaeological study of the town of Rust'avi:] *See* Tchilashvili (L. A.)

RUSUDANIANI. [For 'Notice du roman géorgien intitulé Rousoudaniani':] *See* Brosset (M.-F.)

S., V. [Trans. 'Ianvris ajanqebis militaruli istoriis mimokhilva'.] *See* Piłsudski (J. K.) *Regent of Poland.*

SAAKADZE (Giorgi). [For 'Великий Моурави', a novel on the life of the 17th century Georgian military leader Giorgi Saakadze:] *See* Antonovskaya (A. A.)

—— [For 'Великий Моурави. Поэма XVII века о Георгии Саакадзе', being a Russian trans. of the poem 'Didmouraviani':] *See* Joseph [Ioseb Saakadze], *Bishop of Tiflis.*

—— [For an account of the life and times of Giorgi Saakadze:] *See* K'variani (S. A.)

SABAKHTARISHVILI (Valeriane Domentisdze). გლეხთა რევოლუციური მოძრაობა დასავლეთ საქართველოში 1905—1907 წ.წ., სენაკისა და ზუგდიდის მაზრები. [Glekht'a revolutsiuri modzraoba dasavlet' Sak'art'veloshi 1905–1907 ds. ds., Senakisa da Zugdidis mazrebi. The revolutionary movement among the peasants of Western Georgia in 1905–7, in the districts of Senaki and Zugdidi.] pp. 246. თბილისი [*Tiflis,*] 1959. 8⁰.   **17075. e. 42**

SABANISDZE (Ioane). წმიდა მოწამე აბო ტფილელი. [Dsmida modsame Abo Tp'ileli. The

SABANISDZE *(cont.)*

holy martyr Abo of Tiflis. A contemporary biography of the saint.] pp. 15. ტფილისი [*Tiflis,*]
1899. 8⁰.　　　　　　　　　　**17076. g. 2. (5.)**

—— Das Martyrium des heiligen Abo von Tiflis
[trans. from the Georgian life by Ioane Sabanisdze,
with introduction] von K. Schultze. pp. 41. *Leipzig,* 1905. 8⁰. [*Texte und Untersuchungen zur Geschichte der altchristlichen Literatur.* Neue Folge.
Bd. 13. Hft. 4.]　　　　　　　　**3628. d. 1/28**

SADZAGELI (GIORGI) *Iverieli.* Ананурскій
Успенскій Соборъ. [Description of Ananuri church
and its antiquities]. pp. 69–80. 1 *plate. Москва,*
1898. 4⁰. [*Матеріалы по Археологіи Кавказа.* вып.
7.]　　　　　　　　　　　　　　**Ac. 5575/3**

SAHAK I, PARTʿEW, called THE GREAT, *Catholicos
of Armenia.* [For ʻО грузинской версіи апокрифическаго Видѣнія Саака Парфянина':] *See* MELIKʿ-
SETʿ-BEGI (L. M.)

SĀHDŌNĀ, *Bishop of Māhōzē dh-Arēwān in Bēth
Garmai.* Le sermon géorgien du moine Martyrius
et son modèle syriaque. [The Georgian text of a
Homily ʻDe paenitentia et humilitate' by Martyrius-Sāhdōnā. Edited, with a Latin translation,
by G. Garitte. Accompanied by the corresponding
passages of the Syriac original in a Latin translation by A. de Halleux.] pp. 243–312. *Louvain,*
1956. 8⁰. [*Le Muséon.* tom. 69.]　　**P. P. 4453**

SAINT-MARTIN (JEAN ANTOINE). Rapport sur
la Littérature géorgienne. pp. 117–25. *Paris,* 1823.
8⁰. [*Journal Asiatique.* tom. 2.]　　**R. Ac. 8808**

SAINT PETERSBURG, afterwards **PETRO-
GRAD,** afterwards **LENINGRAD.**—*Academia
Scientiarum Imperialis, afterwards* Академия Наук
СССР. *See* MARR (N. Y.). Описание грузинских ру-
кописей синайского монастыря. 1940. 8⁰.　**11916. k. 16**

—— [For ʻИзвестия Кавказского Историко-Архео-
логического Института в Тифлисе':] *See* TIFLIS.—
Kavkazsky Istoriko-Arkheologichesky Institut.
　　　　　　　　　　　　　　　Ac. 1125. qc

—— *See* ZHIRKOV (L. I.). Лакский язык. Фонетика
и морфология. 1955. 8⁰.　　　　**17076. i. 8**

—— Bulletin de la Classe Historico-Philologique
de l'Académie Impériale des Sciences. 16 tom.
St.-Pétersbourg, Leipzig. 1844–59. 4⁰.　**Ac. 1125/7**

—— Bulletin Scientifique publié par l'Académie
Impériale des Sciences. 10 tom. *St.-Pétersbourg,
Leipzig.* 1836–42. 4⁰.　　　　　**Ac. 1125/6**

—— Эпиграфика Востока. Сборник статей под редакцией проф. В. А. Крачковской. вып. 1— *Москва,
Ленинград,* 1947— 4⁰. *In progress.*　**Ac. 1125. gd/3**

—— Известия Академии Наук СССР. (Bulletin de
l'Académie des Sciences de l'URSS.) VII серия.
Отделение Гуманитарных Наук. (Classe des Huma-
nités.) 3 tom. *Ленинград,* 1928–30. 8⁰.
　　　　　　　　　　　　　Ac. 1125/44. (2.)

—— Извѣстія Императорской Академіи Наукъ.
(Bulletin de l'Académie Impériale des Sciences.)
VI серія. 21 томъ. *С.-Петербургъ,* 1907–27. 8⁰.
　　　　　　　　　　　　　　Ac. 1125/44

—— Христіанскій Востокъ. Серія, посвященная
изученію христіанской культуры народовъ Азіи и
Африки. tom. 1; 2, pt. 1, 2; 4–6. *С.-Петербургъ,* 1912–
22. 4⁰.　　　　　　　　　　　**Ac. 1125/105**

—— Mélanges Asiatiques, tirés du Bulletin His-
torico-Philologique de l'Académie Impériale des
Sciences. tom. 1–9; Nouvelle Série, tom. 1–2.
St.-Pétersbourg, 1849–1919. 8⁰. *Incomplete; lacks
tom. 9, livr. 1 and tom. 10 of the original series.*
　　　　　　　　　　　　　　Ac. 1125/11

—— Советская этнография. Сборник статей. no. 1—
Москва, Ленинград, 1938— 8⁰. *In progress.*
　　　　　　　　　　　　　　Ac. 1125. nd

—— Тексты и разыскания по кавказской филологии.
Textes et recherches dans le domaine de la philologie caucasienne. tom 1. pp. 125. 1 *plate. Ленинград,*
1925. 4⁰.　　　　　　　　　　**Ac. 1125/228**

——Византійскій Временникъ. (Βυζαντινὰ Χρονικά).
Издаваемый … подъ редакціею В. Г. Васильевскаго

SAINT PETERSBURG *(cont.)*

и В. Э. Регеля. tom. 1–25. *Санктпетербургъ,* 1894–1928. 8⁰.   **Ac. 1125/56**

—— [New series.] том 1 (26)—. *Москва,* 1947—. 8⁰. *In progress.*   **Ac. 1125. wb/25**

—— Записки Коллегии Востоковедов при Азиатском Музее Российской Академии Наук. том 1–5. *Ленинград,* 1925–30. 8⁰.   **Ac. 1125. qb**

—— *Грузинский Филиал. See* TIFLIS.—*Academy of Sciences of the U.S.S.R.—Georgian Filial.*

—— *Институт Антропологии и Этнографии.* Советский Фольклор. Статьи и материалы. вып. 1–7. *Ленинград,* 1934–41. 8⁰.   **Ac. 1125. nba**

—— *Институт Этнографии им. Н. Н. Миклухо-Маклая.* Кавказский этнографический сборник. (Ответственный редактор М. О. Косвен.) том 1, 2, *etc. Москва,* 1955—8⁰. [*Труды Института Этнографии. Новая серия.* том 26, 46, *etc.*] *In progress.*   **Ac. 1125. nd/5**

—— *Институт Истории Материальной Культуры. See* KAPANADZE (D. G.). Грузинская нумизматика. 1955. 4⁰.   **17080. f. 4**

—— Советская археология. no. 1— *Москва, Ленинград,* 1936— 8⁰. *In progress.*   **Ac. 1125. nb/2**

—— *Институт Востоковедения. See* RUDENKO (B. T.). Грамматика грузинского языка. 1940. 8⁰. [*Труды Института Востоковедения.* no. 32.]   **17076. f. 3**

—— Грузинские рукописи Института Востоковедения. [Catalogue of the Georgian manuscripts in the Oriental Institute of the Academy of Sciences of the U.S.S.R. Compiled by R. R. Orbeli.] вып. 1 [containing descriptions of the manuscripts relating to History, Geography, Travel, Archaeology, Laws, Philosophy, Linguistics and Bibliography.] pp. 184. 30 *plates. Москва, Ленинград,* 1956. 8⁰. *In progress.*   **17080. f. 3**

—— [Another copy.]   **W. P. 7226**

—— Собрание грузинских рукописей Института Востоковедения Академии Наук СССР. [By R. R. Orbeli.] pp. 30–66. 2 *plates. Москва, Ленинград,* 1954. 8⁰. [*Ученые записки Института Востоковедения.* том 9.]   **Ac. 1125. ik/9**

—— Советское Востоковедение. том 1— *Москва, Ленинград,* 1940— 8⁰. *In progress.*   **Ac. 1125. ik/7**

—— *Институт Языкознания.* Труды Института Языкознания. том 1— *Москва,* 1952— 8⁰. *In progress.*   **Ac. 1125. sf**

—— *Кабардино-балкарский научно-исследовательский институт. See* NAL'CHIK.—*Кабардино-балкарский научно-исследовательский институт.*

—— *Яфетический Институт,* afterwards *Институт языка и мышления. See* TURCHANINOV (G. F.) and TSAGOV (M. N.). Грамматика кабардинского языка. том 1. 1940. 8⁰.   **Ac. 1125. t/4**

—— Памяти академика Н. Я. Марра, 1864–1934. [A collection of essays, edited by I. I. Meshchaninov.] pp. iv. 476. 5 *plates. Москва, Ленинград,* 1938. 8⁰.   **Ac. 1125. t/3**

—— *Яфетический сборник.* Recueil japhétique. (Редактор .... Н. Я. Марр.) вып. 4–6. *Ленинград,* 1926–30. 8⁰.   **Ac. 1125. t**

—— Язык и мышление. Le langage et la mentalité. (Редактор .... Н. Я. Марр.) вып. 1–11. *Ленинград,* 1933–48. 8⁰.   **Ac. 1125. t/2**

—— *Bibliothèque Imperiale Publique. See* below: *Императорская Публичная Библіотека.*

—— *Императорская Публичная Библіотека.* [For 'Notice sur un manuscrit géorgien de la Bibliothèque Impériale Publique':] *See* BROSSET (M.-F.)

—— Краткій каталогъ собранія грузинскихъ рукописей пріобрѣтеннаго Императорскою Публичною Библіотекою въ 1896 году. Составилъ Н. Я. Марръ. pp. 13. *С.-Петербургъ,* 1900. 8⁰.   **17031. d. 6**

—— *Императорскій,* afterwards *Государственный,*

SAINT PETERSBURG (cont.)

Эрмитажъ. Памятники эпохи Руставели. [By various authors. With illustrations, including a portrait.] pp. viii. 406. 66 *plates. Ленинград,* 1938. 8⁰.

Ac. 5583. b/65

—— *Императорское Общество Востоковѣдѣнія.* Грамматика грузинскаго языка. (Курсы кавказскихъ туземныхъ языковъ для кандидатовъ на судебныя должности Министерства Юстиціи.) Составилъ I. А. Кипшидзе. pp. 95. *С.-Петербургъ,* 1911. fol. *Lithographed from the Ms.* **Ac. 2355/2**

—— *Императорское Русское Археологическое Общество.* Записки Восточнаго Отдѣленія Императорскаго Русскаго Археологическаго Общества .... под редакціею ... Барона В. Р. Розена. томъ 1–22. *Санктпетербургъ,* 1887–1915. 8⁰. *Томъ* 22 *lacks* вып. 1 *and* 2. **Ac. 5584**

—— *Ленинградский Институт Живых Восточных Языков имени А. С. Енукидзе.* Восточные Записки. том 1. pp. 326. 1 *plate. Ленинград,* 1927. 8⁰.

Ac. 1096. d. 3

—— *Православное,* afterwards *Российское Палестинское Общество.* Православный Палестинскій Сборникъ. [With illustrations and supplements, including maps.] вып. 1–59. *С.-Петербургъ,* 1881—1911. **Ac. 2058**

—— [Continued as:] Палестинский Сборник. вып. 1(63)— *Москва, Ленинград,* 1954— 8⁰. *In progress.* **Ac. 1125. eh**

SAKHOKIA (Tʿedo Timotʿes-dze). ეგნატე ნინოშვილი. [Egnate Ninoshvili. A biographical sketch of E. Ninoshvili (Ingoroqva), the Georgian man of letters.] pp. 116–36. ტფილისი [*Tiflis,*] 1895. 8⁰. [*Moambe.* tom. 2. no. 12.] **17089. b. 1**

—— ქართული ხატოვანი სიტყვა-თქმანი. [Kʿartʿuli khatovani sitqva-tʿkʿmani. Dictionary of Georgian figurative and metaphorical expressions. Edit. by G. Chitaia.] tom. 2 [comprising letters ჱ — ჵ] and 3 [comprising letters ჯ — ჰ]. თბილისი [*Tiflis,*] 1954–55. 8⁰. *Note: The first volume was published in 1950.* **17076. i. 6**

—— Les Proverbes géorgiens. [Translated and arranged, by Tʿ. Sakhokia.] Extrait de la Revue des Traditions Populaires. pp. 34. *Paris,* 1903. 8⁰.

17076. d. 1

SALAMANES, *Saint.* [For 'La Passion géorgienne des S. S. Théodore ... et Salamanes':] *See* Theodore, *Saint and Martyr, of Pella.*

SALIA (Kalistrate Zosimes-dze). [Editor of journal 'Bedi Kʿartʿlisa'.] *See* Periodical Publications.—*Paris.*

SAMTʿAVRO. [For Catalogue of the gems discovered in the Samtʿavro burial ground, compiled by M. N. Lortʿkʿipʿanidze:] *See* Tiflis.—*Museum of Georgia.*

SAMTSKHE. [For 'Samtskhis khurotʿmodzghvreba', a study of the architecture of Samtskhe:] *See* Beridze (V. V.)

—— [For 'Khalkuri meskhuri lekʿsebi':] *See* Gvaramadze (K.) called Meskhi.

—— [For 'К грузинским надписям из Месхии':] *See* Marr (N. Y.)

SAMUKASHVILI (Nino). [Trans. 'Latviuri zghaprebi'.] *See* Latvian Tales.

SANAKOEV (Pavel Alekseevich). ქართულ-ოსური ლექსიკონი. [Kʿartʿul-osuri lekʿsikoni. Georgian-Ossete dictionary.] Гуырдзиаг-ирон дзырдуат. (Грузинско-осетинский словарь.) pp. 483. *Сталинир,* 1955. 8⁰. **17076. h. 12**

SAORBISI. [For a description of the ancient church at Saorbisi, with reproductions of inscriptions:] *See* Chubinashvili (G. N.)

SAQVARELIDZE (Tʿamar Nikolozis-asuli). [Joint author of 'Бронзы древней Грузии'.] *See* Tʿavadze (Pʿ. N.) and Saqvarelidze (Tʿ. N.)

SARAJISHVILI (Alekʿsandre). [Joint edit. of 'Visramiani'.] *See* Sargis, *of Tʿmogvi.*

SARAJISHVILI (cont.)

—— "ვეფხის-ტყაოსნის" ყალბი ადგილები. ["Vep'khis-tqaosnis" qalbi adgilebi. Spurious passages in "The Man in the Panther's Skin". A critical study of Shot'a Rust'aveli's epic.] 2 pt. pp. 1–20; 1–30. ტფილისი [*Tiflis,*] 1895. 8⁰. [*Moambe.* tom. 2. no. 11, 12.]   **17089. b. 1**

SARGIS, *of T'mogvi.* The Georgian Version of the Story of the Loves of Vis and Ramīn. [Trans., with notes,] by Oliver Wardrop. [Selected extracts only.] pp. 493–507. *London,* 1902. 8⁰. [*Journal of the Royal Asiatic Society* for 1902.]   **R. Ac. 8820/3**

—— ვისრამიანი. [Visramiani. A romance imitated from the Persian tale of the loves of Vīs and Rāmīn, by Gurgānī. Edited by I. Tchavtchavadze, A. Sarajishvili and P. Umikashvili.] pp. xiii. 477, 6. ტფილისი [*Tiflis,*] 1884. 8⁰.   **17076. c. 4**

—— Visramiani. The Story of the Loves of Vis and Ramin. A romance of Ancient Persia. Translated from the Georgian version by Oliver Wardrop. pp. xii. 409. *London,* 1914. 8⁰. [*Royal Asiatic Society.—Oriental Translation Fund.* New series. vol. 23.]   **14003. bb. 18**

SARGISEAN (NERSĒS). [For 'Inscriptions .... recueillies par le Père Nersès Sargisian':] *See* BROSSET (M.-F.)

—— [For 'Notice concernant les inscriptions géorgiennes recueillies par le P. Nersès Sargisian':] *See* BROSSET (M.-F.)

SATUNIN (KONSTANTIN ALEKSANDROVICH). Млекопитающие кавказского края. (Mammalia Caucasica.) [Illustrated.] tom. 2. pp. ii. 223, iii. ტფილისი [*Tiflis,*] 1920. 8⁰. [*Sak'art'velos muzeumis shromebi.* no. 2.]   **17080. b. 1**

SAVVA, *the Monk* [*Prince* SULKHAN ORBELIANI]. [*Life.*] *See* BARAMIDZE (A. G.)

—— [For 'Notice sur le dictionnaire géorgien de Soulkhan Saba Orbéliani':] *See* BROSSET (M.-F.)

—— [For 'Саба Орбеліани и его грузинскій "Лексиконъ"':] *See* GAMREKELI (N.)

—— [For '*Wisdom and lies:* variations on a Georgian literary theme', being a study of the 'Book of Wisdom and Lies' by S.-S. Orbeliani:] *See* LANG (D. M.)

—— [For 'Sulkhan-Saba Orbelianis literaturuli moghvadseobidan':] *See* LOLASHVILI (I. A.)

—— [For French rendering of selected tales by, included in 'Contes et légendes du Caucase':] *See* MOURIER (J.)

—— [For a supplement to S.-S. Orbeliani's Georgian lexicon:] *See* TCHQONIA (I. M.)

—— [For 'Dsigni "Sibrdzne sitsruisa" da k'art'uli khalkhuri makhvilsitqvaoba':] *See* TSANAVA (A. B.)

—— The Book of Wisdom and Fiction. Selections. Translated and adapted for the IX–Xth forms of Georgian schools by J. Mchedlishvili [Mtchedlishvili] and I. Petrova. [Illustrated.] pp. 97. *Tbilisi,* 1959. 12⁰.   **17076. b. 45**

—— The Book of Wisdom and Lies. [Translated, with notes, by J. O. Wardrop.] pp. xvi. 256. *London,* 1894. 8⁰. *Printed by William Morris at the Kelmscott Press.*   **C. 43. e. 18**

—— Книга мудрости и лжи. Грузинскія басни и сказки XVII.–XVIII. стол. Саввы-Сулхана Орбеліани. Переводъ и объясненія А. Цагарели. pp. xix. 217. *Санктпетербургъ,* 1878. 8⁰.   **12430. h. 25**

—— О мудрости вымысла. (Перевод Елены Гогоберидзе.) pp. 235. *Москва,* 1951. 8⁰.   **12431. ppp. 42**

—— სულხან-საბა ორბელიანი, 1658–1958 : საიუბილეო კრებული. [Sulkhan-Saba Orbeliani, 1658–1958 : saiubileo krebuli. A collection of essays by various hands on aspects of the life and literary work of Sulkhan-Saba Orbeliani, published in commemoration of the third centenary of his birth. Edit. by a committee of scholars of the Georgian Academy of Sciences.] pp. 291. თბილისი [*Tiflis,*] 1959. 8⁰.   **17076. f. 32**

—— თხზულებანი ოთხ ტომად. [T'khzulebani

ot'kh tomad. Collected works in four volumes. Edited by S. I. Qubaneishvili and R. Baramidze. With plates, including a portrait.] tom. I— თბილისი [*Tiflis,*] 1959— 8⁰. *In progress.*

17076. b. 47

SAYEADEANÇ (Arut'in) called Sayeat'-Nōva. [For selected poems, in Russian translation:] *See* Gol'tsev (V. V.) and Chik'ovani (S. I.). Поэзия Грузии. 1949. 4⁰.   **17075. dd. 1**

—— [*Biography.*] *See* Melik'set'-Begi (L. M.)

SAYEAT'-NŌVA, *pseud. See* Sayeadeanç (A.)

SCHIEFNER (Franz Anton von). [*Obituary.*] *See* Tsagareli (A. A.)

—— Ausführlicher Bericht über des Generals Baron Peter von Uslar Abchasische Studien. pp. viii. 62. *St.-Petersburg,* 1863. 4⁰. [*Mémoires de l'Académie Impériale des Sciences.* sér. 7. tom. 6. no. 12.]   **Ac. 1125/3**

—— Ausführlicher Bericht über Baron P. v. Uslar's Awarische Studien. pp. viii. 180. *St.-Pétersbourg,* 1872. 4⁰. [*Mémoires de l'Académie Impériale des Sciences.* sér. 7. tom. 18. no. 6.]   **Ac. 1125/3**

—— Ausführlicher Bericht über Baron P. v. Uslar's Hürkanische Studien. pp. iv. 200. *St.-Pétersbourg,* 1871. 4⁰. [*Mémoires de l'Académie Impériale des Sciences.* sér. 7. tom. 17. no. 8.]   **Ac. 1125/3**

—— Ausführlicher Bericht über Baron P. v. Uslar's Kasikumükische Studien. pp. viii. 136. *St. Petersburg,* 1866. 4⁰. [*Mémoires de l'Académie Impériale des Sciences.* sér. 7. tom. 10. no. 12.]   **Ac. 1125/3**

—— Ausführlicher Bericht über Baron P. v. Uslar's Kürinische Studien. pp. iv. 256. *St.-Pétersbourg,* 1873. 4⁰. [*Mémoires de l'Académie Impériale des Sciences.* sér. 7. tom. 20. no. 2.]   **Ac. 1125/3**

—— Awarische Texte. pp. l. 113. *St.-Petersburg,* 1873. 4⁰. [*Mémoires de l'Académie Impériale des Sciences.* sér. 7. tom. 19. no. 6.]   **Ac. 1125/3**

—— Kurze Charakteristik der Thusch-Sprache. pp. 402–26. *St.-Pétersbourg,* 1854. 8⁰. [*Mélanges Asiatiques de l'Académie des Sciences.* tom. 2.]

Ac. 1125/11

—— Tschetschenzische Studien. pp. viii. 72. *St.-Petersburg,* 1864. 4⁰. [*Mémoires de l'Académie Impériale des Sciences.* sér. 7. tom. 7. no. 5.] **Ac. 1125/3**

—— Versuch über das Awarische. pp. 54. *St. Petersburg,* 1862. 4⁰. [*Mémoires de l'Académie Impériale des Sciences.* sér. 7. tom. 5. no. 8.] **Ac. 1125/3**

—— Versuch über die Sprache der Uden. pp. 110. *St. Petersburg,* 1863. 4⁰. [*Mémoires de l'Académie Impériale des Sciences.* sér. 7. tom. 6. no. 8.]

Ac. 1125/3

—— Versuch über die Thusch-Sprache oder die khistische Mundart in Thuschetien. pp. I–160. *St.-Pétersbourg,* 1859. 4⁰. [*Mémoires de l'Académie des Sciences.* 6ᵐᵉ *série.—Sciences Politiques.* tom. 9.]

Ac. 1125/2

SCHMERLING (Renée Oskarovna). ქართულ ხელნაწერთა მორთულობის ნიმუშები. [K'ar-t'ul khelnadsert'a mort'ulobis nimushebi. Specimens of Georgian manuscript illuminations. Edit. by G. Chubinashvili. Illustrated.] (Образцы декоративного убранства грузинских рукописей. Échantillons des enluminures des manuscrits géorgiens. Album de 32 planches dont 11 en couleurs. Introduction et notice des planches par Renée Schmerling.) *Georg. & Russ.* pp. 76. 32 *plates.* ტფილისი [*Tiflis,*] 1940. 4⁰.   **17080. g. 4**

SCHMIDT (Carl). Eine Benutzung des Testamentum Domini nostri Jesu Christi. [An analysis of one of the sources of the Georgian recension of the apocryphal legend of Joseph of Arimathea.] pp. 263–67. *Leipzig,* 1921. 8⁰. [*Harnack-Ehrung: Beiträge zur Kirchengeschichte... Adolf von Harnack zu seinem siebzigsten Geburtstage dargebracht.*]

04530. i. 7

SCHOTA RUSTAWELI. *See* Rust'aveli (Shot'a).

SCHULTZE (KARL). [Trans. life and martyrdom of St. Abo of Tiflis, by Ioane Sabanisdze.] *See* SABANISDZE (I.)

SERAPION, *Saint, of Zarzma.* [*Life.*] *See* PEETERS (P.). Histoires monastiques géorgiennes. 1917–19. 8⁰.　　　　　　　　　　　　　**2002. f**

SERDYUCHENKO (GEORGY PETROVICH). [For Russian-Abaza dictionary, with a study of the Abaza language by G. P. Serdyuchenko:] *See* CHERKESSK.—*Cherkessky Nauchno-Issledovatel'sky Institut.*

—— Языки Северного Кавказа и Дагестана. Сборник лингвистических исследований. Под редакцией ... Г. П. Сердюченко. (вып. 2. Под редакцией И. И. Мещанинова и Г. П. Сердюченко.) [With summaries in German.] 2 вып. *Москва, Ленинград,* 1935–49. 8⁰.　　　　　　　　　　　　　**Ac. 9890**

SEVAST'YANOV (PETR IVANOVICH). [For 'Explication de quelques inscriptions, photographiées par M. Sévastianof':] *See* BROSSET (M.-F.)

SEVERIAN, *Bishop of Gabala.* Un fragment géorgien de l'homélie IX de Sévérien de Gabala. [Edit., with Latin trans., by] G. Garitte. pp. 97–102. *Louvain,* 1953. 8⁰. [*Le Muséon.* tom. 66.]　　　　　　　　　　　　　**P. P. 4453**

SEVEROV (NIKOLAI PAVLOVICH) and **CHUBINASHVILI** (GIORGI NIKOLOZIS-DZE). Кумурдо и Никорцминда. pp. 24. 28 *plates. Москва,* 1947. fol. [*Памятники грузинской архитектуры.* no.1.]　　　　　　　　　　　　　**Ac. 4828/2**

SEXTUS, *Pythagoraeus.* Vingt-deux "Sentences de Sextus" en géorgien. [Edit. with Latin trans. by G. Garitte.] pp. 355–63. 2 *plates. Louvain,* 1959. 8⁰. [*Le Muséon.* tom. 72.]　　　　　　　　　　　　　**P. P. 4453**

SHADURI (VANO). [For introductory essay by V. Shaduri to selected writings of Pushkin:] *See* PUSHKIN (A. S.)

—— Декабристская литература и грузинская общественность. pp. 577. 12 *plates. Тбилиси,* 1958. 8⁰.　　　　　　　　　　　　　**17076. f. 23**

SHAHNAVAZ I, *King of Georgia. See* VAKHTANG V.

SHAHSEVANIDZE (G.). [Trans. 'Prak'tikis shesakheb':] *See* MAO (TSÊ-TUNG).

SHAKSPERE (WILLIAM). [For a study of A. D. Matchavariani's ballet on the theme of Othello:] *See* ORJONIKIDZE (G. S.)

—— [*Biography.*] *See* QIASASHVILI (N. A.)

—— [For 'K'art'uli Shek'spiriana':] *See* QIASASHVILI (N. A.)

—— იულიოს კეისარი. [Iulios Keisari. Julius Caesar. Translated into Georgian by I. Machabeli.] pt. 1 and 2. ტფილისი [*Tiflis,*] 1896. 8⁰. [*Moambe.* tom. 3. no. 1, 2.]　　　　　　　　　　　　　**17089. b. 1**

—— რიჩარდ მესამე. [Richard Mesame. The Tragedy of Richard the Third, translated into Georgian by I. Machabeli.] pp. 146. ტფილისი [*Tiflis,*] 1893. 8⁰.　　　　　　　　　　　　　**17075. d. 7**

—— სონეტები. [Sonetebi.] (Shakespeare's Sonnets. Translated into Georgian by Givi Gachechiladze.) [With notes and a biographical sketch.] pp. 192. თბილისი [*Tiflis,*] 1952. 8⁰.　**17076. d. 13**

—— ტრაგედიები. (თხზულებანი.) [Tragediebi. (T'khzulebani.) The Tragedies of Shakspere, trans. into Georgian by Ivane Machabeli, and edit. by G. Gachechiladze, in three vols.; followed by the other works of Shakspere, trans. by various hands and edit. by G. Gachechiladze. With portraits.] tom. 1–5, *etc.* თბილისი [*Tiflis,*] 1953— 8⁰. *In progress.*　　　　　　　　　　　　　**17075. d. 40**

SHAMS AL-DĪN AISKHANOV. Поэты Чечено-Ингушетии. [Part composed by Sh. Aiskhanov, the rest collected by him. Translated by Z. Shishova and others. With portraits of the authors.] pp. 153, 7. *Москва,* 1935. 8⁰.　**17077. a. 5**

SHANIDZE (AKAKI GABRIELIS-DZE). [Joint edit. of 'Balavarianis k'art'uli redak'tsiebi'.] *See* BARLAAM, *Saint, of India.*

SHANIDZE *(cont.)*

—— [For 'Le fragment géorgien de l'Évangile de Thomas', trans. into Latin from the edition by A. G. Shanidze:] *See* BIBLE.—New Testament.—*Apocrypha.*

—— [Joint edit. of Georgian version of the Shāhnāmeh.] *See* ḤASAN (ABU'L-ḲāSIM) called FIRDAUSĪ, *Ṭūsī.*

—— [Edit. concordance and dictionary to the Georgian Gospels.] *See* IMNAISHVILI (I. B.)

—— [Edit. Sinai polycephalon of A. D. 864.] *See* LITURGIES.—Greek Rite.—*Lectionaries.*

—— [Joint edit. of 'Vep'khis tqaosani'.] *See* RUST'AVELI (SHOT'A).

—— [Joint edit. of selected works of Vazha-P'shavela.] *See* VAZHA-P'SHAVELA, *pseud.*

—— Библіографія: отдѣльныя изданія и статьи на грузинскомъ языкѣ, появившіяся въ 1911–1912 гг. pp. 253–62. С.-Петербургъ, 1913. 4⁰. [*Христіанскій Востокъ.* томъ 2. вып. 2.]   **Ac. 1125/105**

—— ძველი ქართულის ქრესტომათია ლექსიკონითურთ. I. ქრესტომათია. [Dzveli k'art'ulis k'restomat'ia lek'sikonit'urt'. I. K'restomat'ia. Chrestomathy of Old Georgian, with a glossary. pt. I. Containing the text material.] pp. xxiii. 112. ტფილისი [*Tiflis,*] 1935. 8⁰. [*Caucasus Polyglottus.* tom. I.]   **17076. g. 1**

—— Глагольные категории акта и контакта на примерах грузинского языка. pp. 165–72. *Москва,* 1946. 8⁰. [*Известия Академии Наук СССР. Classe des Sciences Littéraires et Linguistiques.* tom. 5. no. 2.]   **Ac. 1125/44 (11)**

—— Издание древнегрузинских рукописей. pp. 255–58. *Москва,* 1945. 8⁰. [*Известия Академии Наук СССР. Classe des Sciences Littéraires et Linguistiques.* tom. 4. no. 6.]   **Ac. 1125/44 (11)**

—— ქართული ენის გრამატიკა. ნაწილი I : მორფოლოგია, *etc.* (ნაწილი II : სინტაქსი, *etc.*) [K'art'uli enis gramatika. Nadsili I : morp'ologia. (Nadsili II : sintak'si.) Grammar of the Georgian language. pt. I: Morphology. (pt. II: Syntax.) Intended for use in Georgian State Schools.] 2 pt. თბილისი [*Tiflis,*] 1955. 8⁰.   **17076. f. 15**

—— ქართული ენის სტრუქტურისა და ისტორიის საკითხები. I. [K'art'uli enis struk'turisa da istoriis sakit'khebi. tom. I. Questions concerning the structure and history of the Georgian language. tom. I. Georgian and Russian texts.] (Вопросы структуры и истории грузинского языка.) pp. vii. 379. თბილისი [*Tiflis,*] 1957. 8⁰. [*T'khzulebani.* tom. I, *etc.*] *In progress.*   **17073. a. 7**

—— Отчетъ о лѣтней командировкѣ 1913 г. въ Душетскій и Тіонетскій уѣзды Тифлисской губерніи. pp. 1069–74. С.-Петербургъ, 1913. 8⁰. [*Извѣстія Акад. Наукъ.* ser. 7. tom. 7.]   **Ac. 1125/44**

—— თხზულებანი. [T'khzulebani. Collected works on Georgian linguistic problems.] tom. I— თბილისი. [*Tiflis,*] 1957— 8⁰. *In progress.*   **17073. a. 7**

—— ვეფხის-ტყაოსნის სიმფონია. [Vep'khis-tqaosnis simp'onia. A glossary and concordance to the epic poem by Rust'aveli, 'The Man in the Panther's Skin', compiled under the direction of A. G. Shanidze.] (Симфония к поэме Ш. Руствели "Витязь в тигровой шкуре".) pp. 037.428,3. თბილისი [*Tiflis,*] 1956. 4⁰. [*Dzveli k'art'uli enis kat'edris shromebi.* no. 3.]   **17076. h. 13**

—— *and others.* ძველი ქართული ლიტერატურა. ქრესტომათია სამშუალო სკოლის VIII კლასისათვის. [Dzveli k'art'uli literatura. K'restomat'ia sashualo skolis VIII klasisat'vis. Ancient Georgian literature. Chrestomathy for the 8th class of Middle Schools. Compiled by A.G. Shanidze, A. G. Baramidze and I. V. Abuladze under the editorship of A. G. Shanidze. Illustrated. 15th edition.] pp. 260. თბილისი [*Tiflis,*] 1956. 8⁰.   **17076. h. 8**

SHANSHIASHVILI (SANDRO ILIAS-DZE). Стихи и поэмы. Перевод с грузинского. pp. 119. *Тбилиси,* 1949. 8⁰.   **11588. b. 30**

SHAP'IRO (IOSIF BORISOVICH) *and others.* თბილისის ღრმად მოხუცებული ადამიანები. [T'bilisis ghrmad mokhutsebuli adamianebi. The oldest inhabitants of Tiflis. A series of studies, by I. B. Shap'iro, G. Z. P'itskhelauri and O. E. Gagua. Illustrated.] pp. 143, 2. თბილისი [*Tiflis*,] 1956. 8⁰.

    17075. e. 31

SHARADZENIDZE (T'INAT'IN SIMONIS-ASULI). ენათა კლასიფიკაციის პრინციპები. [Enat'a klasip'ikatsiis printsipebi. Principles of the classification of languages.] (Классификации языков и их принципы.) [Georgian text with summary in Russian.] pp. 540, 4. თბილისი [*Tiflis*,] 1958. 8⁰.   **17076. f. 29**

SHARASHIDZE (K'RISTINE GIORGIS-ASULI). [Joint compiler of Catalogue of Georgian manuscripts in the Georgian State Museum.] *See* TIFLIS.—*Museum of Georgia.*

—— [Joint author of Guide to the collections of ancient manuscripts in the Georgian State Museum.] *See* TIFLIS.—*Museum of Georgia.*

SHATBERASHVILI (GIORGI IVANES-DZE). მოთხრობები. [Mot'khrobebi. Collected short stories.] pp. 300. თბილისი [*Tiflis*,] 1954. 8⁰.   **17076. b. 6**

SHATBERD CODEX. [For 'Die unter Hippolyts Namen überlieferte Schrift Ueber den Glauben', trans. from the Georgian version in the Shatberd Codex and edit. by G. N. Bonwetsch:] *See* HIPPOLYTUS, *Saint, of Rome.*

SHAUMYAN (RAFAEL M.). Грамматический очерк агульского языка, с текстами и словарем. [Edit. by K. D. Dondua, under the general editorship of I. I. Meshchaninov. With a map.] pp. 198. 10 *plates*. Москва, Ленинград, 1941. 8⁰. [*Труды Института Языка и Мышления*. no. 15.]

    Ac. 1125. fd. (5.)

—— Предварительное сообщение об агульском языке. pp. 203–44. Москва, Ленинград, 1935. 8⁰. [*Язык и мышление*. вып. 3–4.]   **Ac. 1125. t/2**

—— Следы грамматических классов (родов) в агульском языке. pp. 219–26. Москва, Ленинград, 1936. 8⁰. [*Язык и мышление*. вып. 6–7.]   **Ac. 1125. t/2**

—— Яфетические языки "шах-дагской подгруппы". pp. 163–94. Москва, Ленинград, 1940. 8⁰. [*Язык и мышление*. вып. 10.]   **Ac. 1125. t/2**

SHAVT'ELI (IOVANE). [For 'Древнегрузинскіе одописцы' including Shavt'eli's ode 'Abdulmesia':] *See* MARR (N. Y.)

—— თამარ მეფისა და მეუღლისა მისისა დავით მეფის შესხმა. [T'amar mep'isa da meughlisa misisa Davit' mep'is sheskhma. Eulogy of Queen T'amar and her consort King David. Edit. by Z. E. Tchitchinadze.] pp. 63. თფილისი [*Tiflis*,] 1883. 12⁰. [*K'art'veli klasikebi*. no. 2.] *Note: This ode is now thought to have been written in praise of King David the Builder.*   **17075. d. 5. (1.)**

SHENGELAIA (DEMNA). [Edit. selected works by Ilia Tchavtchavadze.] *See* TCHAVTCHAVADZE (I. G.) *Prince.*

SHENGELAIA (LEON MIKHEILIS-DZE). *See* K'IACHELI (L.) *pseud.*

SHERVINSKY (SERGEI VASIL'EVICH). [Edit. 'Великий Моурави':] *See* JOSEPH [Ioseb Saakadze] *Bishop of Tiflis.*

SHILLING (EVGENY MIKHAILOVICH). Кубачинцы и их культура. Историко-этнографические этюды. [Illustrated.] pp. 222. 5 *plates*. Москва, Ленинград, 1949. 8⁰. [*Труды Института Этнографии*. Новая серия. том 8.]   **Ac. 1125. nd/5**

SHIO-MGHVIME, *Monastery.* [For 'Сигель грузинскаго царя Баграта IV, 1027–1072', granted to the Mghvime Monastery:] *See* T'AQAISHVILI (E. S.)

—— [For 'Рельефы Шиомгвиме и их место в развитии грузинской средневековой скульптуры':] *See* VOL'SKAYA (A. I.)

SHISHMAREV (VLADIMIR FEDOROVICH). Шота Руставели. Несколько параллелей и аналогий. pp. 29–47. Москва, Ленинград, 1938. 8⁰. [*Известия Академии Наук СССР. Classe des Sciences Sociales*. no. 3.]

    Ac. 1125/44 (9)

SHISHOVA (Zinaida Konstantinovna) *and others*. [Russian translation of 'Поэты Чечено-Ингушетии'.] *See* Shams al-Din Aiskhanov.

SHOGENTSUKOV (Adam Ogurlievich). [Edit. Russian-Kabardo-Circassian dictionary.] *See* Kardanov (B. M.) and Bichoev (A. T.)

—— Восхождение. Стихи. Перевод с кабардинского. pp. 142. *Москва*, 1959. 12⁰.   **17075. c. 38**

SHOGENTSUKOV ('Alī Askhadovich). Избранное. Перевод с кабардинского. [With a portrait.] pp. 310. *Москва*, 1957. 8⁰.   **11589. aa. 45**

—— Поэмы. Перевод с кабардинского Семена Липкина. [With a portrait.] pp. 170. [*Ленинград*,] 1949. 8⁰.   **11588. ee. 12**

—— Поэмы и стихотворения. Перевод с кабардинского. [With a portrait.] pp. 199. *Москва*, 1950. 8⁰.   **011586. n. 71**

—— *and others*. Заря над Эльбрусом. Кабардинские повести и рассказы. (Авторизованные переводы с кабардинского.) [With an introduction by V. Goffenshefer.] pp. 403, 5. *Москва*, 1957. 8⁰.   **17076. b. 32**

SHORA-BEKMURZIN-NOGMOV. Die Sagen und Lieder des Tscherkessen-Volks, gesammelt vom Kabardiner Schora-Bekmursin-Nogmow, bearbeitet und mit einer Vorrede versehen von Adolf Bergé. pp. xxxi. 144. *Leipzig*, 1866. 8⁰.   **12431. f. 10**

SHOT'A, *of Rust'avi*. *See* Rust'aveli (Shot'a).

SHTAIN (Moisei Grigorievich). [Trans. comedy 'Стрекоза'.] *See* Barat'ashvili (M.)

SHUSHANIK, *Saint and Martyr*. [For 'Sainte Šoušanik, martyre en Arméno-Géorgie':] *See* Peeters (P.)

SIKHARULIDZE (K'senia Alek'sis-asuli). [Introduction to 'P'shav-Khevsuruli poezia'.] *See* Khornauli (I. G.)

SIMEON, *Metaphrastes*. [For 'Iоаннъ Ксифилинъ, продолжатель Симеона Метафраста':] *See* Kekelidze (K. S.)

SIMEON, *Saint, of Mons Admirabilis*. [For 'Историко-агиографическіе отрывки', containing extraits from the life of Simeon of Mons Admirabilis:] *See* Kekelidze (K. S.)

SIMEON, *Stylites, Saint*. Vies géorgiennes [made from the Syriac] de S. Syméon Stylite, l'Ancien, et de S. Éphrem. Éditées (traduites [into Latin]) par Gérard Garitte. 2 tom. pp. x. 124, 1; ii. 87, 1. *Louvain*, 1957. 8⁰. [*Corpus Scriptorum Christianorum Orientalium*. vol. 171–172 = Scriptores Iberici. tom. 7–8.]   **14005. a**

SIMON, *King of Georgia*. [*Biography*.] *See* Karitchashvili (D. G.)

SINAI, *Mount*. [For 'Greek script and Georgian scribes on Mt. Sinai':] *See* Blake (R. P.)

—— [For 'Catalogue des manuscrits géorgiens littéraires du Mont Sinaï':] *See* Catharine, *Saint, of Alexandria*.—Convent of, on Mount Sinai.

—— [For 'Описание грузинских рукописей синайского монастыря':] *See* Catharine, *Saint, of Alexandria*.—Convent of, on Mount Sinai.

—— [For 'Le calendrier palestino-géorgien du Sinaiticus 34':] *See* Liturgies.—Greek Rite.—*Calendar*.

—— [For 'Sinuri mravalt'avi 864 dslisa':] *See* Liturgies.—Greek Rite.—*Lectionaries*.

—— [For 'Памятники грузинской старины . . . . на Синаѣ':] *See* Tsagareli (A. A.)

SJOEGREN (Andreas Johan). [For 'Рукописные материалы акад. Шёгрена по черкесским языкам':] *See* Turchaninov (G. F.)

—— Rapport sur un ouvrage manuscrit intitulé: "Словарь Русско-черкесскій". pp. 165–76. *St.-*

Pétersbourg, 1848. 4⁰. [*Bulletin Historico-Philolo-gique de l'Académie des Sciences.* tom. 4.]

Ac. 1125/7

SJÖGREN (JOHAN ANDREAS). *See* SJOEGREN (A. J.)

SKAMKOCHAISHVILI (SHALVA) and **MELUA** (MIRIAN). ქართული ლექსიკონი. [K'art'uli lek'si-koni.] Le dictionnaire géorgien. pp. 130. პარიზი [*Paris*,] 1948. 4⁰.   **17076. f. 7**

SKOSYREV (PETR). [Joint edit. of 'Тамарджвеба'.] *See* ABASHELI (A. B.) *and others.*

SMEDT (CHARLES DE). [Joint edit. of 'Analecta Bollandiana'.] *See* BRUSSELS.—*Société des Bollandistes.*

SOCIALIST-FEDERALIST PARTY. *See* GEORGIA.—*Socialist-Federalist Revolutionary Party.*

SOLOMON II, *King of Imeret'i.* [For 'Variétés géorgiennes: ... Tombeau et épitaphe du roi Solomon II, d'Iméreth, à Trébisonde':] *See* BROSSET (M.-F.)

—— მეფე სოლომონ მეორის დროს წერილები. [Mep'e Solomon meoris drois dserilebi. Letters of the time of King Solomon II, mainly concerning the Russian annexation of Imeret'i.] pp. 84–100. ტფილისი [*Tiflis*,] 1896. 8⁰. [*Moambe.* tom. 3. no. 4.]   **17089. b. 1**

SOLOMON, *King of Israel.* [For Georgian version of the commentary of St. Hippolytus on the Song of Solomon:] *See* HIPPOLYTUS, *Saint, of Rome.*

SONG OF SONGS. *See* BIBLE.—Old Testament. —*Song of Solomon.*

SOPHRONIUS, *Saint, Patriarch of Jerusalem.* [Author of sketches of lives of the Evangelists.] *See* BIBLE.—New Testament.

SOVIET UNION.—*Communist Party. See* RUSSIA. — *Российская Коммунистическая Партия.*

SPEUSIPPUS, ELEUSIPPUS and **MELEU-SIPPUS,** *Saints and Martyrs, of Cappadocia.* Дѣянія святыхъ близнецовъ мучениковъ Спевсипа, Еласипа и Меласипа. [Georgian text of the Acts of Saints Speusippus, Eleusippus and Meleusippus, edited with Russian translation and commentary by N. Y. Marr.] pp. 285–344. С.-Петербургъ, 1907. 8⁰. [*Записки Восточнаго Отдѣленія Имп. Русскаго Археологическаго Общества.* томъ 17.]   **Ac. 5584**

STALIN (IOSIF VISSARIONOVICH). [For 'Dideba Stalins', a collection of poems in honour of Stalin:] *See* ABASHELI (A. B.) *and others.*

—— [For 'Великому Сталину', a collection of poems in honour of Stalin:] *See* ABASHELI (A. B.) *and others.*

—— [*Biography.*] *See* ALEKSANDROV (G. F.), *and others.*

—— [For 'Сталин. Детство и отрочество. Эпопея':] *See* LEONIDZE (G. N.)

—— ანარქიზმი თუ სოციალიზმი? [Anark'izmi t'u sotsializmi? Anarchism or socialism? Trans. from the collected works of Stalin, vol. 1.] pp. 163. [თბილისი. *Tiflis*,] 1951. 8⁰.   **17075. f. 11**

—— დიალექტიკური და ისტორიული მატერია-ლიზმის შესახებ. [Dialek'tikuri da istoriuli ma-terializmis shesakheb. On dialectical and historical materialism. Trans. from the 11th edition of the volume 'Questions of Leninism', 1951.] pp. 100. [თბილისი. *Tiflis*,] 1951. 8⁰.   **17075. f.10**

—— საანგარიშო მოხსენება პარტიის XVIII ყრილობაზე საკავშირო к. п. (б.) ცენტრალური კომიტეტის მუშაობის შესახებ. [Saangarisho mokhseneba partiis XVIII qrilobaze sakavshiro k.p.(b) tsentraluri komitetis mushaobis shesakheb. Report delivered at the 18th Congress of the Party on the work of the Central Committee of the Communist Party of the Soviet Union. Trans. from the 11th edition of the volume 'Questions of Leninism', 1951.] pp. 172. 1 *plate.* [თბილისი. *Tiflis*,] 1952. 8⁰.   **17075. f. 12**

STALIN *(cont.)*

—— სიტყვა პარტიის XIX ყრილობაზე, 14 ოქ-ტომბერი, 1952 წ. [Sitqva partiis XIX qrilobaze, 14 ok'tomberi, 1952 ds. Speech at the 19th Party Congress, October 14th, 1952. Trans. from the Russian. With a portrait.] pp. 14. თბილისი [*Tiflis,*] 1952. 8⁰.   **17075. f. 8 (3.)**

—— სოციალიზმის ეკონომიკური პრობლემები სსრ კავშირში. [Sotsializmis ekonomikuri problemebi SSR Kavshirshi. Economic problems of Socialism in the U.S.S.R.] pp. 102. [თბილისი. *Tiflis,*] 1953. 8⁰.   **17075. f. 8 (5)**

STAL'SKY (SULAIMĀN). Избранные песни и стихи. [Selected songs and poems. Translated from the Lezghian by various hands, and edited by Efendi Kapiev, with a preface by P. Pavlenko.] pp. 105, 3. 1 *plate.* Москва, 1938. 12⁰.   **17075. d. 35**

STAROSTIN (A.). [Trans. 'Восстание в Гурии. Исторический роман'.] *See* NINOSHVILI (E.) *pseud.*

STEGENSEK (AUGUSTIN). Neuere russische Arbeiten zur armenisch-georgischen Philologie. pp. 373–78. Rom, 1901. 8⁰. [*Oriens Christianus.* Jahrg. 1.]   **Ac. 2002. b**

STEIN (ERNST EDUARD AUREL). [For review of E. Stein's 'Histoire du Bas-Empire. Tome II, De la disparition de l'Empire d'Occident à la mort de Justinien (476–565)', with special reference to Byzantine policy in Georgia:] *See* TOUMANOFF (C. L.) *Prince.*

STEIN (MOISEI GRIGORIEVICH). *See* SHTAIN (M. G.)

STEPANOVA (K.). [Joint edit. of essay on Rust'aveli's poem 'Vep'khis-tqaosani'.] *See* TSERET'ELI (A. R.) *Prince.*

STEPHEN, *Laurae S. Sabae Monachus,* called THAUMATURGUS. Un extrait géorgien de la Vie d'Étienne le Sabaïte. [Edit., with Latin trans., by] G. Garitte, pp. 71–92. *Louvain*, 1954. 8⁰. [*Le Muséon.* tom. 67].   **P. P. 4453**

STESHENKO-KUFTINA (VALENTINA KONSTANTINOVNA). Древнейшие инструментальные основы грузинской народной музыки. I. Флейта Пана. Les plus anciens fondements instrumentaux de la musique populaire géorgienne. I. La flûte de Pan. [Russian text with summary in French. With musical notations, and illustrations.] pp. xvi. 282. 16 *plates.* Тбилиси, 1936. 8⁰.   **Ac. 1128. db/2**

STEVENSON (ROBERT HORNE). [Trans. 'Amiran-Darejaniani'.] *See* MOSES, *of Khoni.*

STOCKHOLM.—*Estonian Theological Society in Exile.* Papers of the Estonian Theological Society in Exile. *Stockholm*, 1951–. 8⁰. *In progress.*

                        754. bbb. 11

STRATIG (ANTIOKH). *See* ANTIOCHUS, *Laurœ S. Sabœ Monachus.*

STURUA (MIKHEIL). [Edit. 'Chveni drosha'.] *See* PERIODICAL PUBLICATIONS.—*Paris.*

STURUA (NIKOLOZ IVANES-DZE) *and others.* თბილისის რევოლუციური წარსული. [T'bilisis revolutsiuri dsarsuli. A history of revolutionary movements in the city of Tiflis.] (Революционное прошлое Тбилиси.) pp. 275. 2 *plates.* თბილისი [*Tiflis,*] 1959. 8⁰.   **17075. ee. 11**

SUJUNA. [For an archaeological study of the ancient church at Sujuna:] *See* T'AQAISHVILI (E. S.)

SUKHUMI.—*Abkhazian Linguistic, Literary and Historical Institute.* დ. გულიას სახელობის აფხა-ზეთის ენის, ლიტერატურის და ისტორიის ინ-სტიტუტის შრომები. [D. Gulias sakhelobis Ap'khazet'is enis, literaturis da istoriis institutis shromebi. Works of the Abkhazian Linguistic, Literary and Historical Institute named after D. I. Gulia. Edit. by K. Bghazhba.] Труды Абхазского Института Языка, Литературы и Истории имени Д. И. Гулиа. tom. 24, 25, 28–30, *etc.* სუხუმი [*Sukhumi,*] 1951–. 8⁰. *In progress.*   **17076. i. 3**

SULTANOV (KAMIL'). Дагестанские повести и рассказы. [An anthology of stories, trans. from languages of Daghestan by various hands, and compiled with an introduction by K. Sultanov.] pp. 355. Москва, 1960. 8⁰.   **17076. b. 50**

SUMBAT, *son of Davitʻ.* [For Sumbat's Life and History of the Bagratids, edit. by S. Qaukhchishvili:] *See* Georgian Annals.

SUMERIAN LANGUAGE. [For 'Sumerian and Georgian: a Study in Comparative Philology':] *See* Tseretʻeli (M. G.)

SURGULADZE (Akaki Nestoris-dze). დიდი რუსი მხედართმთავრები. [Didi rusi mkhedartʻmtʻavrebi. Great Russian military leaders. Historical studies.] pp. 250. თბილისი [*Tiflis*,] 1953. 8⁰.   **17075. e. 16**

—— ნარკვევები რევოლუციური მოძრაობის ისტორიიდან საქართველოში, 1917–1921 წწ. [Narkvevebi revolutsiuri modzraobis istoriidan Sakʻartʻveloshi, 1917–1921 dsds. Studies in the history of the revolutionary movement in Georgia, 1917–1921.] pp. 410. თბილისი [*Tiflis*,] 1954. 8⁰.   **17075. e. 32**

SURMANIDZE (Moedin). Советский Аджаристан. [Soviet Ajaristan. A description of the western Georgian A. S. S. R. of Atchara.] pp. 297–308. Москва, 1928. 8⁰. [*Новый Восток.* кн. 20–21.]   **Ac. 1096. b/5**

SUSANNA, *Saint and Martyr, of Tsurtavi.* [For 'Sainte Šoušanik, martyre en Arméno-Géorgie':] *See* Peeters (P.)

SVAN FOLK-SONGS. [For 'Gesänge russischer Kriegsgefangener. III. Band: Kaukasusvölker, *etc.*', including Svan folk-songs:] *See* Lach (R.)

SVAN LANGUAGE. [For 'Гдѣ сохранилось сванское склоненіе?':] *See* Marr (N. Y.)

—— [For 'Русско-сванскій словарь':] *See* Nizharadze (I. I.)

—— [For 'Original Vocabularies of Five West Caucasian Languages', including Svanian:] *See* Peacock (D. R.)

—— [For 'Svanuri prozauli tekʻstebi':] *See* Tiflis.—*Marr Language Institute,* afterwards *Institute of Linguistics.*

—— [For 'English-Svanetian Vocabulary':] *See* Wardrop (*Sir* J. O.) *K.B.E.*

SVANETʻI. [For 'Изъ поѣздокъ въ Сванію лѣтомъ 1911 и 1912 г.':] *See* Marr (N. Y.)

TABASARAN LANGUAGE. [For 'Das Tabassaranische':] *See* Bouda (K.). Beiträge zur kaukasischen und sibirischen Sprachwissenschaft, No. 3. 1939. 8⁰.   **753. f. 32**

—— [For 'Грамматическій очеркъ табассаранскаго языка':] *See* Dirr (A.)

—— [For 'Тайна Дюрка. Поэма', trans. from Tabasaran:] *See* Jafarov (A.)

TABIDZE (Galaktion Basilis-dze). რჩეული. [Rcheuli. Selected poetic works, chosen and arranged by B. Chikʻobava.] pp. 245. 1 *plate.* თბილისი [*Tiflis*,] 1954. 4⁰.   **17075. dd. 3**

TABIDZE (Titsian Iustines-dze). Три поэмы. Перевод с грузинского. [By B. Brik and K. Chernyavsky. With a portrait.] pp. 71. Тифлис, 1935. 8⁰.   **17075. c. 6**

—— *and others.* ნიკო ფიროსმანიშვილი. ტექსტი ტ. ტაბიძის, გ. რობაკიძის, გ. ქიქოძის, კ. ზდანევიჩის და კ. ჩერნიავსკის. [Niko Pʻirosmanishvili. Tekʻsti T. Tabidzis, G. Robakʻidzis, G. Kʻikʻodzis, K. Zdanevichis da K. Cherniavskis. A collection of articles on the Georgian painter N. Pʻirosmanishvili. Georgian, Russian and French texts.] (Нико Пиросманишвили.). pp. viii. 203. 55 *plates.* ტფილისი [*Tiflis*,] 1926. 4⁰.   **17080. d. 14**

TʻAMAR, *Queen of Georgia.* [For 'Четыре портрета царицы Тамары':] *See* Alibegashvili (G.V.)

—— [For 'Notice sur le mari russe de Thamar':] *See* Brosset (M.-F.)

—— [For 'Tʻamariani':] *See* Gugunava (S.) *Prince.*

T'AMAR *(cont.)*

—— [For 'Древнегрузинскіе одописцы', including Chakhrukhadze's eulogy of Queen T'amar:] *See* MARR (N. Y.)

T'AQAISHVILI (EK'VT'IME SVIMONIS-DZE). [Edit. 'Мудрость Балавара'.] *See* BARLAAM, *Saint, of India.* [The Legend of Barlaam and Josaphat.—*Georgian*].

—— [For 'L'inscription d'Épiphane', trans. from the Russian of N. Y. Marr by E. S. T'aqaishvili:] *See* EPIPHANIUS, *Catholicos of Georgia.*

—— *See* TIFLIS.—*Tiflis State University.* Album d'architecture géorgienne. Rédigé par M. E. Takaïchvili, *etc.* 1924. 4⁰.   **17080. d. 1**

—— ახალი ვარიანტი წმ. ნინოს ცხოვრებისა. [Akhali varianti dsm. Ninos tskhovrebisa. A new variant of the Life of St. Nino.] pp. lix. 78. ტფილისი [*Tiflis*,] 1891. 8⁰. *Imperfect: wants pp. xxxi–xlvi.*   **17075. e. 4. (2.)**

—— Antiquités géorgiennes. [Illustrated.] 2 pt. *Bruxelles*, 1935, 37. 8⁰. [*Byzantion.* tom. 10, 12.]   **P. P. 4748. pc**

—— Antiquities of Georgia. pp. 96–116. 26 *plates. London*, 1937. 8⁰. [*Georgica.* vol. I. nos. 4–5.]   **Ac. 8821. e**

—— Древности Гулекарской церкви. pp. 299–302. 8 *plates.* Петроградъ, 1922. 4⁰. [*Христіанскій Востокъ.* томъ 6. вып. 3.]   **Ac. 1125/105**

—— ძველი საქართველო. [Dzveli Sak'art'velo. Ancient Georgia.] Древняя Грузія. L'Ancienne Géorgie. Mémoires de la Société géorgienne d'histoire et d'ethnographie, sous la rédaction de M. E. Takaïchvili. tom. 1, 2. *Tiflis*, 1909, 13. 8⁰.   **17080. d. 10**

—— Еще одинъ изъ источниковъ исторіи Грузіи царевича Вахушта. Гуджаръ Баратовыхъ изъ Бетаніи. [Edit., with trans. and commentary, of a charter used as a source by the historian Vakhushti pp. 113–28. С.-Петербургъ, 1894. 8⁰. [*Записки Восточнаго Отдѣленія Имп. Русскаго Археологическаго Общества.* томъ 8.]   **Ac. 5584**

—— Four Basilican Churches of the Qvirila Valley. [With facsimiles in the text.] pp. 154–73. 28 *plates. London*, 1936. 8⁰. [*Georgica.* vol. I. nos. 2–3.]   **Ac. 8821. e**

—— Georgian Chronology and the Beginnings of Bagratid Rule in Georgia. pp. 9–27. *London*, 1935. 8⁰. [*Georgica.* vol. I. no. I.]   **Ac. 8821. e**

—— [Another copy, being an offprint.] **17075. f. 5**

—— The Icon of the Crucifixion in the Dsalenjikha Church in Megrelia. pp. 12–13. 4 *plates. London*, 1936. 8⁰. [*Georgica.* vol. I. nos. 2–3.]   **Ac. 8821. e**

—— Христіанскіе памятники. [Christian Monuments. Report on an archaeological expedition undertaken in 1902, including inscriptions from ancient Georgian churches and reproductions of icons and manuscripts]. pp. xii. 164. 25 *plates.* Москва, 1909. 4⁰. [*Матеріалы по Археологіи Кавказа.* вып. 12.]   **Ac. 5575/3**

—— პალეოგრაფიული ალბომი. დამატება "საქართველოს სიძველენის" II ტომისა. [Paleograp'iuli albomi. Damateba "Sak'art'velos sidzvelenis" II tomisa.] Album paléographique. Supplément du II tome "Des Antiquités Géorgiennes". livr. I [containing facsimiles of charters of Kings Bagrat IV and David IV.] pp. 10. *lith. Tiflis*, 1909. fol.   **17080. d. 9**

—— საქართველოს სიძველენი. [Sak'art'velos sidzveleni. Antiquities of Georgia. A collection of charters and historical documents.] 10 pt. pp. 1–176; 449–64. ტფილისი [*Tiflis*,] 1895–97. 8⁰. [*Moambe.* tom. 2–4.] *Incomplete: wanting pp. 177–448 and all after p. 464.*   **17089. b. 1**

—— საქართველოს სიძველენი. [Sak'art'velos sidzveleni. Antiquities of Georgia.] Грузинскія Древности. Les Antiquités Géorgiennes. Édition de la Société géorgienne d'histoire et d'ethnographie, sous la rédaction de M. E. Takaïchvili. tom. 2 and Album. *Tiflis*, 1909. 8⁰ and fol.   **17080. d. 9**

—— Сигель грузинскаго царя Баграта IV, 1027–1072. [A royal charter granted to the Mghvime

T'AQAISHVILI *(cont.)*
Monastery.] pp. 59–68. 4 *plates*. С.-Петербургъ, 1896. 8⁰. [*Записки Восточнаго Отдѣленія Имп. Русскаго Археологическаго Общества.* томъ 9.]

Ac. 5584

—— Les sources des notices du Patriarche de Jérusalem Dosithée sur les rois d'Aphkhazie. pp. 357–68. *Paris*, 1927. 8⁰. [*Journal Asiatique.* sér. 12. tom. 9.]   **R. Ac. 8808**

—— Суджунская церковь и ея древности. pp. 40–50. 14 *plates*. Петроградъ, 1916. 4⁰. [*Христіанскій Востокъ.* томъ 5. вып. 1.]   **Ac. 1125/105**

—— Тквирская церковь въ Мингреліи и ея древности. pp. 284–300. 14 *plates*. Петроградъ, 1916. 4⁰. [*Христіанскій Востокъ.* томъ 4. вып. 3.]   **Ac. 1125/105**

—— Церковь въ Ванѣ, въ Имеріи, и ея древности. pp. 86–110. 16 *plates. Leningrad*, 1927. 4⁰. [*Извѣстія Кавказскаго Историко-археологическаго Института.* том 2.]   **Ac. 1125. qc**

—— Церкви и церковные древности Мегреліи. pp. 69–85. 7 *plates. Leningrad*, 1927. 4⁰. [*Извѣстія Кавказскаго Историко-археологическаго Института.* том 2.]   **Ac. 1125. qc**

TARCHNIŠVILI (MICHAEL). *See* T'ARKHNISHVILI (M.)

T'ARKHNISHVILI (MIKHEIL). [Edit., with Latin trans., 'Typicon Gregorii Pacuriani']. *See* BAKURIANI (G.)

—— [For 'Lettres géorgiennes chrétiennes', being a summary of the book 'Geschichte der kirchlichen georgischen Literatur' by M. T'arkhnishvili and J. Assfalg:] *See* BRIÈRE (M.)

—— [Edit. and trans. the Lectionary of the Church of Jerusalem, 5th–8th centuries.] *See* LITURGIES.—Greek Rite.—*Lectionaries.*

—— [Edit. with Latin trans. 'Liturgiae Ibericae Antiquiores'.] *See* LITURGIES.—Greek Rite.— *Leitourgikon I.*

—— [Trans. 'Eine neue georgische Jakobosliturgie'.] *See* LITURGIES.—Greek Rite.—*Leitourgikon I.*

—— [Edit.' Corpus Scriptorum Christianorum Orientalium. Scriptores Iberici'.] *See* LOUVAIN.— *Academia Lovaniensis.*

—— À propos de la plus ancienne version géorgienne des Actes des Apôtres. pp. 347–68. *Louvain*, 1956. 8⁰. [*Le Muséon.* tom. 69.]   **P. P. 4453**

—— À propos des travaux de philologie géorgienne de M. G. Garitte. pp. 369–84. *Louvain*, 1955. 8⁰. [*Le Muséon.* tom. 68.]   **P. P. 4453**

—— Die Anfänge der schriftstellerischen Tätigkeit des hl. Euthymius und der Aufstand von Bardas Skleros. pp. 113–24. *Wiesbaden*, 1954. 8⁰. [*Oriens Christianus.* Bd. 38. (Vierte Serie. Bd. 2.)]   **Ac. 2002. b**

—— Les deux recensions du "Barlaam" géorgien. pp. 65–86. *Louvain*, 1958. 8⁰. [*Le Muséon.* tom. 71.]   **P. P. 4453**

—— Die Entstehung und Entwicklung der kirchlichen Autokephalie Georgiens. pp. 107–26. *Louvain*, 1960. 8⁰. [*Le Muséon.* tom. 73.]   **P. P. 4453**

—— Die geistliche Dichtung Georgiens und ihr Verhältnis zur Byzantinischen. pp. 76–96. *Wiesbaden*, 1957. 8⁰. [*Oriens Christianus.* Bd. 41. (Vierte Serie. Bd. 5.)]   **Ac. 2002. b**

—— Geschichte der kirchlichen georgischen Literatur, auf Grund des ersten Bandes der georgischen Literaturgeschichte von K. Kekelidze bearbeitet von P. Michael Tarchnišvili in Verbindung mit Dr. Julius Assfalg. pp. xvii. 521. *Città del Vaticano*, 1955. 8⁰. [*Studi e Testi.* no. 185.]   **17076. i. 15**

—— [Another copy.]   **012211. b. 1/185**

—— Kurzer Überblick über den Stand der georgischen Literaturforschung. pp. 89–99. *Wiesbaden*, 1953. 8⁰. [*Oriens Christianus.* Bd. 37. (Vierte Serie. Bd. 1.)]   **Ac. 2002. b**

T'ARKHNISHVILI *(cont.)*

—— Il monachesimo georgiano nelle sue origini e nei suoi primi sviluppi. pp. 307–19. *Roma,* 1958. 8⁰. [*Il Monachesimo Orientale: Orientalia Christiana Analecta.* no. 153.]   **Ac. 2002. bb**

—— Publications récentes relatives à la littérature géorgienne. pp. 173–89. *Louvain,* 1958. 8⁰. [*Le Muséon.* tom. 71.]   **P. P. 4453**

—— Les récentes découvertes épigraphiques et littéraires en géorgien. pp. 249–60. *Louvain,* 1950. 8⁰. [*Le Muséon.* tom. 63.]   **P. P. 4453**

—— Le roman de Balahvar et sa traduction anglaise. [Containing a critical discussion of D. M. Lang's trans. of the shorter Georgian version of the legend of Barlaam and Josaphat.] pp. 83–92. *Roma,* 1958. 8⁰. [*Orientalia Christiana Periodica.* vol. 24. no. 1–2.]   **Ac. 2002. bb/2**

—— Sources arméno-géorgiennes de l'histoire ancienne de l'Église de Géorgie. pp. 29–50. *Louvain,* 1947. 8⁰. [*Le Muséon.* tom. 60.]   **P. P. 4453**

—— Das Verhältnis von Kirche und Staat im Königreich Georgien. pp. 79–92. *Wiesbaden,* 1955. 8⁰. [*Oriens Christianus.* Bd. 39. (Vierte Serie. Bd. 3.)]   **Ac. 2002. b**

TATISHVILI (Vladimer Ivanes-dze). Грузины в Москве. Исторический очерк, 1653–1722. pp. 230, 4. 36 *plates.* Тбилиси, 1959. 8⁰.   **17075. e. 40**

T'AVADZE (Ambrosi Giorgis-dze). ილია ჭავჭავაძის ფილოსოფიური და ესთეტიკური შეხედულებანი. [Ilia Tchavtchavadzis p'ilosop'iuri da est'etikuri shekhedulebani. Ilia Tchavtchavadze's philosophical and aesthetic views.] pp. 150. თბილისი [*Tiflis,*] 1954. 8⁰.   **17075. f. 15**

T'AVADZE (P'erdinand Nestoris-dze) and **SAQVARELIDZE** (T'amar Nikolozis-asuli). Бронзы древней Грузии. (Bronzes of ancient Georgia.) [With a summary in English.] pp. 84. 41 *plates.* Тбилиси, 1959. 8⁰.   **17080. d. 29**

T'AVART'K'ILADZE (Kodsia). [Edit. epic poem 'Vep'khis-tqaosani'.] *See* Rust'aveli (Shot'a).

T'AVZISHVILI (Giorgi Iasonis-dze). Яков Гогебашвили. Общественно-педагогическая и литературная деятельность. pp. 150, 2. Тбилиси, 1957. 8⁰.   **17075. b. 3**

T'BILELI (Iosif). *See* Joseph [Ioseb Saakadze], *Bishop of Tiflis.*

TBILISI. *See* Tiflis.

TCHAN LANGUAGE. *See* Laz.

TCHARAIA (Petre Giorgis-dze). *See* Charaya (P. G.)

TCHAVTCHAVADZE (Alek'sandre Garsevanis-dze) *Prince.* [For selected poems, in Russian translation:] *See* Gol'tsev (V. V.) and Chik'ovani (S. I.). Поэзия Грузии. 1949. 4⁰.   **17075. dd. 1**

TCHAVTCHAVADZE (Ilia Grigolis-dze) *Prince.* [For selected poems, in Russian translation:] *See* Gol'tsev (V. V.) and Chik'ovani (S. I.). Поэзия Грузии. 1949. 4⁰.   **17075. dd. 1**

—— *See* Jedlička (J.). Kamenité cesty Gruzie. Povídky gruzínských klasiků. [Including a Czech translation of two stories by Ilia Tchavtchavadze.] 1958. 12⁰.   **17076. b. 44**

—— [Edit. newspaper 'Iveria'.] *See* Periodical Publications.—*Tiflis.*

—— [For 'Ilia Tchavtchavadze: p'ilosop'iuri da sotsialur-politikuri shekhedulebani':] *See* Ratiani (P. K.)

—— [Joint edit. of 'Visramiani'.] *See* Sargis, *of T'mogvi.*

—— [For 'Ilia Tchavtchavadzis p'ilosop'iuri da est'etikuri shekhedulebani':] *See* T'avadze (A. G.)

—— აი ისტორია. [Ai istoria. Here is history for you! Critical articles, reprinted from the Georgian

TCHAVTCHAVADZE (cont.)
journal 'Iveria' of 1887.] pp. 176. ტფილისი [Tiflis,] 1910. 8⁰.   **17075. f. 4. (3.)**

—— The Hermit: a legend, by Prince Ilia Chav-chavadze. Translated from the Georgian by Marjory Wardrop. pp. 38. 1 *plate*. *London*, 1895. 16⁰.   **17077. a. 2**

—— ილია ჭავჭავაძე. პორტრეტები და ილუს-ტრაციები. [Ilia Tchavtchavadze. Portretebi da ilustratsiebi. A biography in pictures of the Georgian writer Ilia Tchavtchavadze, compiled by N. Alania and others under the artistic direction of L. Grigolia. With a portrait frontispiece in colour.] pp. 139. თბილისი [Tiflis,] 1959. fol.   **17080. g. 9**

—— ილია ჭავჭავაძე. საიუბილეო კრებული. [Ilia Tchavtchavadze. Saiubileo krebuli. A collection of essays by various hands, published to commemorate the 50th anniversary of the death of Ilia Tchavtchavadze.] (Илья Чавчавадзе. Юбилейный сборник.) pp. 370. 1 *plate*. თბილისი [Tiflis,] 1957. 8⁰.   **17075. f. 42**

—— Избранные произведения. Перевод, *etc*. (Редакция В. В. Гольцева.) pp. 422. *Москва*, 1950. 8⁰.   **O12264. b. 31**

—— Избранные произведения. Перевод с грузинского Е. Гогоберидзе. (რჩეული თხზულებანი. [Rcheuli t'khzulebani.]) [Selected works in Russian translation, comprising tales and novels. Edit. by D. Shengelaia.] pp. 283. *Тбилиси*, 1955. 8⁰.   **17076. b. 13**

—— კრიტიკული წერილები. [Kritikuli dserilebi. Critical essays.] pp. 127. ტფილისი [Tiflis,] 1909. 8⁰.   **17075. f. 4. (2.)**

—— პოლემიკური წერილები. [Polemikuri dserilebi. Polemical letters.] pp. 48. ტფილისი [Tiflis,] 1909. 8⁰.   **17075. f. 4. (4.)**

—— თხზულებანი ილია ჭავჭავაძისა. [T'khzule-bani Ilia Tchavtchavadzisa. Works of Ilia Tchav-

chavadze. Poems and stories. With a portrait and one facsimile.] tom. 1, 2. ტფილისი [Tiflis,] 1892. 8⁰.   **17075. c. 4**

—— თხზულებანი. პავლე ინგოროყვას შესავალი წერილით. [T'khzulebani. Pavle Ingoroqvas shesavali dserilit'. Selected works, with an introductory essay by Pavle Ingoroqva.] pp. lxxxi. 544. 21 *plates*. თბილისი [Tiflis,] 1957. 4⁰.   **17075. dd. 8**

—— თხზულებათა სრული კრებული ათ ტომად. [T'khzulebat'a sruli krebuli at' tomad. Complete collection of works in ten volumes. Edit. by P. I. Ingoroqva.] tom. 6, 7, *etc*. თბილისი [Tiflis,] 1956, *etc*. 8⁰. *In progress*.   **17076. h. 9**

—— ცხოვრება და კანონი. [Tskhovreba da kanoni. Life and Law. Articles reprinted from the Georgian journal 'Iveria' of 1877–81.] pp. 131. ტფილისი [Tiflis,] 1909. 8⁰.   **17075. f. 4. (1.)**

TCHEISHVILI (Alek'sandre Nikolozis-dze). Лело. Роман. Перевод с грузинского (Г. Аккермана и А. Кочеткова). pp. 340. *Москва*, 1950. 8⁰.   **12594. f. 7**

—— [Another edition.] Авторизованный перевод с грузинского Г. Аккермана и А. Кочеткова. [With a portrait.] pp. 369. *Москва*, 1952. 8⁰.   **O12589. l. 18**

TCHELIDZE (Vakhtang). [Trans. 'Robinson Crusoe'.] *See* DEFOE (D.)

——[Trans. 'Nicholas Nickleby'.] *See* DICKENS (C.)

—— [Trans. 'Paradise Lost. Paradise Regained'.] *See* MILTON (J.)

—— [Joint trans. of works of Shakspere.] *See* SHAKSPERE (W.)

—— ცხოვრება ივანე მაჩაბლისა. [Tskhovreba Ivane Machablisa. A novel based on the life of the Georgian dramatist I. Machabeli. Edit. by G. Leonidze.] pp. 379, 4. თბილისი [Tiflis,] 1955. 8⁰.   **17076. b. 16**

—— [Second edition.] pp. 383, 4. თბილისი [Tiflis,] 1957. 8⁰.   **17075. b. 2**

TCHILAIA (Sergi Estates-dze). [Edit. 'Arsena Marabdeli'.] *See* Javakhishvili (M. S.)

TCHILASHVILI (Levan Alek'sandres-dze). ქალაქი რუსთავი. ისტორიულ-არქეოლოგიური ნარკვევი. [K'alak'i Rust'avi. Istoriul-ark'eologiuri narkvevi. The town of Rust'avi. A historical and archaeological study. With a summary in Russian.] (Город Рустави. Историко-археологический очерк.) pp. 228. 39 *plates.* თბილისი [*Tiflis,*] 1958. 8⁰.
17075. e. 50

TCHITCHINADZE (Konstantine Archilis-dze). [Joint edit. of selected writings of Pushkin.] *See* Pushkin (A. S.)

—— [Trans. 'Цыгане' and 'Полтава'.] *See* Pushkin (A. S.)

TCHITCHINADZE (Zak'aria Egnates-dze). [Edit. 'Profesori Patkanovi da k'art'uli istoriis dsqaroebi'.] *See* Bak'radze (D. Z.)

—— [Edit. poems of B. Gabashvili.] *See* Gabashvili (B. I.)

—— [Edit. 'Davit'iani'.] *See* Guramishvili (D.)

—— [Edit. 'Svimon mep'e'.] *See* Karitchashvili (D. G.)

—— [Edit. drama 'Mep'e Davit' Aghmashenebeli'.] *See* Orbeliani (A. V. Jambakurian-).

—— [Edit. A. N. P'urtseladze's dramatic works.] *See* P'urtseladze (A. N.)

—— [Edit. eulogy of Queen T'amar and her consort King David.] *See* Shavt'eli (Iovane).

—— [Edit. poems of King T'eimuraz I.] *See* T'eimuraz I, *King of Georgia.*

—— [Edit. 'Ramdenime lek'si'.] *See* Tsakheli, *pseud.*

—— დავით ერისთავი. [Davit' Erist'avi. A bio-

graphical sketch by Z. Tch., i. e. Z. E. Tchitchinadze.] pp. 40. ტბილისი [*Tiflis,*] 1892. 8⁰.
17075. d. 1. (6.)

—— იოსებ დავითაშვილი. [Ioseb Davit'ashvili, 1850–1887. Biography of the Georgian poet.] pp. 50. თბილისი [*Tiflis,*] 1887. 8⁰. **17075. d. 1. (3.)**

—— ისტორია ქართული სტამბისა და მწიგნობრობის ბეჭდვისა. [Istoria k'art'uli stambisa da mdsignobrobis betchdvisa. History of printing and book production in Georgia.] pp. 99–151. ქუთაისი [*K'ut'aisi,*] 1900. 8⁰. [*Krebuli.* tom. 2. no. 12.]
17089. b. 4

—— ქართლის ცხოვრება. [K'art'lis tskhovreba. The life of Georgia. A Georgian historical chronicle. Edited by Z. E. Tchitchinadze. Part I only, containing chronicle up to reign of King Vakhtang Gorgasali, 5th century. Second edition.] pp. 210, ii. ტფილისი [*Tiflis,*] 1897. 8⁰. **17075. e. 6**

—— ქართული მწერლობა მეჩვიდმეტე საუკუნეში. [K'art'uli mdserloba mechvidmete saukuneshi. Georgian literature in the 17th century.] pp. 40. თბილისი [*Tiflis,*] 1888. 8⁰. **17076. g. 2. (3.)**

—— ქართული მწერლობა მეთორმეტე საუკუნეში. [K'art'uli mdserloba met'ormete saukuneshi. Georgian literature in the 12th century.] pp. 34. თბილისი [*Tiflis,*] 1887. 8⁰. **17076. g. 2. (2.)**

—— ქართული მწერლობა მეცამეტე საუკუნიდამ მეთექვსმეტე საუკუნემდე. [K'art'uli mdserloba metsamete saukunidam met'ek'vsmete saukunemde. Georgian literature from the 13th to the 16th century.] pp. 34. თბილისი [*Tiflis,*] 1885. 8⁰.
17076. g. 2. (1.)

—— ქართველთ მაჰმადიანთ სახალხო ლექსები. [K'art'velt' Mahmadiant' sakhalkho lek'sebi. Georgian Muhammadan popular verses, collected in Batum, K'obulet'i, *etc.*] pp. 20. თფილისი [*Tiflis,*] 1891. 8⁰. **17075. d. 1. (4.)**

—— პლატონ იოსელიანი. [Platon Ioseliani, a biography of the Georgian historian and man of letters, 1809–1875.] pp. 36. *Тифлисъ,* 1893. 8⁰.
17075. ee. 2

TCHITCHINADZE *(cont.)*

—— შოთა რუსთაველი, 1172–1216. [Shot'a Rust'aveli, 1172–1216. Biographical and critical study of the Georgian poet. Edit. by K. I. Meskhievi.] pp. ii. 68. 1 *plate.* თბილისი [*Tiflis,*] 1884. 8⁰.

17075. d. 1. (1.)

—— სოლომონ დოდაშვილი. [Solomon Dodashvili. A biography of the 19th century Georgian pedagogue and man of letters.] pp. 30. თფილისი [*Tiflis,*] 1893. 8⁰. **17076. g. 2. (4.)**

TCHKHIKVICHVILI (J.). *See* CHKHIKVISHVILI (I. D.)

TCHONK'ADZE (DANIEL GIORGIS-DZE). *See* JEDLIČKA (J.). Kamenité cesty Gruzie. Povídky gruzínských klasiků. [Including a Czech translation of the story 'Suramis tsikhe' by D. Tchonk'adze.] 1958. 12⁰. **17076. b. 44**

—— [For dramatisation of the story 'Suramis tsikhe' by D. Tchonk'adze:] *See* MT'VARADZE (S.)

TCHOUBINOF (DAVID). *See* CHUBINOV (D. I.)

TCHQONIA (ALEK'SANDRE). [Editor of monthly review 'Moambe'.] *See* PERIODICAL PUBLICATIONS. —*Tiflis.*

TCHQONIA (ILIA MIRIANIS-DZE). სიტყვის-კონა: საბა-სულხან ორბელიანის და დავით ჩუბინაშვილის ლექსიკონებში გამოტოვებული სიტყვები. [Sitqvis-kona: Saba-Sulkhan Orbelianis da Davit' Chubinashvilis lek'sikonebshi gamotovebuli sitqvebi. A glossary of words omitted in the dictionaries of Saba-Sulkhan Orbeliani and Davit' Chubinashvili.] Грузинскій глоссарій, *etc.* pp. vii. 74. С.-Петербургъ, 1910. 8⁰. [*Матеріалы по яфетическому языкознанію.* no. 1.] **17073. a. 3**

TCHUBINIDZÉ (VALIKO). *See* CHUBINIDZE.

TCHUMBURIDZE (ZURAB GALAKTIONIS-DZE). ქართული სალიტერატურო ენისა და სტილის საკითხები. [K'art'uli saliteraturo enisa da stilis sakit'khebi. Questions of Georgian literary language and style. Critical essays.] pp. 182, 3. თბილისი [*Tiflis,*] 1956. 8⁰. **17076. h. 7**

T'EIMURAZ I, *King of Georgia.* [For 'T'eimuraz I and his Poem "The Martyrdom of Queen K'et'evan":] *See* AVALISHVILI (Z. D.)

—— ლექსნი. [Lek'sni. Poems of King T'eimuraz I. Edited with introduction and notes by Z. E. Tchitchinadze.] pp. 64. თფილისი [*Tiflis,*] 1886. 8⁰. **17075. d. 1. (2.)**

T'EIMURAZ GIORGIS-DZE, *Prince of Georgia.* [Author of 'Précis des guerres qu'eut à soutenir.... le Prince-Royal Dawith', in 'Mémoires inédits, relatifs à l'histoire et à la langue géorgiennes':] *See* BROSSET (M.-F.)

—— Dissertation sur les monnaies géorgiennes, traduite d'une lettre du prince Théimouraz, avec des éclaircissements, par M. Brosset. [With a plate.] 2 pt. *Paris,* 1835–36. 8⁰. [*Nouveau Journal Asiatique.* tom. 15; *Journal Asiatique.* sér. 3. tom. 2.]

R. Ac. 8808

TEUNOV (KHACHIM ISKHAKOVICH). Литература и писатели Кабарды. Авторизованный перевод с кабардинского [by various hands, with a preface by V. Goffenshefer. Second edition.] pp. 380, 4. *Москва,* 1958. 8⁰. **17076. f. 18**

T'EVZADZE (ANDRO RAZHDENIS-DZE). წიგნი ლექსების. [Dsigni lek'sebis. Book of verses.] pp. 268. 1 *plate.* თბილისი [*Tiflis,*] 1958. 12⁰. **17075. c. 36**

THEODORE, *Saint and Martyr, of Pella.* La Passion géorgienne des SS. Théodore, Julien, Eubulus, Malcamon, Mocimus et Salamanes. [Edited with introduction and Latin translation by Robert P. Blake and Paul Peeters.] pp. 70–101. *Bruxelles,* 1926. 8⁰. [*Analecta Bollandiana.* tom. 44.] **2002. f** *Note: The connection of these martyrs with Pella has been called in question, and should be treated as conjectural.*

—— [Another copy, being an offprint.] **17073. f. 1**

THOMAS, *Saint and Apostle.* [For 'Le fragment géorgien de l'Évangile de Thomas':] *See* BIBLE.— New Testament.—*Apocrypha.*

THORNICIUS, afterwards JOHANNES, *Monk at Mount Athos.* Un colophon géorgien de Thornik le Moine. [Edit., with Latin trans. and commentary, by P. Peeters.] pp. 358–71. *Bruxelles,* 1932. 8⁰. [*Analecta Bollandiana.* tom. 50.]   **2002. g**

—— [Another copy, being an offprint.]   **20003. k. 3**

TIFLIS. [For an anthology of poems and verses about Tiflis:] *See* CHIK'OVANI (S. I.)

—— [For 'Тбилиси в XIX столетии, 1865–1869':] *See* CHKHETIA (SH. Q.)

—— [For 'Тбилиси, столица Грузинской ССР':] *See* OTAROVA (N. A.)

—— [For 'T'bilisis ghrmad mokhutsebuli adamianebi', being studies of the oldest inhabitants of Tiflis:] *See* SHAP'IRO (I. B.) *and others.*

—— [For 'T'bilisis revolutsiuri dsarsuli':] *See* STURUA (N. I.) *and others.*

—— [For a symposium of essays, published on the occasion of the 1500th anniversary of the foundation of Tiflis:] *See* TIFLIS.—*Tiflis State University.*

—— [For 'Тбилиси. Архитектура старого города и жилые дома первой половины XIX столетия':] *See* TSINTSADZE (V. G.)

—— *Academy of Sciences of the Georgian S.S.R.* *See* BOTCHORISHVILI (L. I.). ქართული კერამიკა. [K'art'uli keramika. Georgian ceramics.]. 1949. 8⁰.
                                                17080. d. 12

—— ქართული ენის განმარტებითი ლექსიკონი. [K'art'uli enis ganmartebit'i lek'sikoni. Explanatory dictionary of the Georgian language.] Толковый словарь грузинского языка. tom. 1–6, *etc.* 1950–. 4⁰. *See* CHIK'OBAVA (A. S.) *and others.*   **17076. i. 1**

—— *See* IMNAISHVILI (I. V.). ქართული ოთხთავის

სიმფონია-ლექსიკონი. [K'art'uli ot'kht'avis simp'onia-lek'sikoni. Concordance and dictionary to the Georgian Gospels.] 1948–1949. 4⁰.   **17071. c. 2**

—— *See* JAP'ARIDZE (V. V.). კერამიკული წარმოება XI–XIII სს. საქართველოში. [K'eramikuli dsarmoeba XI–XIII ss. Sak'art'veloshi. Ceramic production in Georgia in the 11th–13th centuries.] 1956. 4⁰.   **17080. g. 2**

—— [For 'K'art'uli sazogadoebrivi da p'ilosop'iuri azris istoriidan':] *See* KHIDASHELI (S. V.)

—— [For 'T'bilisis ark'eologiuri dzeglebi':] *See* K'ORIDZE (D. L.)

—— [For descriptive Catalogue of Georgian manuscripts in the K'ut'aisi State Historical Museum:] *See* K'UT'AISI.—*K'ut'aisi State Historical Museum.*

—— [For 'Ashkharuli dialek'ti', a study of one of the Abkhazo-Abazinian dialects:] *See* LOMT'AT'IDZE (K'. B.)

—— [For 'N. Nikoladzis ark'ivis katalogi':] *See* NIKOLADZE (N. I.)

—— [For 'Les Brachiopodes du Crétacé inférieur de la Géorgie Occidentale', being an offprint from the 'Travaux de l'Institut Géologique':] *See* NUTSUBIDZE (K'.SH.)

—— [For 'K'art'velt'a udzvelesi sardsmunoebis istoriidan':] *See* OCHIAURI (T'. A.)

—— [For 'Kolek'tiuri nadirobis gadmonasht'ebi Ratchashi':] *See* ROBAK'IDZE (A. I.)

—— *See* SAVVA, *the Monk* [*Prince* SULKHAN ORBELIANI]. სულხან-საბა ორბელიანი, 1658—1958: საიუბილეო კრებული. [Sulkhan-Saba Orbeliani, 1658–1958: saiubileo krebuli.] 1959. 8⁰. **17076. f. 32**

—— [For 'D. Gulias sakhelobis Ap'khazet'is enis, literaturis da istoriis institutis shromebi':] *See* SUKHUMI. — *Abkhazian Linguistic, Literary and Historical Institute.*

TIFLIS *(cont.)*

—— [For 'Enat'metsnierebis institutis shromebi':] *See* TIFLIS.—*Marr Language Institute.*

—— [For Catalogue of the gems in the Georgian State Museum:] *See* TIFLIS.—*Museum of Georgia.*

—— [For descriptive Catalogue of Georgian manuscripts in the Georgian State Museum:] *See* TIFLIS.—*Museum of Georgia.*

—— [For Guide to the collections of ancient manuscripts in the Georgian State Museum:] *See* TIFLIS.—*Museum of Georgia.*

—— [For 'Muzeumshi 1904–1920 dslebshi shemosuli, Sak'art'veloshi aghmochenili ark'eologiuri masalebis aghdseriloba':] *See* TIFLIS.—*Museum of Georgia.*

—— [For 'Transactions of the J. Beritashvili Physiological Institute':] *See* TIFLIS.—*Tiflis State University.*

—— ასპირანტთა და ახალგაზრდა მეცნიერ მუშაკთა IX სამეცნიერო კონფერენცია, 1958 . . . მუშაობის გეგმა და მოხსენებათა თეზისები. [Aspirantt'a da akhalgazrda metsnier mushakt'a IX sametsniero konp'erèntsia, 1958... Mushaobis gegma da mokhsenebat'a t'ezisebi. 9th Scientific Conference of Young Scholars, 1958... Programme of proceedings and résumés of communications. Georgian and Russian texts.] IX научная конференция аспирантов и молодых научных работников, 1958, *etc.* pp. 177, iv. თბილისი [*Tiflis,*] 1958. 8⁰.
17080. d. 27

—— ძველი ქართული ენის ძეგლები. [Dzveli k'art'uli enis dzeglebi. Monuments of the ancient Georgian language.] (Памятники древнегрузинского языка.) no. 6–11, *etc.* თბილისი [*Tiflis,*] 1948–. 4⁰ & 8⁰. *In progress.*
17071. c. 2

—— რუსულ-ქართული ლექსიკონი. [Rusul-k'art'uli lek'sikoni. Russian—Georgian dictionary. Compiled and edited by G. S. Akhvlediani and others.] (Русско-грузинский словарь.) 3 tom. თბილისი [*Tiflis,*] 1956–59. 4⁰.
Ac. 1140/3

—— საქართველოს სსრ მეცნიერებათა აკადემიის გამოცემათა ბიბლიოგრაფია, 1937–1956 წწ. [Sak'art'velos SSR metsnierebat'a akademiis gamotsemat'a bibliograp'ia, 1937–1956 dsds. Bibliography of the publications of the Academy of Sciences of the Georgian S. S. R., 1937–1956. Compiled by E. Zhuzhunadze.] (Библиография изданий Академии Наук Грузинской ССР, 1937–1956.) pp. 945. თბილისი [*Tiflis,*] 1959. 4⁰.
17080. d. 28

—— საქართველოს სსრ მეცნიერებათა აკადემიის მოამბე : ძირითადი, ქართული გამოცემა. [Sak'art'velos SSR metsnierebat'a akademiis moambe: dzirit'adi, k'art'uli gamotsema. Bulletin of the Academy of Sciences of the Georgian S.S.R.: original Georgian edition.] tom. 6–7 (geological section only), 10— თბილისი [*Tiflis,*] 1945–. 8⁰.
17080. d. 11

—— შრომის ორგანიზაციის ფორმები ძველი საქართველოს სახალხო მეურნეობაში. [Shromis organizatsiis p'ormebi dzveli Sak'art'velos sakhalkho meurneobashi.] Les formes d'organisation du travail dans l'économie sociale de l'ancienne Géorgie. tom. 1— თბილისი [*Tiflis,*] 1941–. 8⁰. *In progress.*
17075. e. 19

—— Сообщения Академии Наук Грузинской ССР. Bulletin of the Academy of Sciences of the Georgian SSR. [Containing translations of articles published in the Georgian edition of the Bulletin, 'Moambe'. Some articles have English summaries.] том 7. no. 1–7; том 10–. Тбилиси, 1946–. 8⁰.
Ac. 1140

—— *Institute of Economics.* ეკონომიკის ინსტიტუტის შრომები. [Ekonomikis institutis shromebi. Works of the Institute of Economics.] (Труды Института Экономики.) tom. 10–. თბილისი [*Tiflis,*] 1957–. 8⁰. *In progress.*
17080. d. 24

—— *Institute of the History of Georgian Art. See* CHUBINASHVILI (G. N.). Архитектура Кахетии, *etc.* 2 tom. 1956–59. 4⁰.
17080. g. 11

—— *See* CHUBINASHVILI (G. N.). ქართული ოქრომჭედლობა VIII—XVIII საუკუნეებისა. [K'art'uli ok'romtchedloba VIII–XVIII saukuneebisa. Ge-

TIFLIS *(cont.)*

orgian gold repoussé work of the 8th to 18th centuries. An album, with five brochures, containing explanatory text in Georgian, Russian, English, French and German.] 1957. fol.

14999. h. 9

—— *See* CHUBINASHVILI (N.). Грузинская средневековая художественная резьба по дереву, перелома X–XI вв. 1958. 4⁰.   **17080. g. 5**

—— *See* TSINTSADZE (V. G.). Тбилиси. Архитектура старого города и жилые дома первой половины XIX столетия. 1958. fol.   **17080. g. 10**

—— *See* VOL'SKAYA (A. I.). Рельефы Шиомгвиме и их место в развитии грузинской средневековой скульптуры. 1957. 8⁰.   **17080. c. 1**

—— ქართული ხელოვნება. ქართული ხელოვნების ისტორიის ინსტიტუტის შრომები. [K'art'uli khelovneba. K'art'uli khelovnebis istoriis institutis shromebi. Georgian Art. Works of the Institute of the History of Georgian Art.] (Ars Georgica. Разыскания Института Истории Грузинского Искусства.)[Edit. by S. Barnaveli and others. Georgian and Russian texts, with a summary in German. Illustrated.] tom. 4, 5–. თბილისი [*Tiflis,*] 1955–. 4⁰. *In progress.*   **17080. g. 1**

—— *Institute of Language Studies. See* TIFLIS.— *Marr Language Institute,* afterwards *Institute of Linguistics.*

—— *Institute of Manuscripts. See* BURJANADZE (SH. V.). ისტორიული დოკუმენტები იმერეთის სამეფოსა და გურია-ოდიშის სამთავროებისა, 1466–1770 წწ. [Istoriuli dokumentebi Imeret'is samep'osa da Guria-Odishis samt'avroebisa, 1466–1770 dsds.] bk. 1–. 1958–. 8⁰.   **17075. ee. 10**

—— *Institute of Plant Protection.* მცენარეთა დაცვის ინსტიტუტის შრომები. [Mtsenaret'a datsvis institutis shromebi. Works of the Institute of Plant Protection.] Труды Института Защиты Растений. tom. 6, 7, 9, 11, 12, *etc.* თბილისი [*Tiflis,*] 1949–. 8⁰. *In progress.*   **17080. d. 15**

—— *Institute of Zoology.* ზოოლოგიის ინსტიტუტის შრომები. [Zoologiis institutis shromebi. Works of the Zoological Institute.] Труды Института зоологии. tom. 9, 10, 12, 14, 15, 16, *etc.* თბილისი [*Tiflis,*] 1950–. 8⁰. *In progress.*   **17080. d. 16**

—— *I. A. Javakhishvili Historical Institute. See* AP'AK'IDZE (A. M.) *and others.* Мцхета. Итоги археологических исследований, *etc.* том I. 1958. fol.   **17080. g. 7**

—— *See* GEGESHIDZE (M. K.). ქართული ხალხური ტრანსპორტი. I. საზმელეთო საზიდი საშუალებანი. [K'art'uli khalkhuri transporti. I. Sakhmelet'o sazidi sashualebani.] (Грузинский народный транспорт. I. Сухопутные средства перевозки. Georgischer Volkstransport. I. Landsbeförderungsmittel.) 1956. 8⁰.   **17080. e. 6**

—— [For Report of First and Second Gudarekhi Archaeological Campaigns:] *See* MUSKHELISHVILI (L. V.) *and others.*   **17080. f. 7**

—— *See* P'UT'URIDZE (V. S.). ქართულ-სპარსული ისტორიული საბუთები. [K'art'ul-sparsuli istoriuli sabut'ebi. Georgian-Persian historical charters.] 1955. 8⁰.   **17075. e. 35**

—— მასალები საქართველოს და კავკასიის არქეოლოგიისათვის. [Masalebi Sak'art'velos da Kavkasiis ark'eologiisat'vis. Materials for the archaeology of Georgia and the Caucasus.] (Материалы по археологии Грузии и Кавказа.) [Georgian text, with summaries in Russian. With plates and facsimiles.] tom. 1, 2, *etc.* თბილისი [*Tiflis,*] 1955–. 4⁰. *In progress.*   **17080. f. 8**

—— მასალები საქართველოს ეთნოგრაფიისათვის. [Masalebi Sak'art'velos et'nograp'iisat'vis. Materials for the Ethnography of Georgia.] (Материалы по этнографии Грузии. Materialien der Ethnographie Georgiens.) tom. 3, 6, 8–11, *etc.* თბილისი [*Tiflis,*] 1940–. 8⁰. *Imperfect; tom. 8 wanting plates 19–22. In progress.*   **17080. d. 22**

—— *Rust'aveli Literary Institute. See* IMEDASHVILI (G.). რუსთველოლოგიური ლიტერატურა, 1712—1956 წლები. [Rust'velologiuri literatura, 1712—

TIFLIS *(cont.)*

1956 dslebi. Bibliography of literature on Shotʻa Rustʻaveli, 1712–1956.] 1957. 8⁰. **17075. c. 23**

—— [For a revised edition of M. S. Wardrop's translation of Shotʻa Rustʻaveli's epic poem, published by the Rustʻaveli Literary Institute, under the title 'The Knight in the Tiger's Skin':] *See* Rustʻaveli (Shotʻa).

—— ქართული ლიტერატურის ისტორია, ოთხ ტომად. [Kʻartʻuli literaturis istoria, otʻkh tomad. History of Georgian literature in four volumes. Edit. by a committee consisting of G. Abzianidze, A. Baramidze and others.] tom. I— თბილისი [*Tiflis,*] 1954–. 8⁰. *In progress.* **17080. e. 5**

—— ლიტერატურული ძიებანი. [Literaturuli dziebani. Essays on Georgian literary history, *etc.*] Литературные разыскания. Literary Researches. [Georgian and Russian texts.] tom. 2, 4–6, 9–12, *etc.* თბილისი [*Tiflis,*] 1945–. 8⁰. *In progress.* **17080. d. 13**

—— ლიტერატურული მემკვიდრეობა. [Literaturuli memkvidreoba. Literary heritage. Containing articles and documents on Georgian literary history.] (Литературное наследство.) bk. I. pp. iv. 672. 3 *plates.* ტფილისი [*Tiflis,*] 1935. 4⁰. **17080. b. 3**

—— *Tiflis Botanical Institute.* მცენარეთა სისტემატიკის და გეოგრაფიის ნარკვევები. [Mtsenaretʻa sistematikis da geograpʻiis narkvevebi.] Заметки по систематике и географии растений. *Georgian and Russ.* fasc. 13, 14, 15, 18, 19, 21, *etc.* თბილისი [*Tiflis,*] 1947–. 8⁰. *In progress.* **Ac. 1140. b/2**

—— თბილისის ბოტანიკის ინსტიტუტის შრომები. [Tʻbilisis botanikis institutis shromebi.] Труды Тбилисского Ботанического Института. *Georgian and Russ.* tom. 12–20, *etc.* თბილისი [*Tiflis,*] 1948–. 8⁰. *In progress.* **Ac. 1140. b**

—— *D. N. Uznadze Institute of Psychology.* ფსიქოლოგია. [Pʻsikʻologia. Psychology. Journal of the Institute. With summaries in Russian.]

Психология. tom. II, *etc.* თბილისი [*Tiflis,*] 1957–. 8⁰. *In progress.* **17080. d. 25**

—— *Academy of Sciences of the U.S.S.R., Georgian Filial.* [For 'Ornement populaire géorgien':] *See* Bardavelidze (V. V.) and Chitaia (G. S.)

—— *See* Chkhetia (Sh. Q.). ტფილისის ისტორიისათვის. [Tpʻilisis istoriisatʻvis. Contribution to the history of Tiflis.] 1938. 8⁰. [*Masalebi Sakʻartʻvelos da Kavkasiis istoriisatʻvis.* fasc. I.] **17075. e. 12**

—— *See* Janashia (S. N.). Сборник Руставели. К 750-летию "Вепхисткаосани". 1938. 8⁰. **17080. d. 7**

—— [For works published by the Georgian Academy after its establishment as a separate institution in 1941:] *See* Tiflis.—*Academy of Sciences of the Georgian S.S.R.*

—— მასალები საქართველოს და კავკასიის ისტორიისათვის. [Masalebi Sakʻartʻvelos da Kavkasiis istoriisatʻvis. Materials for the History of Georgia and the Caucasus.] (Материалы по Истории Грузии и Кавказа). [Georgian and Russian texts.] fasc. I–7, 25, 29–33, *etc.* ტფილისი [*Tiflis,*]. 1937–. 8⁰. *In progress.* **17075. e. 12**

—— *Georgian Geographical Society.* საქართველოს სსრ გეოგრაფიული საზოგადოების შრომები. [Sakʻartʻvelos S.S.R. geograpʻiuli sazogadoebis shromebi. Works of the Geographical Society of the Georgian S.S.R. With summaries in Russian.] Труды географического общества Грузинской ССР. tom. 3, *etc.* თბილისი [*Tiflis,*] 1958–. 8⁰. *In progress.* **17080. d. 26**

—— *Georgian Society of History and Ethnography.* *See* Tʻaqaishvili (E. S.). საქართველოს სიძველენი. [Sakʻartʻvelos sidzveleni.] Les Antiquités Géorgiennes. tom. 2 and Album. 1909. 8⁰ and fol. **17080. d. 9**

—— ძველი საქართველო. [Dzveli Sakʻartʻvelo.] Древняя Грузія. L'Ancienne Géorgie. Mémoires de la Société géorgienne d'histoire et d'ethnographie,

TIFLIS *(cont.)*

sous la rédaction de M. E. Takaïchvili. tom. I, 2. *Tiflis*, 1909–13. 8⁰.   **17080. d. 10**

—— პალეოგრაფიული ალბომი. დამატება 'საქართველოს სიძველის' II ტომისა. [Paleograpʻiuli albomi. Damateba 'Sakʻartʻvelos sidzvelenis' II tomisa.] Album paléographique. Supplément du II tome 'Des Antiquités Géorgiennes'. [Livr. I, containing charters of kings Bagrat IV and David IV. Edited by E. S. Tʻaqaishvili.] pp. 10. *lith.* ტფილისი [*Tiflis*,] 1909. fol.   **17080. d. 9**

—— *Georgian Theatrical Society.* [For 'Kʻartʻuli khalkhuri simgheris ostatebi':] *See* GEGETCHKORI (L.)

—— [For 'Davitʻ Rondeli', a study of the life and work of the Georgian film producer:] *See* LOLADZE (V.)

—— [For 'Suramis tsikhe', a tragedy adapted from the story by D. Tchonkʻadze:] *See* MTʻVARADZE (S.)

—— [For biography of the Georgian actor Vaso Abashidze:] *See* PʻAGHAVA (A.)

—— *Государственная Республиканская Библиотека им. К. Маркса. See* TIFLIS.—*Karl Marx State Library.*

—— *Государственный Музей Грузии. See* TIFLIS. —*Museum of Georgia.*

—— *Institut Caucasien d'Histoire et d'Archéologie. See* TIFLIS.—*Kavkazsky Istoriko-Arkheologichesky Institut.*

—— *Karl Marx State Library.* [For 'N. Nikoladzis arkʻivis katalogi':] *See* NIKOLADZE (N. I.)

—— კარლ მარქსის სახელობის საქართველოს სსრ სახელმწიფო ბიბლიოთეკის შრომები. [Karl Markʻsis sakhelobis Sakʻartʻvelos SSR sakhelmdsipʻo bibliotʻekis shromebi.] Works of the Karl Marx State Library of the SSR of Georgia. [Edit.

by S. Euli-Kʻuridze. With tables and plates.] bk. I. pp. 248. ტფილისი [*Tiflis*,] 1934. 8⁰.   **17075. e. 2**

—— *Кавказская Археографическая Коммиссія.* Акты собранные Кавказскою Археографическою Коммиссіею ... под редакціею ... А. Берже. [Illustrated.] 12 томъ. *Тифлисъ*, 1866–1904. fol.   **1712. a. 1**

—— *Kavkazsky Istoriko-Arkheologichesky Institut.* Известия Кавказского Историко-Археологического Института в Тифлисе. Bulletin de l'Institut Caucasien d'Histoire et d'Archéologie à Tiflis. tom. I, 2 and part of tom. 3. *Leningrad, Tiflis*, 1923–27. 4⁰.   **Ac. 1125. qc**

—— Законъ о Кавказскомъ Историко-Археологическомъ Институтѣ, *etc.* pp. 955–1006. *Петроградъ*, 1917. 8⁰. [*Извѣстія Академіи Наукъ*. VI серія. томъ 9.]   **Ac. 1125/44**

—— *Marr Language Institute*, afterwards *Institute of Linguistics. See* BARDAVELIDZE (V. V.) and CHITAIA (G. S.). ქართული ხალხური ორნამენტი. [Kʻartʻuli khalkhuri ornamenti.] Ornement populaire géorgien. 1939. 8⁰.   **17080. e. 3**

—— *See* BERIDZE (V. M.) *and others.* ტექნიკური ტერმინოლოგია. [Tekʻnikuri terminologia. A Russo-Georgian technical dictionary, compiled by a committee of scholars, and edited by V. M. Beridze and others.] 1957. 8⁰.   **17076. h. 17**

—— *See* JANASHIA (S. N.). Сборник Руставели. К 750-летию "Вепхисткаосани". 1938. 8⁰.   **17080. d. 7**

—— *See* KʻASHAKASHVILI (N. V.) and GHAMBASHIDZE (R. B.). მეტალურგიის ტერმინოლოგია. [Metalurgiis terminologia. A dictionary of metallurgical terminology.] 1959. 8⁰.   **17076. h. 20**

—— *See* KETSKHOVELI (N. N.) *and others.* სოფლის მეურნეობის ტერმინოლოგია. [Sopʻlis meurneobis terminologia. A dictionary of agricultural terms.] 1959. 8⁰.   **17076. h. 19**

—— აკად. ნ. მარის სახელობის ენის, ისტორიისა და მატერიალური კულტურის ინსტიტუტის მოამბე. [Akad. N. Maris sakhelobis enis, istoriisa da

TIFLIS *(cont.)*

materialuri kulturis institutis moambe.] Bulletin de l'Institut Marr de Langues, Histoire et de Culture Matérielle. tom. I, 3, *etc.* ტფილისი [*Tiflis,*] 1937–. 8⁰.   **17080. d. 5**

—— ენათმეცნიერების ინსტიტუტის შრომები. აღმოსავლურ ენათა სერია. [Enat'metsnierebis institutis shromebi. Aghmosavlur enat'a seria. Works of the Language Institute. Oriental Language series. Edit. by G. V. Tseret'eli.] Труды Института Языкознания. Серия Восточных Языков. tom. I–3, *etc.* თბილისი [*Tiflis,*] 1954–. 8⁰. *In progress.*   **17076. i. 4.**

—— იბერიულ-კავკასიური ენათმეცნიერება. [Iberiul-kavkasiuri enat'metsniereba.] (Иберийско-кавказское языкознание. Ibero-Caucasica.) tom. 2–5, 7–12, *etc.* თბილისი [*Tiflis,*] 1948–. 8⁰. *In progress.*   **17080. f. 10**

—— ქართული დიალექტოლოგია. [K'art'uli dialek'tologia. Georgian dialect studies.] Грузинская диалектология. tom. I— თბილისი [*Tiflis,*] 1956–. 8⁰. *In progress.*   **17080. f. 11**

—— ქართველურ ენათა სტრუქტურის საკითხები. [K'art'velur enat'a struk'turis sakit'khebi. Problems of the structure of Georgian and related languages. Articles in Georgian, with summaries in Russian.] (Вопросы структуры картвельских языков.) tom. I, *etc.* თბილისი [*Tiflis,*] 1959–. 8⁰. *In progress.*   **17076. f. 31**

—— სვანური პროზაული ტექსტები. II. ბალს-ქვემოური კილო. [Svanuri prozauli tek'stebi. II. Balsk'vemouri kilo. Svanian prose texts. II. Balsk'vemouri dialect. Texts collected by A. Davit'iani, V. T'op'uria and M. K'aldani, and edited by V. T'op'uria.] (Сванские прозаические тексты. II. Нижнебальское наречие.) pp. xiv. 361. თბილისი [*Tiflis,*] 1957. 8⁰.   **17076. c. 14**

—— *Marx, Engels, Lenin and Stalin Institute, Georgian Filial.* [For 'Sabtchot'a kavshiris komunisturi partia .... rezolutsiebsa da gadadsqvetilebebshi':] *See* RUSSIA. — *Российская Коммунистическая Партия.*

—— *Museum of Georgia. See* GABASHVILI (TIMOT'E) *Metropolitan of K'ut'aisi.* მიმოსლვა. [Mimoslva. Travels to Mount Athos, Jerusalem and other Holy Places, undertaken in 1755–59.] 1956. 8⁰.   **17075. e. 34**

——*See* JAP'ARIDZE (V. V.). კერამიკული წარმოება XI–XIII სს. საქართველოში. [Keramikuli dsarmoeba XI–XIII ss. Sak'art'veloshi. Ceramic production in Georgia in the 11ᵗʰ–13ᵗʰ centuries.] 1956. 4⁰.   **17080. g. 2**

—— [For 'T'bilisis ark'eologiuri dzeglebi':] *See* K'ORIDZE (D. L.)

—— მუზეუმში 1904—1920 წლებში შემოსული, საქართველოში აღმოჩენილი არქეოლოგიური მასალების აღწერილობა. [Muzeumshi 1904–1920 dslebshi shemosuli, Sak'art'veloshi aghmochenili ark'eologiuri masalebis aghdseriloba. Description of archaeological materials discovered in Georgia and acquired by the Museum in the years 1904–20. Compiled by M. M. Badriashvili and others, and edited by A. M. Ap'ak'idze.] Описание археологических материалов, обнаруженных в Грузии и поступивших в Музей в 1904–1920 годах. *Georgian and Russian texts.* pp. 108. 61 *plates.* თბილისი [*Tiflis,*] 1955. 4⁰. [*Ark'eologiuri masalebis katalogi.* tom. 2.]   **17080. f. 5**

—— საქართველოს მუზეუმის მოამბე. [Sak'art'velos muzeumis moambe.] Bulletin du Musée de Géorgie. tom. I, 3–8, 9A–15B, 16B–19B, 20B, 21B, *etc.* ტფილისი [*Tiflis,*] 1922–. 8⁰.   **17080. d. 6**

—— საქართველოს მუზეუმის შრომები. [Sak'art'velos muzeumis shromebi.] Travaux du Musée de Géorgie. no. I, 2, 4–6. ტფილისი [*Tiflis,*] 1920–33. 8⁰ & 4⁰.   **17080. b. 1**

—— საქართველოს სახელმწიფო მუზეუმის ძველ ხელნაწერთა საცავების გზამკვლევი. [Sak'art'velos sakhelmdsip'o muzeumis dzvel khelnadsert'a satsavebis gzamkvlevi. Guide to the collections of ancient manuscripts in the Georgian State Museum. Composed by K'. Sharashidze and others, and edit. by K. G. Grigolia. Illustrated.] (Путеводитель по хранилищам древних рукописей Госу-

TIFLIS *(cont.)*

дарственного Музея Грузии.) pp. 345. თბილისი
[*Tiflis*,] 1951. 8⁰.   **17080. b. 8**

—— საქართველოს სახელმწიფო მუზეუმის გემები. [Sakʻartʻvelos sakhelmdsipʻo muzeumis gemebi. A catalogue of the engraved gems in the
Georgian State Museum. Compiled by M. N. Lortʻ-
kʻipʻanidze. With plates, illustrations in the text,
a bibliography, and summaries in Russian.]
(Геммы Государственного Музея Грузии.) tom. 1, 2,
etc. თბილისი [*Tiflis*,] 1954–. 8⁰. *In progress.*
        17080. e. 4

—— [Another copy of tom. 1.]   **17080. e. 4***

—— საქართველოს სახელმწიფო მუზეუმის ქართულ ხელნაწერთა აღწერილობა. [Sakʻartʻvelos
sakhelmdsipʻo muzeumis kʻartʻul khelnadsertʻa
aghdseriloba.] Description des manuscrits géorgiens
du Musée d'État de Géorgie. [Edit. by S. N. Janashia, K. S. Kekelidze and others.] Collection A,
tom. 4, 5. Collection H, tom. 1–6. Collection Q,
tom. 1, 2. Collection S, tom. 1, თბილისი [*Tiflis*,]
1946–. 8⁰. *In progress. tom. 1 of Collection H is
defective, lacking pp. 33–48.*   **17075. e. 9**

—— [Another copy of the catalogue of Collection
H, tom. 3, 4, 5.] 1948–50. 8⁰.   **17075. e. 9***

—— *National Theatre of Georgia. See* GEORGIA.—
National Theatre.

—— *Rustʻaveli Literary Institute. See* TIFLIS.—
*Academy of Sciences of the Georgian S.S.R. —
Rustʻaveli Literary Institute.*

—— *Society for the Spreading of Literacy among the
Georgians.* წიგნების კატალოგი ქ. შ. წერა-კითხვის
გამავრცელებელის საზოგადოების წიგნის მაღა-
ზიისა. [Dsignebis katalogi kʻ. sh. dsera-kitʻkhvis
gamavrtselebelis sazogadoebis dsignis maghaziisa.
Catalogue of books in the bookshop of the Society
for the Spreading of Literacy among the Georgians. Fifth edition.] pp. 54. ტფილისი [*Tiflis*,]
1898. 8⁰.   **17077. a. 7**

—— *Tiflis Botanical Garden. See* TIFLIS.—*Academy*

*of Sciences of the Georgian S.S.R.—Tiflis Botanical
Institute.*

—— *Tiflis State University.* [For Festschrift in
honour of Professor K. S. Kekelidze:] *See* KEKE-
LIDZE (K. S.)

—— *See* MARR (N. Y.). О Кавказскомъ Университетѣ
въ Тифлисѣ. 1918. 8⁰.   **Ac. 1125/11**

—— აკად. ივ. ბერიტაშვილის სახელობის ფიზი-
ოლოგიის ინსტიტუტის შრომები. [Akad. Iv. Beritashvilis sakhelobis pʻiziologiis institutis shromebi.] Transactions of the J. Beritashvili Physiological Institute, edited by Prof. J. S. Beritoff.
tom. 4–6. თბილისი [*Tiflis*,] 1941–45. 8⁰.
        17080. d. 18

—— Album d'architecture géorgienne. (Compre-
nant 80 tableaux des dessins exécutés d'après les
mesurages. Édition de l'Université de Tiflis.)
Rédigé par M. E. Takaïchvili. Gravures dessinées
par les architectes et peintres MM. Ebralidzé,
Kalachnikov, Kalguine, Kern, Kühne, Riabov et
Severov. *Fr. and Georg.* pp. vii. 80. Tiflis, 1924.
4⁰.   **17080. d. 1**

—— ძველი ქართული ენის კათედრის შრომები.
[Dzveli kʻartʻuli enis katʻedris shromebi. Works of
the Department of Old Georgian language.]
no. 3–5, *etc.* თბილისი [*Tiflis*,] 1956–. 4⁰. *In
progress.*   **17076. h. 13**

—— ნარკვევები საქართველოს ისტორიის წყა-
როთმცოდნეობიდან. [Narkvevebi Sakʻartʻvelos
istoriis dsqarotʻmtsodneobidan. Studies in the
sources for Georgian history.] tom. 1— თბილისი
[*Tiflis*,] 1954–. 8⁰. *In progress.*   **17075. e. 20**

—— საქართველოს საერთაშორისო ურთიერთობანი უცხო ქვეყნებთან. [Sakʻartʻvelos saertʻasho-
riso urtʻiertʻobani utskho kʻveqnebtʻan. Georgia's
international relations with foreign powers.] Меж-
дународные сношения Грузии с иноземными
странами. no. 1, 2. ტფილისი [*Tiflis*,] 1926–28. 8⁰.
        17075. e. 11

—— თბილისი 1500. საიუბილეო კრებული. [Tʻbilisi 1500. Saiubileo krebuli. 1500 years of Tiflis. A symposium of essays on historical, archaeological, literary and other topics, published under the auspices of Tiflis University on the occasion of the 1500th anniversary of the foundation of the city. Edited by S. Zhghenti. Illustrated.] (Тбилиси 1500. Юбилейный сборник.) pp. 297, 6. 22 *plates.* თბილისი [*Tiflis,*] 1958. 4⁰. **17075. b. 9**

—— ტფილისის სახელმწიფო უნივერსიტეტი, 1918–1928. I: ზოგადი მიმოხილვა, *etc.* [Tp'ilisis sakhelmdsip'o universiteti, 1918–1928. I: Zogadi mimokhilva, *etc.* Tiflis State University, 1918–1928, a general survey. Part I, comprising reports of the faculties and account of student organisations. Illustrated.] pp. 414, ii. ტფილისი [*Tiflis,*] 1928. 8⁰. **17080. b. 6**

—— ტფილისის სახელმწიფო უნივერსიტეტის შრომები. [Tp'ilisis sakhelmdsip'o universitetis shromebi.] Travaux de l'Université d'État de Tiflis. tom. 1–4. ტფილისი [*Tiflis,*] 1936. 8⁰. *The series, though numbered consecutively throughout, is divided into two sections: 1, Social sciences; 2, Mathematics and Natural Sciences.* **17080. d. 4**

—— ტფილისის უნივერსიტეტის მოამბე. [Tp'ilisis universitetis moambe.] Bulletin de l'Université de Tiflis. tom. 4, 5, 7–10. ტფილისი [*Tiflis,*] 1924–30. 8⁰. **17080. d. 3**

—— ზოგადი ენათმეცნიერების კათედრის შრომები. [Zogadi enat'metsnierebis kat'edris shromebi. Publications of the Department of General Linguistics.] (Труды кафедры общего языкознания.) no. 1–3, *etc.* თბილისი [*Tiflis,*] 1956–. 8⁰. *In progress.* **17076. f. 33**

—— *Union of Soviet Georgian Writers.* [For 'Mnat'obi', monthly journal of the Georgian Soviet writers' union:] *See* PERIODICAL PUBLICATIONS.—*Tiflis.*

TIKHONOV (NIKOLAI SEMENOVICH). [Trans. 'Сталин. Детство и отрочество'.] *See* LEONIDZE (G. N.)

—— [Joint trans. of 'Поэты Грузии'.] *See* MIDSISHVILI (N.)

TIMOTHY, *Archbishop of Imeret'i. See* GABASHVILI (TIMOT'E) *Metropolitan of K'ut'aisi.*

TLUKAANT'I (DAVID). Dottrina Cristiana per uso delle missioni della Giorgia... tradotta dalla lingua Italiana in lingua civile Giorgiana da David Tlukaanti Giorgiano. Seconda edizione. (საქრისტიანო მოძღვარება, გინა წურთნა შვიდთა საიდუმლოთა ზედა. [Sak'ristiano modzghvareba, gina dsurt'na shvidt'a saidumlot'a zeda. Christian doctrine, or instruction in the Seven Sacraments. Based in part on the manual by Cardinal Bellarmino. Second edition, revised by Grigol Baghinant'i.]) pp. 416. *Roma,* 1797. 8⁰. **17071. a. 1**

T'MOGVELI (SARGIS). *See* SARGIS, *of T'mogvi.*

TOGONIDZE (GIORGI). ლტოლვილის სიმღერა. [Ltolvilis simghera.] La chanson du réfugié. *Geo. & Fr.* bk. 2. pp. 88. პარიზი [*Paris,*] 1953. 8⁰. **17075. f. 24**

T'OIDZE (IRAKLI MOSES-DZE). [Joint illustrator of 'The Man in the Panther's Skin'.] *See* RUST'AVELI (SHOT'A).

TOKAREV (G.). Lettre à M. Brosset sur quelques antiquités chrétiennes et autres, des environs de l'Elbrouz. pp. 232–40 *St.-Pétersbourg,* 1850. 4⁰. [*Bulletin Historico-philologique de l'Académie des Sciences.* tom. 7.] **Ac. 1125/7**

TOKAYSHVILI (E.). *See* T'AQAISHVILI (E. S.)

TOLOCHANOV (NIKIFOR MATVEEVICH). [For a report on the diplomatic mission of Tolochanov and Ievlev to Imeret'i:] *See* POLIEVKTOV (M. A.)

T'OMAANT' KOBA, *pseud.* [i.e. IAKOB TSINTSADZE]. რას იცინი? [Ras itsini? Why do you laugh? A satirical fable.] pp. 20. თბილისი [*Tiflis,*] 1896. 8⁰. **17076. a. 5**

T'OP'URIA (GURAM VARLAMIS-DZE). ლეზგიური ზმნის ძირითადი მორფოლოგიური კატეგორიები, კიურიული და ახტის დიალექტების მონაცემთა მიხედვით. [Lezgiuri zmnis dzirit'adi morp'ologiuri kategoriebi, kiuriuli da akhtis dialek'tebis monatsemt'a mikhedvit'. The basic morphological categories of the Lezgian verb, according to data derived from the Kiuri and Akhty dialects.] (Основные морфологические категории лезгинского глагола.) [Georgian text with summary in Russian.] pp. 135. თბილისი [*Tiflis*,] 1959. 8⁰.   **17076. f. 34. (4.)**

T'OP'URIA (VARLAM TRIP'ONIS-DZE). [Edit. 'K'art'uli enis kakhuri dialek'ti'.] *See* MARTIROSOV (A. G.) and IMNAISHVILI (G. M.)

—— [Edit. 'Svanuri prozauli tek'stebi':] *See* TIFLIS.—*Marr Language Institute*, afterwards *Institute of Linguistics*.

—— and **GIGINEISHVILI** (IVANE MOSES-DZE). ორთოგრაფიული ლექსიკონი. [Ort'ograp'iuli lek'sikoni. A lexicographical guide to Georgian spelling, for use in schools. Edit. by S. Qaukhchishvili. Third edition.] pp. 8. 3. 278. თბილისი [*Tiflis*,] 1949. 8⁰.   **17076. g. 12**

T'ORNIKE, *Erist'avi*. *See* THORNICIUS, afterwards JOHANNES, *Monk at Mount Athos*.

TOUMANOFF (CYRIL LÉON) *Prince*. Chronology of the Kings of Abasgia and other Problems. pp. 73–90. *Louvain*, 1956. 8⁰. [*Le Muséon*. tom. 69.]   **P. P. 4453**

—— The Early Bagratids. Remarks in Connexion with some recent Publications. [Including extracts from the Georgian Annals.] pp. 21–54. *Louvain*, 1949. 8⁰. [*Le Muséon*. tom. 62.]   **P. P. 4453**

—— The Fifteenth-Century Bagratids and the Institution of Collegial Sovereignty in Georgia. [With a genealogical table]. pp. 169–221. *New York*, 1949–1951. 8⁰. [Offprint from *Traditio*. vol. 7.]   **17089. d. 2**

—— Iberia on the eve of Bagratid rule. An enquiry into the political history of Eastern Georgia between the VIth and the IXth century. [With a genealogical table.] 3 pt. tom. 65. pp. 17–49; 199–258; tom. 66. pp. 103–104. *Louvain*, 1952–53. 8⁰. [*Le Muséon*. tom. 65–66.]   **P. P. 4453**

—— [Another copy, being an offprint.] **17089. d. 1**

—— Review of 'Histoire du Bas-Empire. Tome II, De la disparition de l'Empire d'Occident à la mort de Justinien (476–565)', by Ernst Stein. [With special reference to Byzantine policy in Georgia.] pp. 481–90. *New York*, 1949–51. 8⁰. [Offprint from *Traditio*. vol. 7.]   **17089. d. 3**

TQVIRI. [For an archaeological study of the ancient church at Tqviri in Mingrelia:] *See* T'AQAISHVILI (E. S.)

TREGUBA (SEMON ADOL'FOVICH). [Trans. 'Абхазские новеллы'.] *See* LAKERBAI (M. A.)

TREVER (KAMILLA VASIL'EVNA). Очерки по истории и культуре кавказской Албании, IV в. до н. э.—VII в. н. э. (Ответственный редактор Акад. И. А. Орбели.) [Illustrated with plans, maps, facsimiles of inscriptions, etc.] pp. 389, 3. 42 *plates*. Москва, Ленинград, 1959. 8⁰.   **17075. b. 4**

TRUBETSKOI (NIKOLAI SERGEEVICH) *Prince*. Erinnerungen an einen Aufenthalt bei den Tscherkessen des Kreises Tuapse. pp. 1–39. *Leipzig*, 1934. 8⁰. [*Caucasica*. fasc. 11.]   **P. P. 3803. eba**

—— Die Konsonantensysteme der Ostkaukasischen Sprachen. pp. 1–52. *Leipzig*, 1931. 8⁰. [*Caucasica*. fasc. 8.]   **P. P. 3803. eba**

—— Studien auf dem Gebiete der vergleichenden Lautlehre der nordkaukasischen Sprachen. I. pp. 7–36. *Leipzig*, 1926. 8⁰. [*Caucasica*. fasc. 3.] *No more published*.   **P. P. 3803. eba**

TSADASA (GAMZAT). Стихотворения и поэмы. [Trans. from Avar into Russian by various hands, with introduction and notes by N. Kapieva. Second edition.] pp. 302. 1 *plate*. Ленинград, 1958. 8⁰.   **17075. d. 44**

TSAGARELI (ALEKSANDR ANTONOVICH). [For a French rendering of selected tales by Sulkhan-Saba Orbeliani, made from the Russian version by Tsagareli, and of Mingrelian tales collected by Tsa-

TSAGARELI *(cont.)*
gareli, included in 'Contes et légendes du Caucase':]
See Mourier (J.)

—— [Trans. 'Книга мудрости и лжи'.] *See* Savva, *the Monk* [*Prince* Sulkhan Orbeliani].

—— Два изслѣдователя кавказскихъ языковъ. Академикъ А. А. Шифнеръ † 1879 г. и баронъ П. К. Усларъ † 1875 г. pp. 29–35. С.-Петербургъ, 1880. 8⁰. [*Журналъ Министерства Народнаго Просвѣщенія.* часть 208. отд. 4.]   **P. P. 1213**

—— Грамоты и другіе историческіе документы XVIII столѣтія, относящіеся до Грузіи. томъ II, вып. 2. pp. lv. 330. С.-Петербургъ, 1902. 8⁰.   **17033. e. 5**

—— Грузинскія надписи, найденныя въ Россіи. [Comprising four inscriptions, dating from the XVIIth and XVIIIth centuries.] pp. 227–32. С.-Петербургъ, 1888. 8⁰. [*Записки Восточнаго Отдѣленія Имп. Русскаго Археологическаго Общества.* томъ 2.].   **Ac. 5584**

—— Мингрельскіе этюды. Первый выпускъ. Мингрельскіе тексты съ переводомъ и объясненіями. (Второй выпускъ. Опытъ фонетики мингрельскаго языка.) 2 вып. С.-Петербургъ, 1880. 8⁰.   **12431. i. 28**

—— Новые архивные матеріалы для исторіи Грузіи XVIII столѣтія. pp. 117–37. С.-Петербургъ, 1883. 8⁰. [*Журналъ Министерства Народнаго Просвѣщенія.* часть 225. отд. 2.]   **P. P. 1213**

—— Памятники грузинской старины въ Святой Землѣ и на Синаѣ. [Includes a Catalogue of Georgian Mss. in the Monastery of the Cross near Jerusalem and the Sinai Monastery, and transcripts of Georgian inscriptions in Palestine.] pp. ix. 310. 11 *plates.* С.-Петербургъ, 1888. 8⁰. [*Православный Палестинскій Сборникъ.* томъ 4. вып. 1.]   **Ac. 2058**

—— Преосвященный Порфирій о грузинскихъ древностяхъ. [Including a description of Georgian ikons in the Sinai Monastery.] pp. 8–18. Санктпетербургъ, 1887. 8⁰. [*Записки Восточнаго Отдѣленія Имп. Русскаго Археологическаго Общества.* томъ 1.]   **Ac. 5584**

—— Свѣдѣнія о памятникахъ грузинской письменности. [Fasc. 1 includes a catalogue of the library of the Georgian monastery on Mt. Athos; fasc. 3 includes documents concerning the life and work of Professor D. Chubinov, and a Georgian version of the tragedy 'Iphigénie' by Racine.] вып. 1, 3. Санктпетербургъ, 1886, 94. 8⁰. *Вып. 3 is defective, lacking title-page, portrait frontispiece and pp. 319–320.*   **7708. d. 3**

TSAGARELI (Archil Lukas-dze). [Joint trans. of selected novels and comedies by Mérimée.] *See* Mérimée (P.)

TSAGARELI (Giorgi Konstantines-dze). [Trans. 'Великий Моурави':] *See* Joseph [Ioseb Saakadze], *Bishop of Tiflis.*

—— [Trans. of the epic poem 'Витязь в тигровой шкуре'.] *See* Rust'aveli (Shot'a).

—— Избранные переводы. Поэты советской Грузии. [An anthology of Georgian verse, in Russian translation by G. Tsagareli. Edit. by G. N. Leonidze.] pp. 185. Тбилиси, 1950. 8⁰.   **17046. aa. 6**

TSAGOV (Mohammed Nurievich). [Joint author of 'Грамматика кабардинского языка'.] *See* Turchaninov (G. F.) and Tsagov (M. N.)

TSAISHVILI (Solomon). [Edit. collected works of K. T'at'arishvili.] *See* Uiaragho, *pseud.*

TSAKHELI, *pseud.* [i. e. Parmen T'valtchrelidze]. რამდენიმე ლექსი. [Ramdenime lek'si. Some verses. Edit. by Z. E. Tchitchinadze.] pp. 32. ტფილისი [*Tiflis,*] 1891. 8⁰.   **17075. d. 1. (5.)**

TSANAVA (Apolon Basilis-dze). წიგნი "სიბრძნე სიცრუისა" და ქართული ხალხური მახვილსიტყვაობა. [Dsigni "Sibrdzne sitsruisa" da k'art'uli khalkhuri makhvilsitqvaoba. The 'Book of Wisdom and Lies', by Sulkhan-Saba Orbeliani, and Georgian popular humour.] pp. 95. თბილისი [*Tiflis,*] 1959. 8⁰.   **17076. b. 46**

—— ქართული მესტვირული პოეზია. [K'art'uli mestviruli poezia. Georgian minstrel poetry. A historical and biographical study.] pp. 224. თბი-ლისი [*Tiflis*,] 1953. 8⁰.   **17075. d. 12**

TSCHENKÉLI (Kita). *See* Chkhenkeli (K.)

TSCHITAIA (Giorgi). *See* Chitaia.

TSERETʻELI (Akaki Rostomis-dze) *Prince*. [For selected poems, in Russian translation:] *See* Gol'-tsev (V. V.) and Chikʻovani (S. I.). Поэзия Грузии. 1949. 4⁰.   **17075. dd. 1**

—— [For 'Творчество А. Р. Церетели':] *See* Nu-tsubidze (Sh. I.)

—— [Editor of the monthly review 'Krebuli'.] *See* Periodical Publications.—*Kʻutʻaisi.*

—— Избранное. Перевод с грузинского под редак-цией В. Гольцева и С. Чиковани. [With portraits and a facsimile.] pp. 327. *Москва*, 1940. 8⁰.   **11587. bb. 31**

—— Неопубликованная рукопись грузинского поэта А. Р. Церетели. [Comprising an essay on Rustʻa-veli's poem 'Vepʻkhis-tqaosani'.] (Вводная статья Н. А. Малеванова, К. Степановой.) pp. 105–110. *Москва*, 1956. 8⁰. [*Исторический архив.* no. 6.]   **Ac. 1125. wb/36**

—— Пережитое. [Reminiscences. Trans. into Rus-sian by E. D. Ghoghoberidze, edit. by E. G. Lund-berg. Second edition.] pp. 144. *Москва*, 1950. 8⁰.   **17076. g. 6**

—— [Another copy.]   **10797. de. 12**

—— თხზულებანი აკაკი წერეთლისა. [Tʻkhzule-bani Akaki Tseretʻlisa. Works of Akaki Tseretʻeli, consisting of his collected poems. With a plate.] 2 tom. ტფილისი [*Tiflis*,] 1893. 8⁰.   **17075. c. 2**

—— თხზულებათა სრული კრებული თხუთმეტ ტომად. [Tʻkhzulebatʻa sruli krebuli tʻkhutʻmet tomad. Complete collection of works, in 15 volumes. Edited by G. Abzianidze and others.] tom. 8, 11, 12, *etc.* თბილისი [*Tiflis*,] 1958–. 8⁰. *In progress.*   **17076. c. 13**

TSERETʻELI (Giorgi Ekʻvtʻimes-dze). [Author of introductory essay to 'Davitʻiani'.] *See* Gura-mishvili (D.)

—— [Editor of Georgian periodical 'Kvali'.] *See* Periodical Publications.—*Tiflis.*

—— Археологическая экскурсія по квирильскому ущелью. [Archaeological excursion through the Qvirila valley. Includes a number of historical inscriptions from Georgian churches]. pp. 83–114. 6 *plates*. *Москва*, 1898. 4⁰. [*Матеріалы по Ар-хеологіи Кавказа.* вып. 7.]   **Ac. 5575/3**

TSERETʻELI (Giorgi Vasilis-dze). [Edit. tom. 2 of 'Kʻartʻuli enis ganmartebitʻi lekʻsikoni'.] *See* Chikʻobava (A. S.) *and others.*

—— [Edit. 'Arabuli zmnis pʻormatʻa paradig-mebi'.] *See* Lekiashvili (A. S.)

—— [Edit. 'Enatʻmetsnierebis institutis shrome-bi'.] *See* Tiflis.—*Marr Language Institute.*

—— არმაზის ბილინგვა. [Armazis bilingva.] A bilingual inscription from Armazi near Mcheta in Georgia. [Georgian and English texts.] pp. 83. 4 *plates*. თბილისი [*Tiflis*,] 1942. 8⁰. [Offprint from the *Bulletin of the Marr Institute of Languages, History and Material Culture.* vol. 13.]   **17080. b. 4**

—— Армазское письмо и проблема происхождения грузинского алфавита. [Illustrated.] 2 pt. вып. 2. pp. 90–101; вып. 3. pp. 59–71. *Москва, Ленинград*, 1948–49. 4⁰. [*Эпиграфика Востока.* вып. 2–3.]   **Ac. 1125. gd/3**

TSERETʻELI (Mikheil Giorgis-dze). The Asi-anic Elements in National Georgian Paganism. pp. 28–66. *London*, 1935. 8⁰. [*Georgica.* vol. 1. no. 1.]   **Ac. 8821. e**

—— ერი და კაცობრიობა. [Eri da katsobrioba. The nation and humanity, a sociological study.] pp. xxxii. 382. თბილისი [*Tiflis*,] 1910. 8⁰.   **17075. e. 7. (1.)**

—— Sumerian and Georgian: a Study in Comparative Philology. 4 pt. 1913. pp. 783–821; 1914. pp. 1–36; 1915. pp. 255–88; 1916. pp. 1–58. *London*, 1913–16. 8⁰. [*Journal of the Royal Asiatic Society for 1913–16.*]   **R. Ac. 8820/3**

TSERET'ELI (Savle Benedik'tes-dze). ლო-გიკური კავშირის დიალექტიკური ბუნების შესახებ. [Logikuri kavshiris dialek'tikuri bunebis shesakheb. Concerning the dialectical nature of logical connection. A metaphysical treatise.] pp. 624. სახელგამი [*State Publishing House: Tiflis*,] 1956. 8⁰.   **17078. d. 1**

—— რაციონალური მარცვალი ჰეგელის დასკვნის თეორიაში. [Ratsionaluri martsvali Hegelis daskvnis t'eoriashi. The rational core in Hegel's theory of judgement.] (Рациональное зерно в теории умозаключения Гегеля.) pp. 334. თბილისი [*Tiflis*,] 1959. 8⁰.   **17078. d. 3**

TSEY IBRĀHĪM. Fables de Tsey Ibrahim—tcherkesse occidental. Traduites et commentées, avec une introduction grammaticale et un index des formes verbales, par Georges Dumézil et Aytek Namitok. pp. 91. *Paris*, 1939. 8⁰. [*Annales du Musée Guimet. Bibliothèque d'études*. tom. 50.]   **1712. e. 50**

TSINTSADZE (Iakob). *See* T'omaant' Koba, *pseud.*

TSINTSADZE (Vakhtang Gerontis-dze). Тбилиси. Архитектура старого города и жилые дома первой половины XIX столетия. [With illustrations, some in colour, and maps, plans and diagrams in the text.] pp. 115. 88 *plates*. Тбилиси, 1958. fol.   **17080. g. 10**

TSKHVILOELI (Polievk'ti). *pseud.* [i. e. Po-lievk'ti Grigolis-dze Karbelashvili]. მეფე ერეკლე და დემეტრე ამილახვარი. [Mep'e Erekle da Demetre Amilakhvari. King Erekle and Demetre Amilakhvari. A historical study.] pp. 1–20. ტფილისი [*Tiflis*], 1896. 8⁰. [*Moambe*. tom. 3. no. 1.]   **17089. b. 1**

T'UMANISHVILI (Kirile). *See* Toumanoff (C. L.) *Prince.*

TURABELIDZE (Elene). [Editor of humorous journal 'Mat'rakhi da salamuri'.] *See* Periodical Publications.—*Tiflis.*

TURCHANINOV (Georgy Fedorovich). Эпиграфические заметки. 2 pt. *Москва*, 1947–48. 8⁰. [*Известия Академии Наук СССР. Отделение литературы и языка*. tom. 6. no. 6; tom. 7. no. 1.]   **Ac. 1125/44 (11)**

—— О категории грамматических классов в кабардинском. pp. 227–30. *Москва, Ленинград*, 1936. 8⁰. [*Язык и мышление*. вып. 6–7.]   **Ac. 1125. t/2**

—— О категории вида в черкесских языках. pp. 254–61. *Москва, Ленинград*, 1949. 8⁰. [*Известия Академии Наук СССР. Отделение литературы и языка*. tom. 8. no. 3.]   **Ac. 1125/44 (11)**

—— Рукописные материалы акад. Шёгрена по черкесским языкам. pp. 157–62. *Москва, Ленинград*, 1940. 8⁰. [*Язык и мышление*. вып. 10.]   **Ac. 1125. t/2**

—— and **TSAGOV** (Mohammed Nurievich). Грамматика кабардинского языка. том I. pp. 159, 1. *Москва, Ленинград*, 1940. 8⁰. *No more published.*   **Ac. 1125. t/4**

T'URDOSPIRELI (Davit'). გაწყვეტილი ზღა-პარი, ნოველები. [Gadsqvetili zghapari, novelebi. The interrupted tale, short stories.] pp. 64. თბი-ლისი [*Tiflis*,] 1919. 8⁰.   **17076. b. 28**

T'URMANIDZE (Khosro). [Georgian translator of the Shāhnāmeh.] *See* Hasan (Abu'l-Kāsim), called Firdausī, *Tūsī.*

TUSH LANGUAGE. [For 'Бацбийский язык':] *See* Desheriev (Y. D.)

—— [For 'Versuch über die Thusch-Sprache':] *See* Schiefner (F. A. von).

T'VALTCHRELIDZE (Parmen). *See* Tsakheli, *pseud.*

T'VALT'VADZE (P'at'ma Antonis-asuli). [Trans. 'Десница великого мастера'.] *See* Gamsakhurdia (K. S.)

T'VALT'VADZE (cont.)

—— [Edit. collected works of E. Ninoshvili.] See NINOSHVILI (E.) pseud.

—— Грузинские повести и рассказы. [Georgian stories and tales, trans. into Russian and edit. by P'. A. T'valt'vadze.] pp. 462. Москва, 1951. 8⁰.

17076. a. 9

UBYKH LANGUAGE. [For 'Die Sprache der Ubychen':] See DIRR (A.)

—— [For 'Contes et légendes des Oubykhs':] See DUMÉZIL (G.)

—— [For 'La langue des Oubykhs':] See DUMÉZIL (G.)

—— [For 'Récits oubykh':] See DUMÉZIL (G.) and NAMITOK (A.)

—— [For 'О языке Убыхов':] See GENKO (A. N.)

UDI LANGUAGE. [For 'Грамматика удинскаго языка':] See DIRR (A.)

—— [For 'Udische Texte':] See DIRR (A.)

—— [For 'К фонетике удинского языка':] See KARBELASHVILI (D. P.)

—— [For 'Versuch über die Sprache der Uden':] See SCHIEFNER (F. A. von).

UIARAGHO, pseud. [i. e. KONDRATE T'AT'ARISHVILI]. თხზულებათა სრული კრებული ორ ტომად. [T'khzulebat'a sruli krebuli or tomad. Complete collection of works, in two volumes.] tom. I. მოთხრობები, ნარკვევები და წერილები. [Mot'khrobebi, narkvevebi da dserilebi. Stories, sketches and articles. Edit. with an introduction and notes by S. Tsaishvili.] pp. xxxiv. 637, 2. თბილისი [Tiflis,] 1957, etc. 8⁰. In progress.

17076. b. 40

UMIKASHVILI (PETRE). [Author of introductory essay to 'Davit'iani'.] See GURAMISHVILI (D.)

—— [Edit. 'Arsenas lek'si'.] See ODZELASHVILI (A.)

—— [Joint edit. of 'Visramiani'.] See SARGIS, of T'mogvi.

UNIVERSITY OF TIFLIS. See TIFLIS.—Tiflis State University.

URATADZE (GRIGOL ILARIONIS-DZE). საზოგადოებრივი მოძრაობა საქართველოში 1821—1921 წ. [Sazogadoebrivi modzraoba Sak'artveloshi 1821–1921 ds. The social movement in Georgia from 1821 to 1921.] pp. 199. პარიზი [Paris,] 1939. 8⁰.

17075. f. 19 (2.)

URBNELI (NIKO) pseud. [i. e. N. KHIZANASHVILI]. მეფე დავით აღმაშენებელი და მისი დრო. [Mep'e Davit' Aghmashenebeli da misi dro. King David the Builder and his time. A historical monograph.] pt. I–3. ტფილისი [Tiflis,] 1894. 8⁰. [Moambe. tom. I. no. I–3.] **17089. b. 1**

URJUMELASHVILI (IVANE). მორანბონი. [Moranboni. A story of the Korean War. Followed by further sketches under the title 'Dgheebshi Koreashi', Days in Korea. With a foreword by V. Baiadze. Illustrated.] pp. 189. I plate. თბილისი [Tiflis,] 1952. 8⁰. **17076. b. 25**

URUSHADZE (SEVERIANE). L'hymne au monde harmonieux. Avec une étude Historico-Mythologique. Ier cahier. pp. ii. 20. Montrouge, n. d. [1956.] 12⁰. **17075. d. 37**

—— კოლხიდეა და პოეზია; ლირიკული პიესა სამი აქტად. [Kolkhidea da poezia; lirikuli piesa sami ak'tad.] Colchidea et la poésie: une pièce lyrique de 3 actes. [Followed by lyric poems in Georgian, French, German and Russian.]. pp. 32. პარიზი [Paris,] 1951. 8⁰. **17075. d. 21. (6.)**

—— საქართველო და კეთილი, თან ცხოვრება და მშვენიერება. [Sak'art'velo da ket'ili, t'an tskhovreba da mshveniereba.] La Géorgie et le Bien, avec la Vie et le Beau. [A miscellany of poems and essays.] pp. 48. პარიზი [Paris,] 1950. 8⁰.

17075. d. 21. (5.)

URUSHADZE (VENERA). Anthology of Georgian Poetry. Translated by V. Urushadze. (ქართული

პოეზიის ანთოლოგია. [K'art'uli poeziis ant'olo-gia.] Edited with an introduction by M. Kveselava.) [Second, enlarged edition.] pp. xxi. 268. 9 *plates.* *Tbilisi*, 1958. 4⁰.   **17075. dd. 5**

USLAR (Petr Karlovich) *Baron.* [For 'Апсща аибан', based on Uslar's work 'Абхазскій языкъ':] *See* Bartholomaei (I. A.)

—— [For 'Ausführlicher Bericht über des Generals Baron P. von U. Abchasische Studien':] *See* Schiefner (F. A. von).

—— [For 'Ausführlicher Bericht über Baron P. v. Uslar's Awarische Studien':] *See* Schiefner (F. A. von).

—— [For 'Ausführlicher Bericht über Baron P. v. Uslar's Hürkanische Studien':] *See* Schiefner (F. A. von).

—— [For 'Ausführlicher Bericht über Baron P. v. Uslar's Kasikumükische Studien':] *See* Schiefner (F. A. von).

—— [For 'Ausführlicher Bericht über Baron P. v. Uslar's Kürinische Studien':] *See* Schiefner (F. A. von).

—— [*Obituary.*] *See* Tsagareli (A. A.)

—— Этнографія Кавказа. Языкознаніе. Абхазскій языкъ. С приложеніемъ статей [of a philological character], *etc.* pp. xv. 193. 120. *Тифлисъ*, 1887. 8⁰.   **O12901. i. 6**

—— Tschetschenzisches und Awarisches. pp. 165–77. *St.-Pétersbourg*, 1865. 8⁰. [*Mélanges Asiatiques de l'Académie des Sciences.* tom. 5. livr. 2–3.]   **Ac. 1125/11**

—— Über die geographische Verbreitung der awarischen Sprache. pp. 109–12. *St.-Pétersbourg*, 1865. 8⁰. [*Mélanges Asiatiques de l'Académie des Sciences.* tom. 5. livr. 2–3.]   **Ac. 1125/11**

USPENSKY (Porfiry). *See* Porfiry [Konstantin Aleksandrovich Uspensky], *Bishop of Chigirin.*

UVAROVA (Praskov'ya Sergyeevna) *Countess.* Матеріалы по Археологіи Кавказа .... под редакціей графини Уваровой. вып. I–II. 1888–1907. 4⁰. *See* Moscow.—*Imperatorskoe Moskovskoe Arkheologicheskoe Obshchestvo.*   **Ac. 5575/3**

—— Поѣздка въ Пшавію, Хевсуретію и Сванетію. [Expedition to P'shavia, Khevsuret'i and Svanet'i. With descriptions of ancient inscriptions and manuscripts, etc., and an appendix by A. S. Khakhanov on the ancient Gospel manuscripts preserved in Svanet'i.] pp. ii. 183, 40. 46 *plates. Москва*, 1904. 4⁰. [*Матеріалы по Археологіи Кавказа.* вып. 10.]   **Ac. 5575/3**

VAKHTANG V, *King of Georgia*, known as Shahnavaz I. [For extracts from poetic life of King Vakhtang V by P'. P'ashvi-Bertkadze, incorporated in 'Histoire de la Géorgie':] *See* Brosset (M.-F.)

VAKHTANG VI, *King of Georgia.* [For 'Notice du Code géorgien, manuscrit de la Bibliothèque royale', comprising the laws of King Vakhtang VI:] *See* Brosset (M.-F.)

—— [For 'Notice historique sur... Wakhtang VI':] *See* Brosset (M.-F.)

—— [For editions of the Georgian Annals, as revised by order of King Vakhtang VI:] *See* Brosset (M.-F.) and Chubinov (D. I.); Georgian Annals; Tchitchinadze (Z. E.)

—— *See* Georgia.—*Laws.* Le Code de Vakhtang VI, édité en version française et annoté par Joseph Karst, *etc.* 1934–40. 8⁰. [*Corpus Juris Ibero-Caucasici.* tom. 1–4, 6.]   **W. P. 5873/1,2**

—— [For 'Laws of King George V, of Georgia.... From the Bodleian Ms. of the Code of Vakhtang VI, *etc.*':] *See* Giorgi V, *King of Georgia*, called The Brilliant.

—— [For 'Georgian Relations with France during the reign of Wakhtang VI, 1711–24':] *See* Lang (D. M.)

—— Détails sur le droit public arménien, extraits

du Code géorgien du roi Wakhtang, et traduits du géorgien par M. Brosset. pp. 21–30. *Paris*, 1832. 8⁰. [*Nouveau Journal Asiatique*. tom. 9.]   **R. Ac. 8808**

VAKHUSHTI, *Prince of Georgia.* [For the first printed Georgian Bible of 1743, edited for publication, with a concluding discourse, by Prince Vakhushti:] *See* BIBLE.

—— [For a French trans. of the histories of the principalities of Georgia by Vakhushti, incorporated in 'Histoire de la Géorgie':] *See* BROSSET (M.-F.)

—— [For 'Nouvelles recherches sur l'historien Wakhoucht':] *See* BROSSET (M.-F.)

—— [For 'Pièces diverses relatives à la Géorgie', including a description of Vakhushti's map of Georgia:] *See* BROSSET (M.-F.)

—— [For 'Rapport sur la publication de la Géographie de la Géorgie par Wakhoucht':] *See* BROSSET (M.-F.)

—— [For text and translation of treatise on the Calendar by Prince Vakhushti:] *See* BROSSET (M.-F.). Études de chronologie technique. 1868. 4⁰.   **Ac. 1125/3**

—— [For the histories of the principalities of Georgia by Vakhushti, incorporated as a continuation to 'K'art'lis tskhovreba':] *See* BROSSET (M.-F.) and CHUBINOV (D. I.)

—— [For 'Еще одинъ изъ источниковъ исторіи Грузіи царевича Вахушта':] *See* T'AQAISHVILI (E. S.)

—— Description géographique de la Géorgie, par le Tsarévitch Wakhoucht, publiée d'après l'original autographe par M. Brosset. *Georg.* and *French.* pp. xxx. 540. 6 *maps. St.-Pétersbourg*, 1842. 4⁰.   **17080. d. 2**

—— Географія Грузіи. Введеніе, переводъ и примѣчанія М. Г. Джанашвили. pp. xlix. 241. *Тифлисъ*, 1904. 8⁰. [*Записки Кавказскаго Отдѣла Имп. Русскаго Географическаго Общества.* кн. 24.]   **Ac. 6134**

—— საქართველოს ისტორია. [Sak'art'velos istoria. History of Georgia. Edited with introduction and notes by D. Z. Bak'radze.] pt. 1. pp. xxxi. 344. 1 *map*. ტფილისი [*Tiflis*,] 1885. 4⁰.   **17075. e. 8**

VARDAN, *Bardzrberdaçi.* [For fragments of the commentary of St. Hippolytus on the Song of Solomon, preserved in the Armenian commentary by Vardan:] *See* HIPPOLYTUS, *Saint, of Rome.*

VARLAAM, *Saint, of Antioch. See* BARLAAM, *Saint, of Asia Minor.*

VARLAAM, *Saint, of India.* [THE LEGEND OF BARLAAM AND JOSAPHAT.—*Georgian.*] *See* BARLAAM, *Saint, of India.*

VASIL'EVSKY (VASILY GRIGOR'EVICH). [Joint edit. 'Византійскій Временникъ'.] *See* ST. PETERSBURG.—*Academia Scientiarum Imperialis.*

VAZHA-P'SHAVELA, *pseud.* [i. e. LUKA RAZIKASHVILI]. [For 'Gadmotsema "Khogais Mindize" da poema "Gvelis mtchameli"':] *See* GACHECHILADZE (A. N.)

—— [For selected poems, in Russian translation:] *See* GOL'TSEV (V. V.) and CHIK'OVANI (S. I.). Поэзия Грузии. 1949. 4⁰.   **17075. dd. 1**

—— ახუნდი. ძველი ამბავი. [Akhundi. Dzveli ambavi. The holy man. An ancient legend, recounted in verse.] pp. 16. ტფილისი [*Tiflis*,] 1898. 12⁰.   **17075. d. 5. (5.)**

—— [Complete works, edited by A. B. Abasheli.] tom. 7. ეთნოგრაფია, ფოლკლორი, კრიტიკა, პუბლიცისტიკა, კორესპონდენციები. [Et'nograp'ia, p'olklori, kritika, publitsistika, korespondentsiebi. Etnography, folklore, criticism, popular articles, correspondence. Edited by P. I. Ingoroqva.] pp. 446, 1. თბილისი [*Tiflis*,] 1956. 8⁰.   **17076. h. 6**

—— Поэмы. Редакция В. Гольцева и С. Чиковани. (Иллюстрации Тамары Абакелиа). [Translations from the Georgian by various hands.] pp. 139. 7 *plates.* Ленинград, 1947. fol.   **11587. d. 1**

VAZHA-P'SHAVELA (*cont.*)

—— Поэмы. [Translated from Georgian into Russian by N. A. Zabolotsky. Edited by P. I. Ingoroqva.] pp. vii. 200. 13 *plates*. *Тбилиси*, 1951. 8⁰.
17075. d. 9

—— Поэмы. [Poems, trans. into Russian by N. A. Zabolotsky.] pp. 256. *Москва*, 1953. 8⁰. **17075. d. 24**

—— რჩეული. ერთტომეული. [Rcheuli. Ert'tomeuli. Selected works. Single volume edition. Comprises poems, drama, fiction and critical articles. Edit. by A. B. Abasheli and A. G. Shanidze.] pp. 399. 9 *plates*. თბილისი [*Tiflis*,] 1953. 4⁰.
17076. d. 9

—— საბავშვო მოთხრობები. [Sabavshvo mot'-khrobebi. Children's tales. Edit. by S. Iordanishvili, with illustrations by S. Maisashvili.] pp. 216. სახელგამი [*State Publishing House: Tiflis*,] 1935. 4⁰.
17076. a. 10

—— Стихотворения и поэмы. (Перевод с грузинского Н. Заболоцкого. Вступительная статья и примечания Симона Чиковани.) [A new edition.] pp. 318, 4. 1 *plate*. *Ленинград*, 1957. 8⁰. **17075. c. 33**

VEIMARN (B. V.) *and others*. Архитектура республик Закавказья. Сборник статей. (Редакционная коллегия : Б. В. Веймарн, В. А. Лавров, Е. Г. Чернов, Ю. С. Яралов.) [Illustrated.] pp. 354, 2. *Москва*, 1951. 8⁰. [*Архитектура народов СССР.*]
Ac. 1106. k/7 (2.)

VEL'TMAN (Mikhail Lazar'evich). *See* Pavlovich (M.) *pseud.*

VERSHIGORA (Petr Petrovich). [Joint trans. of 'Кровью героев'.] *See* Bak'radze (D.)

VIENNA.—*Nationalbibliothek*. Buchkunst des Morgenlandes. — Katalog der Ausstellung im Prunksaal, Juni-Oktober 1953. [Abschnitt 1, Kapitel 3 comprises the description of two Georgian ecclesiastical manuscripts.] pp. 70. 13 *plates*. *Wien*, 1953. 8⁰. **754. bbb. 9**

VĪS and **RĀMĪN.** [For Georgian version of the romance of Vīs and Rāmīn:] *See* Sargis, *of T'mogvi*.

VIS (Henri de). [Joint edit. and translator of 'Epiphanius de gemmis'.] *See* Epiphanius, *Saint, Bishop of Constantia in Cyprus*.

VLADIKAVKAZ.—*Gorsky Institut Narodnogo Obrazovaniya*. Известия Горского Института Народного Образования. вып. 1–3. *Владикавказ*, 1923–26. 8⁰.
Ac. 2652. g

VLADIMIRTSOV (Boris Yakovlevich). Анонимный грузинскій истôрикъ XIV в. о монгольскомъ языкѣ. pp. 1487–1501. *Петроградъ*, 1917. 8⁰. [*Извѣстія Акад. Наукъ. VI серія. томъ II.*] **Ac. 1125/44**

VOGT (Hans Kamstrup). Esquisse d'une grammaire du géorgien moderne. 2 pt. *Oslo*, 1938. 8⁰. [*Norsk tidsskrift for sprogvidenskap*. bd. 9, 10.]
P. P. 5044. dd

—— Structure phonémique du géorgien. Étude sur le classement des phonèmes et des groupes de phonèmes. pp. 5–90. *Oslo*, 1958. 8⁰. [*Norsk tidsskrift for sprogvidenskap*. bd. 18.] **P. P. 5044. dd**

—— Le système des cas en géorgien ancien. pp. 98–140. *Oslo*, 1947. 8⁰. [*Norsk tidsskrift for sprogvidenskap*. bd. 14.] **P. P. 5044. dd**

VOL'SKAYA (Aneli Ivanovna). Рельефы Шиомгвиме и их место в развитии грузинской средневековой скульптуры. [With facsimiles in the text and a summary in German.] pp. 100, 3. 27 *plates*. *Тбилиси*, 1957. 8⁰. **17080. c. 1**

VÖÖBUS (Arthur). Early Versions of the New Testament: Manuscript Studies. [With a chapter on the Old Georgian version.] pp. xvii. 411. *Stockholm*, 1954. 8⁰. [*Papers of the Estonian Theological Society in Exile*. no. 6.] **754. bbb. 11. (6)**

—— Zur Geschichte des altgeorgischen Evangelientextes. pp. 40. *Stockholm*, 1953. 8⁰. [*Papers of the Estonian Theological Society in Exile*. no. 4.]
754. bbb. 11. (4.)

WARDROP (Sir JOHN OLIVER), *K.B.E.* [Trans. 'Laws of King George V, of Georgia'.] *See* GIORGI V, *King of Georgia*, called THE BRILLIANT.

—— [Joint trans. of 'The Georgian Version of the Liturgy of St. James'.] *See* LITURGIES.—Greek Rite.—*Leitourgikon I.*

—— [Compiler of catalogue of Georgian Manuscripts in the British Museum, published as an appendix to the catalogue of Armenian Manuscripts.] *See* LONDON.—*British Museum.*

—— [Joint trans. of 'Life of St. Nino'.] *See* NINO, *Saint, of Cappadocia.*

—— [Trans. extracts of the Georgian version of the Loves of Vīs and Rāmīn.] *See* SARGIS, *of T'mogvi.*

—— [Trans. 'Visramiani'.] *See* SARGIS, *of T'mogvi.*

—— [Trans. 'The Book of Wisdom and Lies'] *See* SAVVA, *the Monk.*

—— English-Svanetian Vocabulary. pp. 589–634. *London*, 1911. 8⁰. [*Journal of the Royal Asiatic Society* for 1911.]   **R. Ac. 8820/3**

WARDROP (MARJORY SCOTT). [Joint trans. of 'Life of St. Nino'.] *See* NINO, *Saint, of Cappadocia.*

—— [Trans. the epic 'The Man in the Panther's Skin'.] *See* RUST'AVELI (SHOT'A).

—— [For a revised edition of M. S. Wardrop's translation of Shot'a Rust'aveli's epic poem, published in Moscow under the title 'The Knight in the Tiger's Skin':] *See* RUST'AVELI (SHOT'A).

—— [Trans. the poetic legend 'The Hermit'.] *See* TCHAVTCHAVADZE (I. G.) *Prince.*

—— Georgian Folk Tales. [Consists of translations of Georgian tales published by Lado Aghniashvili; Mingrelian tales, taken from A. A. Tsagareli,

Mingrel'skie Etyudy; and Gurian tales.] pp. xii. 175. *London*, 1894. 8⁰. [*Grimm Library.* no. 1.]
     2346. c. 1

WATERSON (NATALIE). [Joint author of 'Notes on the Phonetics of the Georgian Word'.] *See* ROBINS (R. H.) and WATERSON (N.)

WELTMANN (MICHAEL). *See* PAVLOVICH (M.) *pseud.*

WESENDONK (OTTO GUENTHER VON). Über georgisches Heidentum. 2 pt. fasc. 1. pp. 1–102; fasc. 2. pp. 121–30. *Leipzig*, 1924–25. 8⁰. [*Caucasica.* fasc. 1, 2.]   **P. P. 3803. eba**

—— [Another copy, being an offprint.] **04504. k. 14**

WOLFF (ROBERT LEE). The Apology of Aristides. —A Re-examination. pp. 233–47. *Cambridge, Mass.*, 1937. 8⁰. [*Harvard Theological Review.* vol. 30.]   **R. Ac. 2692/13**

—— Barlaam and Ioasaph. pp. 131–39. *Cambridge, Mass.*, 1939. 8⁰. [*Harvard Theological Review.* vol. 32.]   **R. Ac. 2692/13**

XIPHILINOS (JOHN) *the Younger.* [For 'Іоаннъ Ксифилинъ, продолжатель Симеона Метафраста':] *See* KEKELIDZE (K. S.)

YAKOVLEV (NIKOLAI FEOFANOVICH). Грамматика литературного кабардино-черкесского языка. pp. 370. *Москва, Ленинград*, 1948. 8⁰.   **012977. ee. 11**

—— Ингуши. Популярный очерк. pp. 134. *Москва, Ленинград*, 1925. 8⁰.   **010290. eee. 41**

—— Kurze Übersicht über die tscherkessischen (adygheischen) Dialekte und Sprachen. [Trans. from the Russian by A. Dirr.] pp. 1–19. 10 *plates. Leipzig*, 1930. 8⁰. [*Caucasica.* fasc. 6.]
     P. P. 3803. eba

—— Новое в изучении Северного Кавказа. pp. 238–54. *Москва*, 1924. 8⁰. [*Новый Восток.* кн. 5.]
     Ac. 1096. b/5

YAKOVLEV *(cont.)*

—— and **ASHKHAMAF** (Daud Alievich). Грамматика адыгейского литературного языка. pp. 462. *Москва, Ленинград,* 1941. 8⁰.   **12977. d. 5**

ZABOLOTSKY (Nikolai Alekseevich). [Trans. 'Давитиани'.] *See* Guramishvili (D.)

——[Trans. poems of Vazha-Pʻshavela.] *See* Vazha-Pʻshavela, *pseud.*

ZACHARIAS, *Rhetor. See* Zacharias, *Scholasticus, Bishop of Mitylene.*

ZACHARIAS, *Scholasticus, Bishop of Mitylene.* ცხოვრება პეტრე ივერისა. [Tskhovreba Petre Iverisa.] (Житіе Петра Ивера.) [A Georgian adaptation by Macarius the Priest of the life of Peter the Iberian, attributed to Zacharias Scholasticus, edited with introduction and Russian translation by N. Y. Marr.] pp. xxxix. 125. 1 *plate.* С.-Петербургъ, 1896. 8⁰. [*Православный Палестинскій Сборникъ.* томъ 16. вып. 2.]   **Ac. 2058**

ZAKʻARIADZE (Germane Iraklis-dze). ნიკო ნიკოლაძის სოციალურ-პოლიტიკური შეხედულებანი. [Niko Nikoladzis sotsialur-politikuri shekhedulebani. The social and political views of N. Nikoladze.] pp. 285. 1 *plate.* სახელგამი [*State Publishing House: Tiflis,*] 1955. 8⁰.   **17075. f. 22**

ZARDIASHVILI (A.). [Joint trans. of historical novel 'Бесики'.] *See* Beliashvili (A. I.)

ZARZMA.[For 'Изъ гурійскихъ народныхъ преданій о постройкѣ Зарзмскаго монастыря':] *See* Marr (N. Y.)

ZDANEVICH (Kirill). [Contributor to symposium 'Niko Pʻirosmanishvili'.] *See* Tabidze (T. I.) *and others.*

ZEDGINIDZE (Elizbar). დაუვიწყარი ზაფხული. [Dauvidsqari zapʻkhuli. The unforgettable summer. A collection of short stories.] pp. 168, 2. 1 *plate.* თბილისი [*Tiflis,*] 1952. 8⁰.   **17076. b. 26**

—— მზის ამოსვლამდე, რომანი. [Mzis amos-

vlamde, romani. Until sunrise, a novel.] pp. 283. 1 *plate.* თბილისი [*Tiflis,*] 1954. 8⁰.   **17076. b. 12**

ZHGHENTI (Besarion Davitʻis-dze). [Foreword to 'Тамарджвеба'.] *See* Abasheli (A. B.) *and others.*

—— [Joint author of 'История грузинской литературы'.] *See* Baramidze (A. G.) *and others.*

—— [Joint edit. of writings of Shalva Dadiani.] *See* Dadiani (Sh. N.)

—— [Author of introduction to prose writings of R. M. Gvetadze.] *See* Gvetadze (R. M.)

—— [Joint edit. of 'Грузинская советская драматургия'.] *See* Kakabadze (P. M.) *and others.*

ZHGHENTI (Leonti). რატომ გვაქვს იმედი!; ბოლშევიკური კომუნიზმი და მუშათა კლასი. [Ratom gvakʻvs imedi!; Bolshevikuri komunizmi da mushatʻa klasi. Why we have hope! Bolshevik communism and the working class. Two political essays.] pp. 31. პარიზი [*Paris,*] 1952. 8⁰.

17075. f. 17

ZHGHENTI (Sergi Mikheilis-dze). [Edit. 'Dziebani kʻartʻuli dialekʻtologiidan'.] *See* Dzidziguri (S. V.)

—— [Edit. symposium of essays, published on the occasion of the 1500th anniversary of the foundation of Tiflis.] *See* Tiflis.—*Tiflis State University.*

—— ქართული ენის ფონეტიკა. [Kʻartʻuli enis pʻonetika. The phonetics of the Georgian language.] (Фонетика грузинского языка.) pp. 312, 4. თბილისი [*Tiflis,*] 1956. 8⁰. [*Zogadi enatʻmetsnierebis katʻedris shromebi.* no. 2.]   **17076. f. 33**

—— ჭანურ-მეგრულის ფონეტიკა. [Tchanur-megrulis pʻonetika. The phonetics of the Lazo-Mingrelian language.] (Фонетика чанско-мегрельского языка.) pp. x. 206. თბილისი [*Tiflis,*] 1953. 8⁰.   **17076. h. 18**

ZHIRKOV (Lev Ivanovich). Аварско-русский словарь. pp. 187. *Москва,* 1936. 8⁰.   **12906. de. 43**

ZHIRKOV *(cont.)*

—— Лакский язык. Фонетика и морфология. [A study, with selected texts, of the Lak language of Daghestan. Edited by E. A. Bokarev.] pp. 158. *Москва*, 1955. 8⁰.   **17076. i. 8**

—— [Another copy.]   **012977. h. 6**

—— Законы лезгинского ударения. pp. 107–117. *Москва, Ленинград*, 1940. 8⁰. [*Язык и мышление*. вып. 10.]   **Ac. 1125. t/2**

ZHIROV (Kн. D.). [Joint edit. of Russian-Abaza dictionary.] *See* CHERKESSK.—*Cherkessky Nauchno-Issledovatel'sky Institut*.

ZHORDANIA (NOE NIKOLOZIS-DZE) *President of Georgia*. [Author of preface to 'Demokratiuli sotsializmi':] *See* RAMISHVILI (N.)

—— ჩემი წარსული.—მოგონებანი. [Chemi dsarsuli.—Mogonebani. My past.—Reminiscences. An autobiography.] pp. 190. 1 *plate*. პარიზი [*Paris*,] 1953. 8⁰.   **17075. f. 19 (5)**

—— ჩვენი ტაქტიკა. [Chveni tak'tika. Our tactics. A political pamphlet.] pp. 23. [*Paris, Arpajon* printed,] 1926. 8⁰.   **17075. f. 30**

—— დემოკრატია. [Demokratia. Democracy. A political brochure.] pp. 63. პარიზი [*Paris*,] 1933. 8⁰.   **17075. f. 29**

—— ეკონომიური წარმატება და ეროვნება. [Ekonomiuri dsarmateba da erovneba. Economic progress and national existence. With a portrait.] pp. 64. პარიზი [*Paris*,] 1937. 8⁰.   **17075. f. 33**

—— პოლიტიკა. [Politika. Politics. A political pamphlet.] pp. 71. პარიზი [*Paris*,] 1926. 8⁰.   **17075. f. 28**

ZHUZHUNADZE (ELENE BAGRATIS-ASULI). [Compiler of bibliography of the publications of the Academy of Sciences of the Georgian S.S.R., 1937–1956:] *See* TIFLIS.—*Academy of Sciences of the Georgian S.S.R.*   **17080. d. 28**

ZICHY (MIHÁLY). [Illustrator of 'The Man in the Panther's Skin'.] *See* RUST'AVELI (SHOT'A).

ZOOLOGICAL INSTITUTE. *See* TIFLIS.—*Academy of Sciences of the Georgian S.S.R.—Institute of Zoology*.

ZORELL (FRANZ). Grammatik zur altgeorgischen Bibelübersetzung. Mit Textproben und Wörterverzeichnis. pp. iv. 164. *Roma*, 1930. 8⁰. [*Scripta Pontificii Instituti Biblici*.] *Lithographed*.   **Ac. 2002. d. (43)**

ZURABISHVILI (IVANE). საქართველოს საერთაშორისო მდგომარეობა. [Sak'art'velos saert'ashoriso mdgomareoba. Georgia's international position.] pp. 95. პარიზი [*Paris*,] 1936. 8⁰.   **17075. f. 7**

—— [Another copy.]   **17075. f. 7***

ZURABISHVILI — ELEP'T'ERIDZE (ILIA). გაროზგილი. თვითმპყრობელობის დროინდელი ჯარისკაცის ცხოვრებიდან. [Garozgili. T'vit'mp-qrobelobis droindeli jariskatsis tskhovrebidan. The Flogged One. From the life of a Soldier under Tsarist Autocracy.] pp. 273. თბილისი [*Tiflis*,] 1953. 12⁰.   **17076. b. 27**

ZVYAGINTSEVA (VERA). [Joint trans. of 'Нарты. Кабардинский эпос'.] *See* NARTY.

GENERAL INDEX OF TITLES

Anthology of Georgian Poetry. URUSHADZE (V.)

Antiquités géorgiennes. T'AQAISHVILI (E. S.)

Les Antiquités Géorgiennes. (Sak'art'velos sidzveleni.) T'AQAISHVILI (E. S.)

Antiquities of Georgia. T'AQAISHVILI (E. S.)

Antologiya darginskoi poezii. ABAKAROV (AḤMAD-KHĀN).

Antologiya gruzinskoi poezii. ABASHIDZE (I. B.) and others.

Aperçu général de la langue géorgienne. BROSSET (M.-F.)

Aperçu général du voyage de M. Brosset dans la Transcaucasie. BROSSET (M.-F.)

Aperçu sur les monnaies russes. CHAUDOIR (S. de) Baron.

Ap'khazet'is enis, literaturisa da istoriis institutis shromebi. SUKHUMI. — Abkhazian Linguistic, Literary and Historical Institute.

Die apokryphe Erzählung des Joseph von Arimathäa über den Bau der ersten christlichen Kirche in Lydda. JOSEPH, of Arimathea.

The Apology of Aristides. — A Re-examination. WOLFF (R. L.)

Apolon Kobakhidze. KOBAKHIDZE (I.)

Ap'sshva anban. Abkhazsky bukvar'. BARTHOLOMAEI (I. A.) Lt.-General.

Arabel da sparsel mdseralt'a geograp'iuli da istoriuli tsnobebi Sak'art'velos shesakheb. DEFRÉMERY (C. F.)

Arabskaya azbuka s drevnegruzinskoi transkriptsiei. MEGRELIDZE (I. B.)

Arabuli zmnis p'ormat'a paradigmebi. LEKIASHVILI (A. S.)

Archéographie géorgienne. BROSSET (M.-F.)

Archiliani. ARCHIL, King of Imeret'i.

Archinsky yazyk. DIRR (A.)

Arili . . . Prop'esor Ivane Javakhishvilisadmi . . . midzghvnili krebuli. JAVAKHISHVILI (I. A.)

Arkheologicheskaya ekskursiya po kviril'skomu ushchel'yu. TSERET'ELI (G. E.)

Arkheologicheskie pamyatniki Armazis-khevi po raskopkam 1937–1946 gg. A'PAK'IDZE (A. M.) and others.

Arkheologicheskie raskopki v drevnegruzinskoi stolitse Mtskheta. LOMT'AT'IDZE (G. A.)

Arkheologicheskoe puteshestvie po Gurii i Adchare. BAK'RADZE (D. Z.)

Arkhitektura Kakhetii. CHUBINASHVILI (G. N.)

Arkhitektura respublik Zakavkaz'ya. Sbornik statei. VEIMARN (B. V.) and others.

Arkhitektura Samtskhe, XIII–XVI vv. BERIDZE (V. V.)

Armazis bilingva. TSERET'ELI (G. V.)

Armazni. Istoriko-arkheologichesky ocherk. MELIK'SET'-BEGI (L. M.)

Armazskoe pis'mo i problema proiskhozhdeniya gruzinskogo alfavita. TSERET'ELI (G. V.)

L'armée géorgienne au Moyen Âge. DADISHKELIANI (T'. T'.) Prince.

Armenisch und Südkaukasisch. DEETERS (G.)

Armyanskiya slova v gruzinskikh Deyaniyakh Pilata. MARR (N. Y.)

Armyansko-gruzinskie materialy dlya istorii Dushepoleznoi Povesti o Varlaame i Ioasafe. BARLAAM, Saint, of India.

Ars Georgica. TIFLIS. – Academy of Sciences of the Georgian S.S.R. – Institute of the History of Georgian Art.

Arsen iz Marabdy. JAVAKHISHVILI (M. S.)

Arsena Marabdeli. JAVAKHISHVILI (M. S.)

Arsenas lek'si. ODZELASHVILI (A.)

L'Art Libéral, ou Grammaire Géorgienne. BROSSET (M.-F.)

Ashkharsky dialekt i ego mesto sredi drugikh abkhazsko-abazinskikh dialektov. LOMT'AT'IDZE (K'. B.)

Ashkharuli dialek'ti da misi adgili skhva ap'khazur-abazur dialek'tt'a shoris. LOMT'AT'IDZE (K'. B.)

The Asianic Elements in National Georgian Paganism. TSERET'ELI (M. G.)

Aspindzis omi. Istoriuli ambavi. GOGEBASHVILI (I. S.)

Aspirantt'a da akhalgazrda metsnier mushakt'a IX sametsniero konp'erentsia, 1958. TIFLIS. – Academy of Sciences of the Georgian S.S.R.

1905–1907 dslebis revolutsia Sak'art'veloshi. KHUTSISHVILI (I. G.) and others.

Atcharis A.S.S.R. NIZHARADZE (N. I.) and JIBUTI (N. M.)

The Athos Codex of the Georgian Old Testament. BLAKE (R. P.)

Ausführlicher Bericht über des Generals Baron Peter von Uslar Abchasische Studien. SCHIEFNER (F. A. von).

Ausführlicher Bericht über Baron P. v. Uslar's Awarische Studien. SCHIEFNER (F. A. von).

Ausführlicher Bericht über Baron P. v. Uslar's Hürkanische Studien. SCHIEFNER (F. A. von).

Ausführlicher Bericht über Baron P. v. Uslar's Kasikumükische Studien. SCHIEFNER (F. A. von).

Ausführlicher Bericht über Baron P. v. Uslar's Kürinische Studien. SCHIEFNER (F. A. von).

Autographie géorgienne. BROSSET (M.-F.)

Avadmqop'oba Pappataci da kogho Phlebotomus'i Sak'art'velosa da mis mezobel k'veqnebshi. KANDELAKI (S.)

The Avâr Language. GRAHAM (C. C.)

Avarsko-russky slovar'. ZHIRKOV (L. I.)

Avarskoe sootvetstvie russkomu tvoritel'nomu predikativnomu padezhu. BOKAREV (A. A.)

L'Avenir de la Géorgie. GEGETCHKORI (E. P.)

Awarische Texte. BOUDA (K.); SCHIEFNER (F. A. von).

Das Awestaalphabet und der Ursprung der armenischen und georgischen Schrift. JUNKER (H. F. J.)

Bagrat, episkop Tavromeniisky. EVAGRIUS, *Bishop of Taormina.*

Bahai-s sardsmunoeba. BAHAISM.

Balavarianis k'art'uli redak'tsiebi. BARLAAM, *Saint, of India.*

Balhvar i Iodasaf. BARLAAM, *Saint, of India.*

Balkharsky dialekt lakskogo yazyka. KHAIDAKOV (S. M.)

Barlaam and Ioasaph. WOLFF (R. L.)

Batsbiisky yazyk. DESHERIEV (YU. D.)

Bedi K'art'lisa. PERIODICAL PUBLICATIONS. – *Paris.*

Beiträge zur Geschichte der kaukasischen Länder und Völker. DORN (B.)

Beiträge zur kaukasischen und sibirischen Sprachwissenschaft. BOUDA (K.)

Beiträge zur Sprach- und Volkskunde des georgischen Stammes der Gurier. BLEICHSTEINER (R.)

Beka Opizari. AMIRANASHVILI (SH. I.)

Die Bekehrung Iberiens und die beiden ältesten Dokumente der iberischen Kirche. MARQUART, afterwards MARKWART (J.)

Eine Benutzung des Testamentum Domini nostri Jesu Christi. SCHMIDT (C.)

Besiki. Roman. BELIASHVILI (A. I.)

Biblia. BIBLE.

Bibliografiya: otdel'nyya izdaniya i stat'i na gruzinskom yazyke, poyavivshiyasya v 1911–1912 gg. SHANIDZE (A. G.)

Bibliografiya izdany Akademii Nauk Gruzinskoi SSR, 1937–1956. TIFLIS. – *Academy of Sciences of the Georgian S.S.R.*

Bibliographia Caucasica et Transcaucasica. MIANSAROV (M. M.)

Bibliographie analytique des ouvrages de Monsieur Marie-Félicité Brosset. BROSSET (L.)

Bibliographie française de la Géorgie. BERIDZE (SH.)

Bibliothèque du Muséon. PERIODICAL PUBLICATIONS. – *Louvain.*

A bilingual inscription from Armazi. TSERET'ELI (G. V.)

Bogi yazycheskoi Gruzii. MARR (N. Y.)

The Book of Wisdom and Fiction. Selections. SAVVA, *the Monk* [*Prince* SULKHAN ORBELIANI].

The Book of Wisdom and Lies. SAVVA, *the Monk* [*Prince* SULKHAN ORBELIANI].

Boshebi. Poltava. PUSHKIN (A. S.)

Les Brachiopodes du Crétacé inférieur de la Géorgie Occidentale. NUTSUBIDZE (K'. SH.)

Brdzola samshoblosat'vis. GOGIBERIDZE (S.)

Britanet'is da Germanet'is samkhedro brdzanebani. EUROPEAN WAR, 1914–1919.

Bronzy drevnei Gruzii. T'AVADZE (P'.N.) and SAQVARELIDZE (T'. N.)

Buchkunst des Morgenlandes. VIENNA. – *Nationalbibliothek.*

Bukhara: mogonebani. 'AINĪ (ŚADR AL-DĪN).

Bulletin de l'Académie des Sciences de l'URSS. SAINT PETERSBURG. – *Academia Scientiarum Imperialis.*

Bulletin de l'Académie Impériale des Sciences. SAINT PETERSBURG. – *Academia Scientiarum Imperialis.*

Bulletin de la Classe Historico-Philologique. SAINT PETERSBURG. – *Academia Scientiarum Imperialis.*

Bulletin de l'Institut Caucasien d'Histoire et d'Archéologie à Tiflis. TIFLIS. – *Kavkazsky Istoriko-Arkheologichesky Institut.*

Bulletin de l'Institut Marr. TIFLIS. – *Marr Language Institute,* afterwards *Institute of Linguistics.*

Bulletin de l'Université de Tiflis. TIFLIS. – *Tiflis State University.*

Bulletin du Musée de Géorgie. TIFLIS. – *Museum of Georgia.*

Bulletin of the Academy of Sciences of the Georgian S.S.R. TIFLIS. – *Academy of Sciences of the Georgian S.S.R.*

Bulletin of the School of Oriental Studies (of the School of Oriental and African Studies). LONDON. – *University of London. – School of Oriental and African Studies.*

Bulletin Scientifique publié par l'Académie Impériale des Sciences. SAINT PETERSBURG. – *Academia Scientiarum Imperialis.*

Burji erovnebisa. GOGEBASHVILI (I. S.)

Βυζαντινὰ Χρονικά. SAINT PETERSBURG. – *Academia Scientiarum Imperialis.*

Le calendrier palestino-géorgien du Sinaiticus 34. LITURGIES. – Greek Rite. – *Calendar.*

Catalogue de livres géorgiens. (Histoire et littérature de la Géorgie.) BROSSET (M.-F.)

Catalogue des manuscrits arméniens et géorgiens de la Bibliothèque Nationale. PARIS. – *Bibliothèque Royale,* afterwards *Impériale,* afterwards *Nationale.*

Catalogue des manuscrits géorgiens de la Bibliothèque de la Laure d'Iviron au mont Athos. ATHOS, *Mount.*

Catalogue des manuscrits géorgiens de la Bibliothèque Patriarcale Grecque à Jérusalem. JERUSALEM. – *Greek Patriarchal Library.*

Catalogue des manuscrits géorgiens littéraires du Mont Sinaï. CATHARINE, *Saint of Alexandria.* – CONVENT OF, ON MOUNT SINAI.

A Catalogue of the Armenian Manuscripts in the British Museum . . . To which is appended a Catalogue of Georgian Manuscripts in the British Museum. LONDON. – *British Museum.*

Catalogue of the Georgian manuscripts in the Cambridge University Library. BLAKE (R. P.)

Caucasian Folk-Tales. DIRR (A.)

Caucasian Review. MUNICH. – *Институт по Изучению СССР.*

Caucasica. BAILEY (*Sir* H. W.)

Caucasica. Zeitschrift für die Erforschung der Sprachen und Kulturen des Kaukasus. PERIODICAL PUBLICATIONS. – *Leipsic.*

The Caucasus. PERIODICAL PUBLICATIONS. – *Munich.*

Caucasus Polyglottus. SHANIDZE (A. G.)

Ch. Rousthawéli: sa vie, son poème, ses maximes, sa philosophie. BERIDZE (SH.)

Chanmetifragmente. Ein Beitrag zur Textgeschichte der altgeorgischen Bibelübersetzung. MOLITOR (J.)

La chanson du réfugié. TOGONIDZE (G.)

Chechensky bukvar'. BARTHOLOMAEI (I. A.). *Lt.-General.*

Chelovek gor. K'IACHELI (L.) *pseud.*

Chemi dsarsuli. – Mogonebani. ZHORDANIA (N. N.) *President of Georgia.*

Chetveroevangelie v drevnegruzinskom perevode. BIBLE. – New Testament. – *Gospels.*

Chetyre portreta tsaritsy Tamary. ALIBEGASHVILI (G. V.)

Chota Rousthavéli, poète géorgien du XIIᵉ siècle. MOURIER (J.)

Chrdili ert'i sinamdvilis. INASARI (I.)

Chrestomatie [*sic*] de la littérature géorgienne ancienne. QUBANEISHVILI (S. I.)

Une chrétienté disparue: les Albaniens du Caucase. DUMÉZIL (G.)

A Christmas Carol. DICKENS (C.)

Chronique géorgienne. BROSSET (M.-F.)

The Chronological-Genealogical Table of the Kings of Georgia. GUGUSHVILI (A. I.)

Chronology of the Kings of Abasgia and other Problems. TOUMANOFF (C. L.) *Prince.*

Chveni drosha. PERIODICAL PUBLICATIONS. – *Paris.*

Chveni simgherebi. GEORGIA. – *Georgian Legion.*

Chveni tak'tika. ZHORDANIA (N. N.) *President of Georgia.*

Le Code de Vakhtang VI. GEORGIA. – *Laws.*

Colchidea et la poésie. URUSHADZE (S.)

La collection "Monuments de l'ancienne langue géorgienne". GARITTE (G.)

Un colophon géorgien de Thornik le Moine. THORNICIUS, afterwards JOHANNES, *Monk at Mount Athos.*

Contes et légendes des Oubykhs. DUMÉZIL (G.)

Contes et légendes du Caucase. MOURIER (J.)

Contes lazes. DUMÉZIL (G.)

Contes orientaux. BORIN (A.)

La conversione ufficiale degl'Iberi al cristianesimo. PALMIERI (A.)

Copie figurée de quelques cachets géorgiens. BROSSET (M.-F.)

Corpus Juris Ibero-Caucasici. GEORGIA. – *Laws.*

Corpus Scriptorum Christianorum Orientalium. – Scriptores Iberici. LOUVAIN. – *Academia Lovaniensis.*

Correspondance en grec des rois géorgiens du Cakheth. BROSSET (M.-F.)

Court aperçu sur les frontières de la Géorgie. I. (P.)

La culture mégalithique en Géorgie. MELIK'SET'-BEGI (L. M.)

D. Gulias sakhelobis Ap'khazet'is enis, literaturis da istoriis institutis shromebi. SUKHUMI. – *Abkhazian Linguistic, Literary and Historical Institute.*

Da budet mir! Stikhi. MARGIANI (R. A.)

Dabadeba da aghzrda Erekle Batonishvilisa. RAZIKASHVILI (N.) *known as* BACHANA.

Dagestanskaya narodnaya lirika. GREBNEV (N.)

Dagestanskie povesti i rasskazy. SULTANOV (K.)

Dakarguli samot'khe. MILTON (J.)

Dargala poeziyala antologiya. ABAKAROV (AḢMAD-KHĀN).

Dasavlet' Sak'art'velos k'veda tsartsis brak'iopodebi. NUTSUBIDZE (K'. SH.)

Dastur-lama. DADIANI (N. G.)

The Date of the Building of the Cathedral "The Living Pillar". KAKABADZE (S. N.)

Dauvidsqari zap'khuli. ZEDGINIDZE (E.)

David Stroitel'. Trilogiya. GAMSAKHURDIA (K. S.)

Davit' aghmashenebeli. Tetralogia. GAMSAKHURDIA (K. S.)

Davit' Erist'avi. TCHITCHINADZE (Z. E.)

Davit' Guramishvili. NASIDZE (M.)

Davit' Rondeli. LOLADZE (V.)

Davit'iani. GURAMISHVILI (D.)

Davitiani. Stikhotvoreniya i poemy. GURAMISHVILI (D.)

Davit'iani. (T'khzulebat'a sruli krebuli.) GURAMISHVILI (D.)

De codice Hiberico Bibliothecae Bodleianae Oxoniensis. PEETERS (P.)

Dsigni akhlisay aght'k'misa. BIBLE. – New Testament.

Dsigni lek'sebis. T'EVZADZE (A. R.)

Dsigni „Sibrdzne sitsruisa" da k'art'uli khalkhuri makhvilsitqvaoba. TSANAVA (A. B.)

Dsignis matiane. PERIODICAL PUBLICATIONS. – TIFLIS.

Dsignis sasakhle. KAKUSHADZE (N. V.)

Dsmida modsame Abo Tp'ileli. SABANISDZE (IOANE).

Dva gruzinskikh arkhitekturnykh termina – "achrdil" i "balavar". MARR (N. Y.)

Dva izsledovatelya kavkazskikh yazykov. Akademik A. A. Shifner . . . i baron P. K. Uslar. TSAGARELI (A. A.)

Dziebani k'art'uli dialek'tologiidan. DZIDZIGURI (S. V.)

Dzirit'adi ukughmart'oba. GOGEBASHVILI (I. S.)

Dzveli da akhali. JORJADZE (A.)

Dzveli k'art'uli enis dzeglebi. TIFLIS. – *Academy of Sciences of the Georgian S.S.R.*

Dzveli k'art'uli enis kat'edris shromebi. TIFLIS. – *Tiflis State University.*

Dzveli k'art'uli literatura. K'restomat'ia sashualo skolis VIII klasisat'vis. SHANIDZE (A. G.) *and others.*

Dzveli k'art'uli literatura: V–XVIII ss. KEKELIDZE (K. S.) and BARAMIDZE (A. G.)

Dzveli k'art'uli literaturis k'restomat'ia. QUBANEISHVILI (S. I.)

Dzveli k'art'ulis k'restomat'ia. SHANIDZE (A. G.)

Dzveli Sak'art'velo. T'AQAISHVILI (E. S.).

The Early Bagratids. TOUMANOFF (C. L.) *Prince.*

Early Versions of the New Testament: Manuscript Studies. VÖÖBUS (A.)

Échantillons des enluminures des manuscrits géorgiens. SCHMERLING (R. O.)

Économie nationale de la Géorgie. KANDELAKI (K.)

L'église géorgienne du Clibanion au Mont Admirable. PEETERS (P.)

Egnate Ninoshvili. SAKHOKIA (T'.T.)

Einführung in das Studium der kaukasischen Sprachen. DIRR (A.)

Einführung in die georgische Sprache. CHKHENKELI (K.)

Ekonomicheskoe razvitie Gruzii i Zakavkaz'ya v XIX–XX vv. GUGUSHVILI (P. B.)

Ekonomikis institutis shromebi. TIFLIS. – *Academy of Sciences of the Georgian S.S.R. – Institute of Economics.*

Ekonomiuri dsarmateba da erovneba. ZHORDANIA (N. N.) *President of Georgia.*

Ekonomiuri krizisi. KANDELAKI (K.)

Ekspeditsii na Kavkaz 1892, 1893 i 1895 g. KHAKHANOV (A. S.)

Ekstserpty iz drevnei "Istorii Armenii" po gruzinskoi rukopisi XVII veka. MELIK'SET'-BEGI (L. M.)

Elementare tscherkessische Texte. DEETERS (G.)

Éléments de la langue géorgienne. BROSSET (M.-F.)

Elissa. QAZBEGI (A. M.)

Eltchek'i da setqvianoba Kakhet'shi. K'URDIANI (I.)

Enat'a klasip'ikatsiis printsipebi. SHARADZENIDZE (T'. S.)

Enat'metsnierebis institutis shromebi. Aghmosavlur enat'a seria. TIFLIS. – *Marr Language Institute,* afterwards *Institute of Linguistics.*

Enat'metsnierebis shesavali. CHIK'OBAVA (A. S.)

English-Svanetian Vocabulary. WARDROP (*Sir J. O.*) *K.B.E.*

Die Entstehung und Entwicklung der kirchlichen Autokephalie Georgiens. T'ARKHNISHVILI (M.)

Epigraficheskie zametki. TURCHANINOV (G. F.)

Epigrafika Vostoka. SAINT PETERSBURG. – *Academia Scientiarum Imperialis.*

Epiphanius de gemmis. EPIPHANIUS, *Saint, Bishop of Constantia in Cyprus.*

Eri da katsobrioba. TSERET'ELI (M. G.)

Erinnerungen an einen Aufenthalt bei den Tscherkessen des Kreises Tuapse. TRUBETSKOI (N. S.) *Prince.*

Eris dideba. PERIODICAL PUBLICATIONS. – *Paris.*

Erovnuli sakit'khi. GOMART'ELI (I. G.)

Ert'oba. PERIODICAL PUBLICATIONS. – *Tiflis.*

Ert'tomeuli. ABASHELI (A. B.); BELIASHVILI (A. I.); GABESKIRIA (V. I.); GRISHASHVILI (I. G.); RURUA (P.)

Ert'tomeuli. Rcheuli. VAZHA-P'SHAVELA, *pseud.*

Ert'tomeuli. (Rcheuli lek'sebi, baladebi da simgherebi.) KALADZE (K. R.)

Eshche odin iz istochnikov istorii Gruzii tsarevicha Vakhushta. T'AQAISHVILI (E. S.)

Esquisse d'une grammaire du géorgien moderne. VOGT (H. K.)

Essai chronologique sur la série des catholicos d'Aphkhazeth. BROSSET (M.-F.)

Essai de classification des suites monétaires de la Géorgie. LANGLOIS (V.)

Essai de déchiffrement des inscriptions de l'église de Manglis. BROSSET (M.-F.)

Essays. GAMSAKHURDIA (K. S.)

Estructura social y costumbres de la sociedad en el Epos Heroico . . . "El Caballero de la Piel de Tigre". NOZADZE (V.)

État actuel de la littérature géorgienne. BROSSET (M.-F.)

L'état actuel des études linguistiques caucasiennes. POLÁK (V.)

Ethnographical and Historical Division of Georgia. GUGUSHVILI (A. I.)

Etiudebi dzveli kʻartʻuli literaturis istoriidan. KEKELIDZE (K. S.)

Etnografiya Kavkaza. Yazykoznanie, *etc.* USLAR (P. K.) *Baron.*

Etʻnograpʻia, pʻolklori, kritika, publitsistika, korespondentsiebi. VAZHA-PʻSHAVELA, *pseud.*

Etʻnograpʻiuli nadserebi. BOTCHORISHVILI (L. I.)

Études comparatives sur les langues caucasiennes du nord-ouest. DUMÉZIL (G.)

Études de chronologie technique. BROSSET (M.-F.)

Études sur les monuments géorgiens photographiés par M. Iermakof. BROSSET (M.-F.)

Evangelienzitate in einem altgeorgischen Väterfragment. MOLITOR (J.)

Examen critique des annales géorgiennes. BROSSET (M.-F.)

Explication de diverses inscriptions géorgiennes, arméniennes et grecques. BROSSET (M.-F.)

Explication de quelques inscriptions . . . au Mont Athos. BROSSET (M.-F.)

Explication de quelques inscriptions géorgiennes. BROSSET (M.-F.)

Un extrait géorgien de la Vie d'Étienne le Sabaïte. STEPHEN, *Laurae S. Sabae Monachus,* called THAUMATURGUS.

Extraits d'une Topographie de la Géorgie, (traduits) par M. Klaproth. GEORGIA. – *Descriptions and Travels.*

Fables de Tsey Ibrahim. TSEY IBRĀHĪM.

Feminiziruyushchy glasny v gruzinskom. DONDUA (K. D.)

Festschrift Prof. Dr. Iwane Dschawachischwili . . . dargebracht. JAVAKHISHVILI (I. A.)

Fialki na skalakh. RAMAZANOV (B.)

The Fifteenth-Century Bagratids and the Institution of Collegial Sovereignty in Georgia. TOUMANOFF (C. L.) *Prince.*

A fifteenth-century Georgian Needle Painting in the Metropolitan Museum, New York. AVALISHVILI (Z. D.)

Fiziolog. Armyano-gruzinsky izvod. PHYSIOLOGUS.

Fonetichesky sbornik. (Trudy kafedry obshchego yazykovedeniya.) TIFLIS. – *Tiflis State University.*

Fonetika chansko-megrelʻskogo yazyka. ZHGHENTI (S. M.)

Fonetika gruzinskogo yazyka. ZHGHENTI (S. M.)

La formation de la nation géorgienne. MANVELISHVILI (A. P.)

Les formes d'organisation du travail dans l'économie sociale de l'ancienne Géorgie. TIFLIS. – *Academy of Sciences of the Georgian S.S.R.*

Four Basilican Churches of the Qvirila Valley. TʻAQAISHVILI (E. S.)

Le fragment géorgien de l'Évangile de Thomas. BIBLE. – New Testament. – *Apocrypha.*

Un fragment géorgien de l'homélie IX de Sévérien de Gabala. SEVERIAN, *Bishop of Gabala.*

Fragment gruzinskoi versii "Detstva Khrista". JESUS CHRIST.

Funktsii ergativnogo padezha v lezginskom yazyke. MEILANOVA (U. A.)

Gabaaseba Tʻeimurazisa da Rustʻvelisa. ARCHIL, *King of Imeretʻi.*

Gabzaruli guli. ARAGVISPIRELI (SH.) *pseud.*

Gadmotsema "Khogais Mindize" da poema "Gvelis mtchameli". GACHECHILADZE (A. N.)

Gadsqvetili zghapari, novelebi. TʻURDOSPIRELI (D.)

Gamardzhveba. Stikhi gruzinskikh poetov, 1941–1944. ABASHELI (A. B.) *and others.*

Gamokʻvabuli nagebobani Sakʻartʻveloshi. MSHVENIERADZE (D. M.)

Gankitʻkhvani Vepʻkhistqaosanisa. NOZADZE (V.)

Garbani. Kʻartʻuli khurotʻmodzghvrebis IX–X ss. dzegli Khevshi. DOLIDZE (V. O.)

Garesdzhiiskaya tetralingva epokhi mongolov 1352 g. MELIKʻSETʻ-BEGI (L. M.)

Garozgili. Tʻvitʻmpqrobelobis droindeli jariskatsis tskhovrebidan. ZURABISHVILI-ELEPʻTʻERIDZE (I.)

Gde sokhranilos' svanskoe sklonenie? MARR (N. Y.)

Die geistliche Dichtung Georgiens und ihr Verhältnis zur Byzantinischen. TʻARKHNISHVILI (M.)

Gemmy Gosudarstvennogo Muzeya Gruzii. TIFLIS. – *Museum of Georgia.*

Geografiya Gruzii. VAKHUSHTI, *Prince of Georgia.*

Géographie et légende dans un écrit apocryphe de Saint Basile. AVALISHVILI (Z. D.)

The Georgian alphabet: Transliteration, pronunciation, and classification of Georgian speech-sounds. GUGUSHVILI (A. I.)

Georgian Chronology and the Beginnings of Bagratid Rule in Georgia. TʻAQAISHVILI (E. S.)

Georgian-English Dictionary. CHERKEZI (E.)

Georgian Folk Tales. WARDROP (M. S.)

Georgian Manuscripts in England. PʻERADZE (G.)

The Georgian Question before the Free World. KANDELAKI (K.)

Georgian Relations with France during the reign of Wakhtang VI, 1711–24. LANG (D. M.)

Georgian repoussé work, VIIIth to XVIIIth centuries. CHUBINASHVILI (G. N.)

Georgian secular literature, epic, romantic and lyric. BLAKE (R. P.)

The Georgian Shakespeariana. QIASASHVILI (N. A.)

Greek script and Georgian scribes on Mt. Sinai. BLAKE (R. P.)

Grozny vlastelin. LORT'K'IP'ANIDZE (N. M.)

Grozy i gradobitiya v Kakhetii. K'URDIANI (I.)

Grundzüge einer vergleichenden Grammatik des Ibero-Kaukasischen. KARST (J.)

Gruzino-persidskie istoricheskie dokumenty. P'UT'URIDZE (V. S.)

Gruzino-russky slovar'. CHUBINOV (D. I.)

Gruzinskaya dialektologiya. TIFLIS. – *Marr Language Institute*, afterwards *Institute of Linguistics*.

Gruzinskaya grammatika. CHUBINOV (D. I.)

Gruzinskaya khudozhestvennaya keramika XI–XIII vv. MAISURADZE (Z. P.)

Gruzinskaya muzykal'naya kul'tura. CHKHIKVADZE (G. Z.) *and others*.

Gruzinskaya numizmatika. KAPANADZE (D. G.)

Gruzinskaya parallel' k drevne-egipetskoi povesti "O dvukh brat'yakh". FRANK-KAMENETSKY (I. G.)

Gruzinskaya poema "Vityaz' v barsovoi shkure" Shoty iz Rustava. MARR (N. Y.)

Gruzinskaya povest' ob Aleksandre Makedonskom i serbskaya Aleksandriya. KHAKHANOV (A. S.)

Gruzinskaya povest' ob Amirane, syne Daredzhana i ostatki skazany o nem v Kartvel'skoi narodnoi literature. GREN (A. N.)

Gruzinskaya sovetskaya dramaturgiya. KAKABADZE (P. M.) *and others*.

Gruzinskaya sovetskaya poeziya. ABASHIDZE (G. G.) *and others*.

Gruzinskaya srednevekovaya khudozhestvennaya rez'ba po derevu. CHUBINASHVILI (N.)

Gruzinskaya versiya Agathangeliya i eya znachenie dlya gruzinskoi istoriografii. MELIK'SET'-BEGI (L. M.)

Gruzinskaya vesna. AKOBIA (SH.) *and others*.

Gruzinskie liriki. PASTERNAK (B. L.)

Gruzinskie narodnye skazki. CHIK'OVANI (M. I.)

Gruzinskie narodnye tantsy. JAVRISHVILI (D. L.)

Gruzinskie novelly. KLDIASHVILI (S. D.)

Gruzinskie povesti i rasskazy. T'VALT'VADZE (P'. A.)

Gruzinskie redaktsii povesti "Varlaam i Ioasaf". BARLAAM, *Saint, of India*.

Gruzinskie rukopisi Instituta Vostokovedeniya. SAINT PETERSBURG. – *Academia Scientiarum Imperialis*. – *Институт Востоковедения*.

Gruzinskie versii apokrificheskikh deyany apostolov. BIBLE. – New Testament. – *Apocrypha*.

Gruzinskie versii Sobornykh Poslany. BIBLE. – New Testament. – *Epistles*.

Gruzinskiya drevnosti. T'AQAISHVILI (E. S.)

Gruzinskiya nadpisi, naidennyya v Rossii. TSAGARELI (A. A.)

Gruzinskiya pripiski grecheskago Evangeliya iz Koridii. MARR (N. Y.)

Gruzinsko-osetinsky slovar'. SANAKOEV (P. A.)

Gruzinsko-russko-frantsuzsky slovar'. CHUBINOV (D. I.)

Gruzinskoe chekannoe iskusstvo s VIII po XVIII vek. CHUBINASHVILI (G. N.)

Gruzinskoe derevyannoe zodchestvo. GARAQANIDZE (M. K.)

Gruzinskoe krasnorechie. KANDELAKI (N.)

Gruzinskoe narodnoe zodchestvo: Adzhara. ADAMIA (I.)

Gruzinsky epos. CHIK'OVANI (M. I.)

Gruzinsky glossary. TCHQONIA (I. M.)

Gruzinsky izvod skazaniya o poste "aradzhavor". MELIK'SET'-BEGI (L. M.)

Gruzinsky (k'art'sky) glossary po imerskomu i rach'inskomu govoram. BERIDZE (V. M.)

Gruzinsky khram "Tkhaba-erdy" na severnom Kavkaze. KRUPNOV (E. I.)

Gruzinsky narodny transport. GEGESHIDZE (M. K.)

Gruzinsky ornament. KRAVCHENKO (A. V.) and QARALASHVILI (N. I.)

Gruzinsky poet XII veka Sh. Rustavelli i ego poema "Barsova kozha". KHAKHANOV (A. S.)

Gruzinsky teatr za sto let. BUKHNIKASHVILI (G. V.)

Gruzinsky veliky nomokanon po spiskam Tiflisskago Tserkovnago Muzeya. GEORGIAN ORTHODOX CHURCH. – *Nomocanon*.

Gruziny v Moskve. Istorichesky ocherk, 1653–1722. TATISHVILI (V. I.)

Gudarekhis pirveli da meore, 1938 da 1939 dsds., ark'eologiuri kampaniis angarishi. MUSKHELISHVILI (L. V.) *and others*.

Guide de conversation français-géorgien. MANVELISHVILI (A. P.)

Guriiskie revolyutsionnye pesni. CHKHIKVADZE (G. Z.)

Gurjistanis vilaiet'is didi davt'ari. JIK'IA (S. S.)

Guyrdziag-iron dzyrduat. SANAKOEV (P. A.)

Gvadi Bigva. K'IACHELI (L.) *pseud*.

[Hagiographical miscellanies.] PEETERS (P.)

Harnack-Ehrung. HARNACK (C. G. A. von).

The Harvard Theological Review. CAMBRIDGE, Mass. – *Harvard University*.

The Hermit: a legend. TCHAVTCHAVADZE (I. G.) *Prince*.

Hippolyts Kommentar zum Hohenlied ... herausgegeben von G. N. Bonwetsch. HIPPOLYTUS, *Saint, of Rome*.

Histoire de la Géorgie. BROSSET (M.-F.); KLAPROTH (H. J. von).

Histoire de la Géorgie depuis l'antiquité ... Réédition faite par N. Marr. BROSSET (M.-F.)

K'art'uli mdserloba met'ormete saukuneshi. TCHIT-
CHINADZE (Z. E.)

K'art'uli mdserloba metsamete saukunidam me-
t'ek'vsmete saukunemde. TCHITCHINADZE (Z.
E.)

K'art'uli mestviruli poezia. TSANAVA (A. B.)

K'art'uli modgmis erovnuli p'ormatsia. MAN-
VELISHVILI (A. P.)

K'art'uli mtchevrmetqveleba. KANDELAKI (N.)

K'art'uli musikaluri kultura. CHKHIKVADZE (G. Z.)
and others.

K'art'uli ok'romtchedloba VIII–XVIII saukuneebisa. CHUBINASHVILI (G. N.)

K'art'uli ornamenti. KRAVCHENKO (A. V.) and
QARALASHVILI (N. I.)

K'art'uli ot'kht'avis simp'onia – lek'sikoni. IMNAI-
SHVILI (I. B.)

K'art'uli p'eodaluri dsqobileba XVI–XVII saukuneebshi. GABASHVILI (V. N.)

K'art'uli p'ilosop'iis istoria. NUTSUBIDZE (SH. I.)

K'art'uli poetikis k'restomat'ia – XVIII–XIX ss.
MIK'ADZE (G. V.)

K'art'uli poeziis ant'ologia. ABASHIDZE (I. B.)
and others; URUSHADZE (V.)

K'art'uli politikis dzveli da akhali gzebi. ASA-
T'IANI (A.)

K'art'uli sabtchot'a poeziis ant'ologia. ABASHELI
(A. B.) and others.

K'art'uli saliteraturo enisa da stilis sakit'khebi.
TCHUMBURIDZE (Z. G.)

K'art'uli sazogadoebrivi da p'ilosop'iuri azris
istoriidan. KHIDASHELI (SH. V.)

K'art'uli Shek'spiriana. QIASASHVILI (N. A.)

K'art'uli t'eatris aghdgenis 100 dseli. GEORGIA. –
National Theatre.

K'art'uli t'vit'-dserileba. BROSSET (M.-F.)

K'art'uli versiebi apokrip'ebisa motsik'ult'a shesakheb. BIBLE. – New Testament. – Apocrypha.

K'art'uli zmnebi. KHUNDADZE (S. T'.)

K'art'vel dramaturgt'a piesebi. BERDZENISHVILI
(G.) and others.

K'art'vel glekhs. GEORGIA. — Socialist-Federalist
Revolutionary Party.

K'art'veli eris istoria. JAVAKHISHVILI (I. A.)

K'art'veli eris tragedia me-17-te saukuneshi.
K'VARIANI (S. A.)

K'art'veli khalkhis literaturuli urt'iert'obani modzme khalkhebt'an. ASAT'IANI (L. N.)

Kart'velt' Mahmadiant' lotsvebi. GURIELI (G. D.)
Prince.

K'art'velt' Mahmadiant' sakhalkho lek'sebi. TCHI-
TCHINADZE (Z. E.)

K'art'velt' mep'et'a tituli, kurt'kheva da regaliebi.
KHAKHANOV (A. S.)

K'art'velt'a udzvelesi sardsmunoebis istoriidan.
OCHIAURI (T'. A.)

K'art'velur enat'a struk'turis sakit'khebi. TIFLIS.
– Marr Language Institute, afterwards Institute
of Linguistics.

Kat'olike epistolet'a k'art'uli versiebi. BIBLE. –
New Testament. – Epistles.

Kat'olikeni Sak'art'veloshi. ISARLISHVILI (L.)

Kaukasische Forschungen ... Erster Teil. Georgische und Mingrelische Texte. BLEICH-
STEINER (R.)

Kaukasische Forschungen im k. u. k. Kriegsgefangenenlager Eger. BLEICHSTEINER (R.)

Kaukasische Märchen. DIRR (A.)

Die kaukasischen Sprachproben in Evliya Çelebi's
Seyahetname. BLEICHSTEINER (R.)

Kavkasiis konp'ederatsia. PARIS. — Caucasian
Confederation.

Kavkaz. PERIODICAL PUBLICATIONS. – Paris.

Kavkaz i pamyatniki dukhovnoi kul'tury. MARR
(N. Y.)

Kavkazovedenie i abkhazsky yazyk. MARR (N. Y.)

Kavkazsky etnografichesky sbornik. SAINT PE-
TERSBURG. – Academia Scientiarum Imperialis. –
Институт Этнографии им. Н. Н. Миклухо-
Маклая.

Kavkazsky kul'turny mir i Armeniya. MARR (N.
Y.)

Keberdei literature. KAMBIEV (KH. P.)

Keberdei-urys slovar'. APAZHEV (M. L.) and others.

Keramika Ozaani. MAISURADZE (Z. P.)

Keramikuli dsarmoeba XI–XIII ss. Sak'art'veloshi. JAP'ARIDZE (V. V.)

Ketskhoveli. Roman. LISASHVILI (I.)

Khalkhuri meskhuri lek'sebi. GVARAMADZE (K.)
called MESKHI.

Khalkhuri poezia. Rcheuli. GOMIASHVILI (A. K.)
and GVETADZE (R. M.)

Khalkhuri zghaprebi. AGHNIASHVILI (L.)

Khalkhuri zghaprebi, Kakhet'shi da P'shavshi
shekrebili. RAZIKASHVILI (T'. P.)

Khalkhuri zghaprebi, K'art'lshi shekrebili. RAZI-
KASHVILI (T'. P.)

Khanmeti palimpsest fragments of the old Georgian version of Jeremiah. BLAKE (R. P.)

Das kharthwelische Verbum. DEETERS (G.)

Les Khazars dans la Passion de S. Abo de Tiflis.
PEETERS (P.)

Khelnadsert'a aghdseriloba. K'UT'AISI. – K'ut'aisi
State Historical Museum.

Khelovneba aznaurebit'i, gina k'art'ulis enisa
t'vit' masdsavlebeli. BROSSET (M.-F.)

Khevsury. GURKO-KRYAZHIN (V. A.)

Khristianskie pamyatniki. Ekskursiya 1902 g.
T'AQAISHVILI (E. S.)

La notice du synaxaire géorgien sur S. Orentius. ORENTIUS, *Saint, of Rize.*

Notice et analyse raisonnée du commencement de la Grammaire géorgienne du patriarche Antoni I. BROSSET (M.-F.)

Notice historique sur les trois dernières années du règne de Wakhtang VI. BROSSET (M.-F.)

Notice sur deux fragments relatifs à l'histoire de la Géorgie, au XIIIme siècle. BROSSET (M.-F.)

Notice sur la Bible géorgienne imprimée à Moscou en 1742. BROSSET (M.-F.)

Notice sur la Langue Géorgienne. BROSSET (M.-F.)

Notice sur le dictionnaire géorgien de Soulkhan Saba Orbeliani. BROSSET (M.-F.)

Notice sur le couvent ibérien du Mont Athos. LANGLOIS (V.)

Notice sur le mari russe de Thamar. BROSSET (M.-F.)

Notice sur quelques auteurs géorgiens. BROSSET (M.-F.)

Notice sur un document géorgien du XVIIe siècle. BROSSET (M.-F.)

Notice sur un manuscrit géorgien. BROSSET (M.-F.)

Notice sur un manuscrit géorgien de la Bibliothèque Impériale publique. BROSSET (M.-F.)

Notice sur un manuscrit géorgien palimpseste. BROSSET (M.-F.)

Notice sur un Nomocanon géorgien. EUTHYMIUS, *of Mtʻa-Dsminda, Saint.*

Notice sur une lettre géorgienne, du roi Artchil à Charles XII. BROSSET (M.-F.)

Notice sur une médaille de l'an 1790. BROSSET (M.-F.)

Notice sur une version géorgienne de la Caverne des Trésors. AVALISHVILI (Z. D.)

Notules kartvéliennes. POLÁK (V.)

Nouvel Orient. MOSCOW. – *Nauchnaya Assotsiatsiya Vostokovedeniya S.S.S.R.*

Nouvelles recherches sur l'historien Wakhoucht, sur le roi Artchil, et sur divers personnages géorgiens enterrés à Moscou. BROSSET (M.-F.)

Novoe v izuchenii Severnogo Kavkaza. YAKOVLEV (N. F.)

Novy Vostok. MOSCOW. – *Nauchnaya Assotsiatsiya Vostokovedeniya S.S.S.R.*

Novye arkhivnye materialy dlya istorii Gruzii XVIII stoletiya. TSAGARELI (A. A.)

Novye stikhi. CHIKʻOVANI (S. I.)

Numizmaticheskie fakty gruzinskago tsarstva. BARATAEV (M. P.) *Prince.*

O drevnem ierusalimskom spiske gruzinskoi minei-chetʻei. BENESHEVICH (V. N.)

O dvukh suffiksakh mnozhestvennosti v gruzinskom. DONDUA (K. D.)

O fragmente gruzinskoi versii "Detstva Khrista". MARR (N. Y.)

O gruzino-grecheskoi rukopisi s miniatyurami. OKUNEV (N. L.)

O gruzinskoi versii apokrificheskago Videniya Saaka Parfyanina o sudʼbe Armenii. MELIKʻ-SETʻ-BEGI (L. M.)

O kategorii grammaticheskikh klassov v kabardinskom. TURCHANINOV (G. F.)

O kategorii vida v cherkesskikh yazykakh. TURCHANINOV (G. F.)

O kavkazskoi versii Biblii v gruzinskikh palimpsestnykh fragmentakh. MARR (N. Y.)

O Kavkazskom Universitete v Tiflise. MARR (N. Y.)

O klassnykh pokazatelyakh v avaro-andotsezskikh yazykakh. BOKAREV (A. A.)

O lingvisticheskikh chertakh kartvelʼskikh yazykov. CHIKʻOBAVA (A. S.)

O meste konchiny i pogrebeniya sv. Maksima Ispovednika. BRILLIANTOV (A. I.)

O mudrosti vymysla. SAVVA, *the Monk* [*Prince* SULKHAN ORBELIANI].

O nekotorykh osetinskikh elementakh v gruzinskom yazyke. ABAEV (V. I.)

O poligenii semantiki. MARR (N. Y.)

O religioznykh verovaniyakh abkhazov. MARR (N. Y.)

O terminakh rodstva v gruzinskom yazyke. PANEK (L. B.)

O tvoritelʼnom padezhe lichnykh mestoimeny 1-go i 2-go litsa v gruzinskom yazyke. RUDENKO (B. T.)

O yazyke ubykhov. GENKO (A. N.)

Ob izdanii gruzinskikh agiograficheskikh pamyatnikov. KEKELIDZE (K. S.)

Ob odnoi lingvisticheskoi kalʼke. Turetskoe vyrazhenie v armyanskom i gruzinskom. DONDUA (K. D.)

Ob odnom anonimnom gruzinskom istorike XIV veka. JAVAKHISHVILI (I. A.)

Ob otnoshenii abkhazskago yazyka k yafeticheskim. CHARAYA (P. G.)

Ob yafeticheskoi teorii. MARR (N. Y.)

Obozrenie Gruzii po chasti prav i zakonovedeniya. DAVID, *Prince-Regent of Georgia.*

Obraztsy dekorativnogo ubranstva gruzinskikh rukopisei. SCHMERLING (R. O.)

Obychnoe semeinoe pravo cherkes. LADYZHENSKY (A. M.)

Obzor istochnikov po istorii Azerbaidzhana. MELIKʻSETʻ-BEGI (L. M.)

Obzor teory i literatury o proiskhozhdenii gruzinskago yazyka. JAVAKHISHVILI (I. A.)

Ocherk grammatiki chamalinskogo yazyka. Bo-
KAREV (A. A.)

Ocherki po etnografii Kavkaza. KOSVEN (M. O.)

Ocherki po istorii gruzinskogo realizma. GAME-
ZARDASHVILI (D. M.)

Ocherki po istorii gruzinskoi slovesnosti. KHA-
KHANOV (A. S.)

Ocherki po istorii i kul'ture kavkazskoi Albanii.
TREVER (K. V.)

Ok'mebi k'art'vel revolutsionert'a pirvel konp'e-
rentsiisa. GEORGIA. – Socialist-Federalist Revolutionary Party.

Ok'ros betchedi. DGEBUADZE-P'ULARIA (P'.)

Oksfordsky fragment drevne-gruzinskoi versii Ieremii. GENKO (A. N.)

The Old Georgian Version of the Gospel of John.
BIBLE. – New Testament. – John.

The Old Georgian Version of the Gospel of Mark.
BIBLE. – New Testament. – Mark.

The Old Georgian Version of the Gospel of Matthew. BIBLE. – New Testament. – Matthew.

The Oldest Structure of Noun Bases in Kartvelian
Languages. CHIK'OBAVA (A. S.)

On the Religious Beliefs of the Abkhazians. MARR
(N. Y.)

Opis' pamyatnikov drevnosti v nekotorykh khra-
makh i monastyryakh Gruzii. KONDAKOV (N. P.)

Opisanie arkheologicheskikh materialov, obnaru-
zhennykh v Gruzii i postupivshikh v Muzei v
1904–1920 godakh. TIFLIS. – Museum of
Georgia.

Opisanie gruzinskikh rukopisei Gosudarstvennogo
Muzeya Gruzii. TIFLIS. – Museum of Georgia.

Opisanie gruzinskikh rukopisei sinaiskogo monastyrya. CATHARINE, Saint, of Alexandria. –
CONVENT OF, ON MOUNT SINAI.

Opisanie persidskago rukopisnago Chetveroevangeliya. BIBLE. – New Testament. – Gospels. –
Appendix.

Opisanie pyati emalevykh medal'onov s gruzin-
skimi nadpisyami. GORDEEV (D.)

Orages et grêle en Kakhétie. K'URDIANI (I.)

Oriens Christianus. ROME. – Collegium des deutschen Campo Santo.

Orient et Byzance. Le tréfonds oriental de l'hagiographie byzantine. PEETERS (P.)

Orientalia Christiana Periodica. ROME. – Pontificio Istituto per gli Studi Orientali.

Original Vocabularies of Five West Caucasian
Languages. PEACOCK (D. R.)

Les origines de la version arménienne et le diatessaron. LYONNET (S.)

Les origines du "Barlaam et Joasaph" grec. À
propos de la thèse nouvelle de M. Nucubidze.
DEVOS (P.)

Ormotsdaat'i dselidsadi samomkhmareblo kooperatsiisa Ruset'shi. KHEISIN (M. L.)

Ornement populaire géorgien. I: Ornement khevsourien. BARDAVELIDZE (V. V.) and CHITAIA
(G. S.)

Ort'ograp'iuli lek'sikoni. T'OP'URIA (V. T.) and
GIGINEISHVILI (I. M.)

Osnovnye morfologicheskie kategorii lezginskogo
glagola. T'OP'URIA (G. V.)

Osnovnye tablitsy k grammatike drevnegruzinskago yazyka. MARR (N. Y.)

Ossetica-Japhetica. MARR (N. Y.)

Oster- und Pfingstfeier Jerusalems im siebten
Jahrhundert. LITURGIES. – Greek Rite. –
Pentekostarion.

Otchet Gudarekhskikh pervoi i vtoroi, 1938 i
1939 gg., arkheologicheskikh kampany. MU-
SKHELISHVILI (L. V.) and others.

Otchet o letnei komandirovke 1913 g. v Dushetsky
i Tionetsky uezdy Tiflisskoi gubernii. SHA-
NIDZE (A. G.)

Otchet o tret'ei lingvisticheskoi poezdke zagra-
nitsu. MARR (N. Y.)

"Otello" A. Machavariani. ORJONIKIDZE (G. S.)

Ozaanis keramika. MAISURADZE (Z. P.)

Une page de saint Hippolyte retrouvée. HIPPO-
LYTUS, Saint, of Rome.

Der Paläolithiker in der Höhle Dewiss-Chwreli.
NIORADZE (G.)

Paleograp'iuli albomi. T'AQAISHVILI (E. S.)

Paleolit'is adamiani Deviskhvrelshi. NIORADZE
(G.)

Palestinsky Sbornik. SAINT PETERSBURG. – Православное, afterwards Российское Палестинское
Общество.

Pamyati akademika N. Ya. Marra, 1864–1934.
SAINT PETERSBURG. – Academia Scientiarum
Imperialis. – Яфетический Институт, after-
wards Институт языка и мышления.

Pamyatniki drevnegruzinskogo yazyka. TIFLIS. –
Academy of Sciences of the Georgian S.S.R.

Pamyatniki epokhi Rustaveli. SAINT PETERS-
BURG. – Императорский, afterwards Государственный, Эрмитажъ.

Pamyatniki gruzinskoi otrechennoi literatury.
KHAKHANOV (A. S.)

Pamyatniki gruzinskoi stariny v Svyatoi Zemle
i na Sinae. TSAGARELI (A. A.)

Pamyatniki tipa Dzhvari. CHUBINASHVILI (G. N.)

Papers of the Estonian Theological Society in
Exile. STOCKHOLM. – Estonian Theological
Society in Exile.

Paradigmy glagol'nykh form literaturnogo arab-
skogo yazyka. LEKIASHVILI (A. S.)

Die Probleme der ältesten Kirchengeschichte Georgiens. PʻERADZE (G.)

Proclamation of General Allenby, *etc*. EUROPEAN WAR, 1914–1919.

Profesori Patkanovi da kʻartʻuli istoriis dsqaroebi. BAKʻRADZE (D. Z.)

Proiskhozhdenie iz okhotnichʼyago byta dvukh gruzinskikh terminov ugolovnago prava: ʻgershiʼ i ʻsanakhshiroʼ. MARR (N. Y.)

Projet dʼun voyage littéraire à exécuter en Géorgie. BROSSET (M.-F.)

Propovednicheskaya deyatelʼnostʼ ap. Andreya i sv. Niny v Gruzii. JAVAKHISHVILI (I. A.)

Prostranny reestr gyurdzhyustanskogo vilaieta. JIKʻIA (S. S.)

Le "protévangile de Jacques" en géorgien. BIBLE. – New Testament. – *Apocrypha*.

Les Proverbes géorgiens. SAKHOKIA (Tʻ. T.)

Pʻsalmuni Davitʻisi. BIBLE. – Old Testament. – *Psalms*.

Pʻshav-Khevsuruli poezia. KHORNAULI (I. G.)

Pʻshavuri lekʻsebi. KHIZANASHVILI (D.)

Pʻsikʻologia. TIFLIS. – *Academy of Sciences of the Georgian S.S.R. – D. N. Uznadze Institute of Psychology*.

Publications récentes relatives à la littérature géorgienne. TʻARKHNISHVILI (M.)

Puteshestvie. GABASHVILI (T.) *Metropolitan of Kʻutʻaisi*.

Putevoditelʼ po khranilishcham drevnikh rukopisei Gosudarstvennogo Muzeya Gruzii. TIFLIS. – *Museum of Georgia*.

Quadragesima und Karwoche Jerusalems im siebten Jahrhundert. LITURGIES. – Greek Rite. – *Triodion*.

Quattuor Evangeliorum versio Georgiana vetus. BIBLE. – New Testament. – *Gospels*.

Quelques remarques sur un livre intitulé: *Reise durch Rußland nach dem kaukasischen Isthmus*. BROSSET (M.-F.)

Ra vaketʻotʻ? LENIN (V. I.)

Ramdenime lekʻsi. TSAKHELI, *pseud*.

Rapport à S. E. le Prince Vorontzof, sur les chartes géorgiennes. BROSSET (M.-F.)

Rapport à Son Excellence M. le Comte Ouvarof. BROSSET (M.-F.)

Rapport à S. E. M. le Ministre . . . sur ses recherches dans les archives de Moscou. BROSSET (M.-F.)

Rapport général sur les résultats dʼun voyage littéraire en Géorgie. BROSSET (M.-F.)

Rapport sur différents documents géorgiens envoyés à lʼAcadémie. BROSSET (M.-F.)

Rapport sur la Littérature géorgienne. SAINT-MARTIN (J. A.)

Rapport sur la publication de la Géographie de la Géorgie par Wakhoucht. BROSSET (M.-F.)

Rapport sur le dictionnaire manuscrit géorgien-russe-latin de M. D. Tchoubinof. BROSSET (M.-F.)

Rapport sur le voyage de M. Dimitri Méghwineth-Khoutzésis-Chwili. BROSSET (M.-F.)

Rapport sur les recherches archéologiques faites par M. Bakradzé dans le Gouria. BROSSET (M.-F.)

Rapport sur les voyages exécutés . . . par M. Dimitri Méghwineth-Khoutsésov. BROSSET (M.-F.)

Rapport sur lʼouvrage manuscrit de M. Bakradzé. BROSSET (M. F.)

Rapport sur un ouvrage manuscrit intitulé: "Slovarʼ Russko-cherkessky". SJOEGREN (A. J.)

Rapport sur un recueil de documents historiques. BROSSET (M.-F.)

Rapport sur un voyage en Géorgie. PEREVALENKO (B.)

Rapports sur un voyage archéologique dans la Géorgie, *etc*. BROSSET (M.-F.)

Ras amboben pʻakʻtebi. KANDELAKI (K.)

Ras itsini? TʻOMAANTʻ KOBA, *pseud*.

Raskopki v Dmanisi. MUSKHELISHVILI (L. V.)

Rasskazy. LOMOURI (N. I.)

Ratom gvakʻvs imedi! ZHGHENTI (L.)

Ratsionaluri martsvali Hegelis daskvnis tʻeoriashi. TSERETʻELI (S. B.)

Razbitoe serdtse. ARAGVISPIRELI (SH.) *pseud*.

Razlozhimostʼ mnimykh primitivov, prostykh slov, i terminy dlya ponyatiya ʻrybaʼ. MARR (N. Y.)

Razyskaniya Instituta Istorii Gruzinskogo Iskusstva. TIFLIS. – *Academy of Sciences of the Georgian S.S.R. – Institute of the History of Georgian Art*.

Rcheuli. GAPʻRINDASHVILI (V. I.); GULIA (D. I.); MIRTSKHULAVA-MASHASHVILI (A. A.); TABIDZE (G. B.)

Rcheuli. Ertʻtomeuli. VAZHA-PʻSHAVELA, *pseud*.

Rcheuli. Lekʻsebi, poemebi, 1934–1953. EULI-KʻURIDZE (S. K.)

Rcheuli nadserebi or tomad. LORTʻKʻIPʻANIDZE (K. A.)

Rcheuli nadserebi otʻkh tomad. PUSHKIN (A. S.)

Rcheuli novelebi da komediebi. MÉRIMÉE (P.)

Rcheuli shairebis krebuli. QIPʻIANI (G.)

Rcheuli tʻkhzulebani. BYELINSKY (V. G.)

Rcheuli tʻkhzulebani khutʻ tomad. DADIANI (SH. N.)

Rcheuli tʻkhzulebani: piesebi. KAKABADZE (P. M.)

Recent work on the Georgian New Testament. LANG (D. M.)

Les récentes découvertes épigraphiques et littéraires en géorgien. TʻARKHNISHVILI (M.)

Recherches comparatives sur le verbe caucasien. DUMÉZIL (G.)

Recherches d'histoire et de philologie orientales. PEETERS (P.)

Recherches sur la poésie géorgienne. BROSSET (M.-F.)

Récits oubykh. DUMÉZIL (G.) and NAMITOK (A.)

Recueil japhétique. SAINT PETERSBURG. — *Academia Scientiarum Imperialis.* - Яфетический Институт, afterwards Институт языка и мышления.

Recueil Rousthavéli. JANASHIA (S. N.)

Registre des cartes géorgiennes manuscrites, acquises par le Musée Asiatique. BROSSET (M.-F.)

Reisen nach Georgien und Imerethi. GUELDENSTAEDT (J. A.)

Rel'efy Nikortsminda. ALADASHVILI (N. A.)

Rel'efy Shiomgvime i ikh mesto v razvitii gruzinskoi skul'ptury. VOL'SKAYA (A. I.)

The Religious Beliefs of the Abkhazians. JANASHIA (N.S.)

Religioznyya verovaniya abkhazov. JANASHIA (N. S.)

Réponse à M. de Bartholomaei. BROSSET (M.-F.)

Review of 'Histoire du Bas-Empire'. TOUMANOFF (C. L.) *Prince.*

Revolyutsionnoe proshloe Tbilisi. STURUA (N. I.) *and others.*

Revolyutsiya 1905–1907 godov v Gruzii. KHUTSISHVILI (I. G.) *and others.*

Revolyutsiya v gruzinskom fol'klore. MEGRELIDZE (I. B.)

Revue de l'Orient chrétien. PERIODICAL PUBLICATIONS. - *Paris.*

Revue des antiquités géorgiennes. BROSSET (M.-F.)

Revue d'Histoire Ecclésiastique. LOUVAIN. - *Academia Lovaniensis.*

Richard Mesame. SHAKSPERE (W.)

Robin Hood. English popular ballads. HOOD (R.)

Robin Hudi. HOOD (R.)

Robinson Crusoe. DEFOE (D.)

Robinzon Kruzo. DEFOE (D.)

Roditel'ny padezh famil'nykh imen na -dze -*de* v zapadnogruzinskom. MEGRELIDZE (I. B.)

Rogor tskhovrobden adamianebi dzvelat'. KUDRYAVSKY (D. N.)

Rogor unda gadadsqdes chvenshi midsis mp'lobelobis sak'me. GEORGIA. – *Socialist-Federalist Revolutionary Party.*

Le roman de Balahvar et sa traduction anglaise. T'ARKHNISHVILI (M.)

Rukopisnye materialy akad. Shögrena po cherkesskim yazykam. TURCHANINOV (G. F.)

Russko-abazinsky slovar'. CHERKESSK. – *Cherkessky Nauchno-Issledovatel'sky Institut.*

Russko-gruzinskie literaturnye svyazi. NIKOLADZE (A. K.)

Russko-gruzinsky slovar'. CHUBINOV (D. I.); TIFLIS. – *Academy of Sciences of the Georgian S.S.R.*

Russko-kabardinsko-cherkessky slovar'. KARDANOV (B. M.) and BICHOEV (A. T.)

Russko-svansky slovar'. NIZHARADZE (I. I.)

Rust'aveli and his Poem. GVAZAVA (G.)

Rustaveli i fol'klor. MEGRELIDZE (I. B.)

Rust'avelis est'etika. NADIRADZE (G. A.)

Rust'avelis krebuli. JANASHIA (S. N.)

Rust'velis da Dantes idumali. BELIASHVILI (L.)

Rustvelologicheskaya literatura, 1712–1956 gody. IMEDASHVILI (G.)

Rust'velologiuri literatura, 1712–1956 dslebi. IMEDASHVILI (G.)

Rusul-k'art'uli lek'sikoni. TIFLIS. – *Academy of Sciences of the Georgian S.S.R.*

Rusuli "apovt'egmatas" k'art'uli redak'tsiebi. DZODSENIDZE (L. G.)

Rutul'sky yazyk. DIRR (A.)

Rutul'tsy. LAVROV (L. I.)

Saangarisho mokhseneba partiis XVIII qrilobaze. STALIN (I. V.)

Saangarisho mokhseneba partiis XIX qrilobaze. MALENKOV (G. M.)

Saba Orbeliani i ego gruzinsky "Leksikon". GAMREKELI (N.)

Sabavshvo lek'sebi da poemebi. ABASHIDZE (I. B.)

Sabavshvo mot'khrobebi. VAZHA-P'SHAVELA, *pseud.*

Sabtchot'a kavshiris komunisturi partia. RUSSIA. – Российская Коммунистическая Партия.

Sabtchot'a kavshiris komunisturi partiis dsesdeba. RUSSIA. – Российская Коммунистическая Партия.

Sabtchot'a Sak'art'velo 17 dslis mandzilze. GEORGIA. – *Soviet Socialist Republic.*

Sabtchot'a sotsialisturi respublikebis kavshiris konstitutsia. RUSSIA. – *Laws, etc.*

Sabtchot'a Ukrainas – K'art'veli mdserlebi. RUSSIA. – *Ukrainian Soviet Socialist Republic.*

Die Sagen und Lieder des Tscherkessen-Volks. SHORA-BEKMURZIN-NOGMOV.

Saiat'novas vinaoba. MELIK'SET'-BEGI (L. M.)

S. Barlaam du Mont Casius. PEETERS (P.)

St. Euthymius the Georgian and the Barlaam and Ioasaph Romance. LANG (D. M.)

S. Hilarion d'Ibérie. HILARION, *Saint, of Iberia.*

S. Ražden le Persan. RAZHDEN, *Saint, of Persia.*

S. Romain le néo-martyr. ROMANUS, *Saint, of Galatia.*

Sainte Šoušanik, martyre en Arméno-Georgie. PEETERS (P.)

Saiubileo krebuli . . . Korneli Samsonis dze Kekelidzes dabadebis 80 dslist'avis aghsanishnavad. KEKELIDZE (K. S.)

Sak'art'velo. Qoveldghiuri sapolitiko, saekonomio da saliteraturo gazet'i. PERIODICAL PUBLICATIONS. – Tiflis.

Sak'art'velo. T'avisup'ali organo. PERIODICAL PUBLICATIONS. – Paris.

Sak'art'velo da ket'ili. URUSHADZE (S.)

Sak'art'velo da saert'ashoriso up'leba. LE FUR (L.)

Sak'art'velo XIX saukunis pirvel nakhevarshi. KHATCHAPURIDZE (G. B.)

Sak'art'velo sabtchot'a kavshiris did samamulo omshi, 1941–1945. IOSELIANI (A. P.)

Sak'art'velos ark'eologia. AP'AK'IDZE (A. M.) and others.

Sak'art'velos deda-k'alak'i Tp'ilisi. JANASHVILI (M. G.)

Sak'art'velos erovnuli meurneoba. KANDELAKI (K.)

Sak'art'velos istoria. VAKHUSHTI, Prince of Georgia.

Sak'art'velos istoria, XIX saukune. KIKVIDZE (A. I.)

Sak'art'velos kherkhemliant'a nomenklatura. CHKHIKVISHVILI (I. D.)

Sak'art'velos khit' khurot'modzghvreba. GARAQANIDZE (M. K.)

Sak'art'velos mokle istoria. Akhali saukuneebis epok'a. KAKABADZE (S. N.)

Sak'art'velos muzeumis moambe. TIFLIS. – Museum of Georgia.

Sak'art'velos muzeumis shromebi. TIFLIS. – Museum of Georgia.

Sak'art'velos respublika. PERIODICAL PUBLICATIONS. – Tiflis.

Sak'art'velos SSR geograp'iuli sazogadoebis shromebi. TIFLIS. – Georgian Geographical Society.

Sak'art'velos SSR metsnierebat'a akademiis gamotsemat'a bibliograp'ia, 1937–1956 dsds. TIFLIS. – Academy of Sciences of the Georgian S.S.R.

Sak'art'velos SSR metsnierebat'a akademiis moambe. TIFLIS. – Academy of Sciences of the Georgian S.S.R.

Sak'art'velos saert'ashoriso mdgomareoba. ZURABISHVILI (I.)

Sak'art'velos saert'ashoriso urt'iert'obani utskho k'veqnebt'an. TIFLIS. – Tiflis State University.

Sak'art'velos sakhelmdsip'o muzeumis dzvel khelnadsert'a satsavebis gzamkvlevi. TIFLIS. – Museum of Georgia.

Sak'art'velos sakhelmdsip'o muzeumis gemebi. TIFLIS. – Museum of Georgia.

Sak'art'velos sakhelmdsip'o muzeumis k'art'ul khelnadsert'a aghdseriloba. TIFLIS. – Museum of Georgia.

Sak'art'velos samart'lisa da kanont'mtsodneobis mimokhilva. DAVID, Prince-Regent of Georgia.

Sak'art'velos sazghvrebi istoriulad da t'anamedrove t'valsazrisit' gankhiluli. JAVAKHISHVILI (I. A.)

Sak'art'velos sidzveleni. T'AQAISHVILI (E. S.)

Sak'art'velos sots.-dem. mushat'a partiis mushaoba sazghvar-garet'. GVARJALADZE (K. I.)

Sak'art'velos teritoriis sazghvrebis shesakheb. I. (P.)

Sak'art'velosa da Amierkavkasiis ekonomikuri ganvit'areba XIX–XX ss. GUGUSHVILI (P. B.)

Sakavshiro komunisturi partiis (bolshevikebis) istoria. RUSSIA. – Российская Коммунистическая Партия. – Центральный Комитет.

Sakhalkho p'urtseli. PERIODICAL PUBLICATIONS. – Tiflis.

Sakhalkho sak'me. PERIODICAL PUBLICATIONS. – Tiflis.

Sakhareba Ioanesi. BIBLE. – New Testament. – John.

Sakharebay ot'kht'avi. BIBLE. – New Testament. – Gospels.

Sakhelgamis gamotsemat'a katalogi. PERIODICAL PUBLICATIONS. – Tiflis.

Sakhelis p'udzis udzvelesi agebuleba k'art'velur enebshi. CHIK'OBAVA (A. S.)

Sakhelmdsip'o da eri. ANCHIN, pseud.

Sakhelt'a bruneba da brunvat'a p'unk'tsiebi dzvel k'art'ulshi. IMNAISHVILI (I. B.)

Sakhisa da khasiat'is problema 'Vep'khistqaosanshi'. BENASHVILI (D.)

Sakit'khavi sueytis tskhovelisay, kuart'isa saup'loysa da kat'olike eklesiisa. NICHOLAS I, Catholicos of Georgia.

Sak'ristiano modzghuareba mokled darigebuli. ROBERT [Bellarmino] Saint, Cardinal, Archbishop of Capua.

Sak'ristiano modzghuareba simokleobit' darigebuli. ROBERT [Bellarmino] Saint, Cardinal, Archbishop of Capua.

Sak'ristiano modzghvareba, gina dsurt'na shvidt'a saidumlot'a zeda. TLUKAANT'I (D.)

Sakut'reba; Midsis sakit'khi Sak'art'veloshi. MANVELISHVILI (A. P.)

Samkhret' sazghvarze. ABASHIDZE (G. G.)

Samok'alak'o omis istoria S.S.R. Kavshirshi. GOR'KY (M.) pseud.

Samsheneblo khelovneba dzvel Sak'art'veloshi. MSHVENIERADZE (D. M.)

Samshoblo. PERIODICAL PUBLICATIONS. – *Paris*.

Samtʿavros samarovanshi mopovebuli gemebis katalogi. TIFLIS. – *Museum of Georgia*.

Samtskhis khurotʿmodzghvreba, XIII–XVI saukuneebi. BERIDZE (V. V.)

Samuslimano Sakʿartʿvelo. PERIODICAL PUBLICATIONS. – *Batum*.

Saorbisskaya tserkovʾ. CHUBINASHVILI (G. N.)

Saqmadsvilo motʿkhrobani. MGALOBLISHVILI (S. Z.)

Sazogadoebrivi modzraoba Sakʿartʿveloshi 1821–1921 ds. URATADZE (G. I.)

Sbornik proizvedeny molodykh pisatelei Sovetskoi Sotsialisticheskoi Respubliki Gruzii. KOLOSOV (M. B.)

Sbornik Rustaveli. JANASHIA (S. N.)

Second rapport adressé à la Conférence de l'Académie Impériale des Sciences. BROSSET (M.-F.)

Les secrets de Rousthaveli et de Dante Aliguiery. BELIASHVILI (L.)

La sépulture de Modeste de Jérusalem. GARITTE (G.)

Serdtse govorit. CHACHKHALIA (K.)

Seriya caucasica. MESHCHANINOV (I. I.)

Le sermon géorgien du moine Martyrius et son modèle syriaque. SĀHDŌNĀ, *Bishop of Māhōzē dh-Arēwān in Bēth Garmai*.

Shahname. Kʿartʿuli versiebi. ḤASAN (ABUʾL-ḲĀSIM) called FIRDAUSĪ, *Ṭūsī*.

Shekʿspiri. QIASASHVILI (N. A.)

Shentʿan amkhanagebi arian. PRILEZHAEVA (M.)

Sheriskhva; mskhverpli. KLDIASHVILI (D. S.)

A short history of the Georgian Church. IOSELIANI (P. E.)

Shotʿa Brolidze. Romani. MALAKʿIASHVILI (V.)

Shota Rustaveli. GOLʾTSEV (V. V.)

Shotʿa Rustʿaveli, 1172–1216. TCHITCHINADZE (Z. E.)

Shota Rustaveli. Neskolʾko parallelei i analogy. SHISHMAREV (V. F.)

Shota Rustaveli i ego poema. GOLʾTSEV (V. V.); INGOROQVA (P. I.)

Shota Rustaveli i ego vremya. Sbornik statei. GOLʾTSEV (V. V.)

Shota Rustaveli i gruzinskaya literatura. DONDUA (K. D.)

Shota Rustaveli i gruzinsky folʾklor. MEGRELIDZE (I. B.)

Shota Rustaveli v russkoi literature. BERKOV (P. N.)

Shotʿa Rustʿavelis epokʿis materialuri kultura. JAVAKHISHVILI (I. A.)

Shrifty dlya nadpisei na chertezhakh. MIKʿELADZE (M. D.)

Shripʿtebi nakhatebze dsardserebisatʿvis. MIKʿELADZE (M. D.)

Shroma. Samushao dsigni. ASLANISHVILI (Tʿ.) *and others*.

Shromebi. KHATCHAPURIDZE (G. B.)

Shromis organizatsiis pʾormebi dzveli Sakʿartʿvelos sakhalkho meurneobashi. TIFLIS. – *Academy of Sciences of the Georgian S.S.R.*

Shuasaukunetʿa kʿartʿuli khis chukʿurtʿma, X–XI saukuneebi. CHUBINASHVILI (N.)

Sibilant correspondences and some questions of the ancient structure of Kartvelian languages. GAMQRELIDZE (Tʿ. V.)

Sibilanttʿa shesatqvisobani da kʿartʿvelur enatʿa udzvelesi strukʿturis zogi sakitʿkhi. GAMQRELIDZE (Tʿ. V.)

Sigelʾ gruzinskago tsarya Bagrata IV, 1027–1072. TʿAQAISHVILI (E. S.)

La Significacion de la Astronomia y Astrologia en el Epos heroico georgiano . . . "El Caballero de la Piel de Tigre". NOZADZE (V.)

La Significacion del Sol en el Epos heroico georgiano . . . "El Caballero de la Piel de Tigre". NOZADZE (V.)

Simfoniya k poeme Sh. Rustveli "Vityazʾ v tigrovoi shkure". SHANIDZE (A. G.)

Simfoniya-slovarʾ k gruzinskomu chetveroglavu. IMNAISHVILI (I. B.)

Sinaisky mnogoglav 864-go goda. LITURGIES. – Greek Rite. – *Lectionaries*.

Sintaksis avarskogo yazyka. BOKAREV (A. A.)

Sinuri mravaltʿavi 864 dslisa. LITURGIES. – Greek Rite. – *Lectionaries*.

Sistema grammaticheskikh klassov v batsbiiskom yazyke. DESHERIEV (YU. D.)

Sitqva partiis XIX qrilobaze. STALIN (I. V.)

Sitqva sakavshiro k. p. (b) XIX qrilobaze. BERIYA (L. P.)

Sitqvis-kona Imerul da Ratchul tʿkʿmatʿa. BERIDZE (V. M.)

Sitqvis-kona: Saba-Sulkhan Orbelianis da Davitʿ Chubinashvilis lekʿsikonebshi gamotovebuli sitqvebi. TCHQONIA (I. M.)

Sitsotskhlis talghebi. GORGANELI (V.)

Skazanie o postroenii pervoi tserkvi v gorode Lidde. JOSEPH, *of Arimathea*.

Sklonenie imen i funktsii padezhei v drevnegruzinskom. IMNAISHVILI (I. B.)

Sklonenie v didoiskom yazyke. MEGRELIDZE (I. B.)

Skruji da Marlei. DICKENS (C.)

Sledy grammaticheskikh klassov (rodov) v agulʾskom yazyke. SHAUMYAN (R. M.)

Sledy rodovogo stroya u mtiulov. PANEK (L. B.)

Sobranie gruzinskikh rukopisei Instituta Vostokovedeniya Akademii Nauk SSSR. SAINT

PETERSBURG. – *Academia Scientiarum Imperialis*. – *Институт Востоковедения*.

Sochineniya v dvukh tomakh. NINOSHVILI (E.) *pseud.*

Solomon Dodashvili. TCHITCHINADZE (Z. E.)

Solomon Dodashvili, tskhovreba da moghvadseoba. GOTSADZE (M. K.)

Some Byzantine accounting practices illustrated from Georgian sources. BLAKE (R. P.)

Sonetebi. SHAKSPERE (W.)

Song of Solomon. BIBLE. – Old Testament. – *Song of Solomon.*

Sonnets. SHAKSPERE (W.)

Soobshcheniya Akademii Nauk Gruzinskoi SSR. TIFLIS. – *Academy of Sciences of the Georgian S.S.R.*

Sop'lis meurneobis terminologia. KETSKHOVELI (N. N.) *and others.*

Sostav i istochniki nachal'noi gruzinskoi letopisi. KHAKHANOV (A. S.)

Sotsialisturi realizmis shesakheb. MERKVILADZE (G. I.)

Sotsializmis ekonomikuri problemebi SSR Kavshirshi. STALIN (I. V.)

Sotsialur-politikuri tskhovrebis gansakut'rebuli pirobebi da glekht'a revolutsiuri modzraobis t'aviseburebani Sak'art'veloshi, 1905–1907 dsds. KATCHARAVA (I. M.)

Sources arméno-géorgiennes de l'histoire ancienne de l'Église de Géorgie. T'ARKHNISHVILI (M.)

Les sources des notices du Patriarche de Jérusalem Dosithée sur les rois d'Aphkhazie. T'AQAISHVILI (E. S.)

Sovetskaya arkheologiya. SAINT PETERSBURG. – *Academia Scientiarum Imperialis*. – *Институт Истории Материальной Культуры.*

Sovetskaya etnografiya. SAINT PETERSBURG. – *Academia Scientiarum Imperialis.*

Sovetskoe Vostokovedenie. SAINT PETERSBURG. – *Academia Scientiarum Imperialis*. – *Институт Востоковедения.*

Sovetsky Ajaristan. SURMANIDZE (M.)

Sovetsky Fol'klor. SAINT PETERSBURG. – *Academia Scientiarum Imperialis*. – *Институт Антропологии и Этнографии.*

Sparset'i da ik'auri k'art'velebi. AGHNIASHVILI (L.)

Spilendz-brinjaos metalurgiis istoriisat'vis Sak'art'veloshi. ABESADZE (Ts. N.) *and others.*

Die Sprache der Ubychen. DIRR (A.)

Die Sprachen des kaukasischen Stammes. ERCKERT (R. von).

Stalin. Detstvo i otrochestvo. Epopeya. LEONIDZE (G. N.)

Stat'i po istorii i drevnostyam Gruzii. BAK'RADZE (D. Z.)

Stikhi i poemy. SHANSHIASHVILI (S. I.)

Stikhi. Perevod s gruzinskogo Borisa Pasternaka. BARAT'ASHVILI (N. M.) *Prince.*

Stikhi, perevod s kabardinskogo. KESHOKOV (A. P.)

Stikhi, pesni, ballady v perevodakh. KALADZE (K. R.)

Stikhotvoreniya. BARAT'ASHVILI (N. M.) *Prince.*

Stikhotvoreniya. Perevod s gruzinskogo. ABASHIDZE (G. G.)

Stikhotvoreniya i poemy. LEONIDZE (G. N.); TSADASA (G.); VAZHA-P'SHAVELA, *pseud.*

Stolniki Tolochanovisa da diaki Ievlevis elchoba Imeret'shi, 1650–1652. POLIEVKTOV (M. A.)

The Story of the Loves of Vis and Ramin (Visramiani). SARGIS, *of T'mogvi.*

Strekoza. BARAT'ASHVILI (M.)

Stroitel'noe iskusstvo v drevnei Gruzii. MSHVENIERADZE (D. M.)

Structure phonémique du géorgien. VOGT (H. K.)

Studien auf dem Gebiete der vergleichenden Lautlehre der nordkaukasischen Sprachen. TRUBETSKOI (N. S.) *Prince.*

Studien zur georgischen Wortbildung. NEISSER (F.)

Studies in the numismatic history of Georgia in Transcaucasia. LANG (D. M.)

Das Studium der altgeorgischen Sprache in Georgien. Bibliographische Übersicht. JEDLIČKA (J.)

Subjekt- und Objektkasus beim awarischen Verbum. BOUDA (K.)

Sudzhunskaya tserkov' i eya drevnosti. T'AQAISHVILI (E. S.)

Sulkhan-Saba Orbeliani, 1658–1958: saiubileo krebuli. SAVVA, *the Monk* [*Prince* SULKHAN ORBELIANI].

Sulkhan-Saba Orbeliani. Tskhovreba da literaturuli mogvadseoba. BARAMIDZE (A. G.)

Sulkhan-Saba Orbelianis literaturuli moghvadseobidan, 1698–1713 dsds. LOLASHVILI (I. A.)

Sumerian and Georgian: a Study in Comparative Philology. TSERET'ELI (M. G.)

Sur la langue géorgienne. BROSSET (M. -F.)

Sur les bénédictions d'Isaac, de Jacob et de Moïse. HIPPOLYTUS, *Saint, of Rome.*

Sur un fragment géorgien d'Agathange. GARITTE (G.)

Sur un projet d'étude des chartes géorgiennes. BROSSET (M.-F.)

Sur une inscription géorgienne de l'église patriarchale de Mtzkhétha. BROSSET (M.-F.)

Suramis tsikhe. Tragedia. MT'VARADZE (S.)

Les survivances de la chasse collective en Ratcha. ROBAKʻIDZE (A. I.)

Svanetskiya rukopisnyya evangeliya. KHAKHA-NOV (A. S.)

Svanskie prozaicheskie teksty. TIFLIS. – *Marr Language Institute*, afterwards *Institute of Linguistics*.

Svanuri prozauli tekʻstebi. TIFLIS. – *Marr Language Institute*, afterwards *Institute of Linguistics*.

Svedeniya o pamyatnikakh gruzinskoi pisʼmennosti. TSAGARELI (A. A.)

Svimon mepʻe, 1557–1600. KARITCHASHVILI (D. G.)

Svobodny Kavkaz. PERIODICAL PUBLICATIONS. – *Munich*.

The Symbolism of Colours in the Georgian romantic epic . . . ʻThe Knight in the Tiger's Skin'. NOZADZE (V.)

Le Synaxaire géorgien. LITURGIES. – Greek Rite. – *Synaxarion*.

Syntagmatων Linguarum Orientalium, quae in Georgiae regionibus audiuntur. MAGGI (F. M.)

Le système des cas en géorgien ancien. VOGT (H. K.)

Taina Dyurka. Poema. JAFAROV (A.)

Tʻamar mepʻisa da meughlisa misisa Davitʻ mepʻis sheskhma. SHAVTʻELI (IOVANE).

Tʻamariani. GUGUNAVA (S.) *Prince.*

Tʻavadi Mishetskisa da diaki Klucharevis elchoba Kakhetʻshi, 1640–1643. POLIEVKTOV (M. A.)

Tʻavadi Rapʻael Eristʻavi. QIPʻSHIDZE (G. Tʻ.)

Tʻavadis N. Baratʻashvilis lekʻsebi. BARATʻA-SHVILI (N. M.) *Prince.*

Tbilisi. Arkhitektura starogo goroda i zhilye doma pervoi poloviny XIX stoletiya. TSINTSADZE (V. G.)

Tʻbilisi 1500. Saiubileo krebuli. TIFLIS. – *Tiflis State University.*

Tbilisi, stolitsa Gruzinskoi SSR. OTAROVA (N. A.)

Tbilisi 1500. Yubileiny sbornik. TIFLIS. – *Tiflis State University.*

Tbilisi v XIX stoletii, 1865–1869. CHKHETIA (SH. Q.)

Tbilisi v poezii. CHIKʻOVANI (S. I.)

Tʻbilisis arkʻeologiuri dzeglebi. Kʻoridze (D. L.)

Tʻbilisis botanikis institutis shromebi. TIFLIS. – *Academy of Sciences of the Georgian S.S.R. – Tiflis Botanical Institute.*

Tʻbilisis ghrmad mokhutsebuli adamianebi. SHA-Pʻiro (I. B.) *and others.*

Tʻbilisis revolutsiuri dsarsuli. STURUA (N. I.) *and others.*

Tchanuri tekʻstebi. CHIKʻOBAVA (A. S.)

Tchanur-megrul-kʻartʻuli shedarebitʻi lekʻsikoni. CHIKʻOBAVA (A. S.)

Tchanur-megrulis pʻonetika. ZHGHENTI (S. M.)

Tʻedzmis kheoba. Istoriul-etʻnograpʻiuli narkvevi. MAKALATʻIA (S. I.)

Tʻeimuraz I and his Poem "The Martyrdom of Queen Kʻetʻevan". AVALISHVILI (Z. D.)

Tekhnicheskaya terminologiya. BERIDZE (V. M.) *and others.*

Tekʻnikuri terminologia. BERIDZE (V. M.) *and others.*

Teksty i razyskaniya po armyano-gruzinskoi filologii. MARR (N. Y.)

Teksty i razyskaniya po kavkazskoi filologii. SAINT PETERSBURG. – *Academia Scientiarum Imperialis.*

Le témoignage de Georges l'Hagiorite sur l'origine du "Barlaam" grec. GARITTE (G.)

Terminologiya selʻskogo khozyaistva. KETSKHO-VELI (N. N.) *and others.*

Texte und Untersuchungen zur Geschichte der altchristlichen Literatur. GEBHARDT (O. von) and HARNACK (C. G. A. von).

Textes avar. DUMÉZIL (G.)

Textes et recherches dans le domaine de la philologie caucasienne. SAINT PETERSBURG. – *Academia Scientiarum Imperialis.*

Textes populaires Inguš. JABAGI (M.)

Theoretisch-praktische Grammatik der modernen georgischen (grusinischen) Sprache. DIRR (A.)

Thrako-armyansky Sabađios-aswaţ i svanskoe bozhestvo okhoty. MARR (N. Y.)

Tʻkhzulebani. BARATʻASHVILI (N. M.) *Prince*; GO-GEBASHVILI (I. S.); SHANIDZE (A. G.)

Tʻkhzulebani. Dsigni mesame. – Naazrevi. JOR-JADZE (A.)

Tʻkhzulebani. Pavle Ingoroqvas shesavali dseri-litʻ. TCHAVTCHAVADZE (I. G.) *Prince.*

Tʻkhzulebani A. Qazbegisa. QAZBEGI (A. M.)

Tʻkhzulebani Akaki Tseretʻlisa. TSERETʻELI (A. R.) *Prince.*

Tʻkhzulebani Anton Pʻurtseladzisa. Pʻurtseladze (A. N.)

Tʻkhzulebani Ilia Tchavtchavadzisa. TCHAVTCHA-VADZE (I. G.) *Prince.*

Tʻkhzulebani or tomad. GVETADZE (R. M.); KLDIA-SHVILI (D. S.); QAZBEGI (A. M.)

Tʻkhzulebani otʻkh tomad. SAVVA, *the Monk [Prince* SULKHAN ORBELIANI].

Tʻkhzulebatʻa sruli krebuli. NINOSHVILI (E.) *pseud.*

Tʻkhzulebatʻa sruli krebuli atʻ tomad. TCHAV-TCHAVADZE (I. G.) *Prince.*

Tʻkhzulebatʻa sruli krebuli or tomad. UIARAGHO, *pseud.*

T'khzulebat'a sruli krebuli ot'kh tomad. LORT'-K'IP'ANIDZE (N. M.)

T'khzulebat'a sruli krebuli t'khut'met tomad. TSERET'ELI (A. R.) *Prince.*

Tkvirskaya tserkov' v Mingrelii i eya drevnosti. T'AQAISHVILI (E. S.)

Tolkovanie Pesni pesnei. HIPPOLYTUS, *Saint, of Rome.*

Tolkovy slovar' gruzinskogo yazyka. CHIK'OBAVA (A. S.) *and others.*

T'ovlian mt'ebshi. Ialbuzi. KETSKHOVELI (N. N.)

Tp'ilisis istoriisat'vis. CHKHETIA (SH. Q.)

Tp'ilisis sakhelmdsip'o universiteti, 1918–1928. TIFLIS. – *Tiflis State University.*

Tp'ilisis sakhelmdsip'o universitetis shromebi. TIFLIS. – *Tiflis State University.*

Tp'ilisis universitetis moambe. TIFLIS. – *Tiflis State University.*

Traditio. PERIODICAL PUBLICATIONS. – *New York.*

Traductions et traducteurs dans l'hagiographie orientale à l'époque byzantine. PEETERS (P.)

Tragediebi. (T'khzulebani.) SHAKSPERE (W.)

Traité géorgien du comput ecclésiastique. ABU-SERIDZE, of *Tbet'i.*

Transactions of the J. Beritashvili Physiological Institute. TIFLIS. – *Tiflis State University.*

Travaux de l'Université d'État de Tiflis. TIFLIS. – *Tiflis State University.*

Travaux du Musée de Géorgie. TIFLIS. – *Museum of Georgia.*

Travaux et mémoires de l'Institut d'Ethnologie. PARIS. – *Université de Paris.* – *Institut d'Ethnologie.*

Tri poemy. TABIDZE (T. I.)

Tristan i Isol'da. Ot geroini lyubvi feodal'noi Evropy do bogini lyubvi matriarkhal'noi Afrevrazii. MARR (N. Y.)

Troisième rapport, adressé à Son Excellence le Prince-Lieutenant du Caucase. BROSSET (M.-F.)

Trudy Abkhazskogo Instituta Yazyka, Literatury i Istorii imeni D. I. Gulia. SUKHUMI. – *Abkhazian Linguistic, Literary and Historical Institute.*

Trudy geograficheskogo obshchestva Gruzinskoi SSR. TIFLIS. – *Georgian Geographical Society.*

Trudy Instituta Ekonomiki. TIFLIS. – *Academy of Sciences of the Georgian S.S.R.* – *Institute of Economics.*

Trudy Instituta Yazykoznaniya. SAINT PETERS-BURG. – *Academia Scientiarum Imperialis.* – *Институт Языкознания.*

Trudy Instituta Yazykoznaniya. Seriya Vostochnykh Yazykov. TIFLIS. – *Marr Language Institute,* afterwards *Institute of Linguistics.*

Trudy Instituta Zashchity Rasteny. TIFLIS. – *Academy of Sciences of the Georgian S.S.R.* – *Institute of Plant Protection.*

Trudy Instituta zoologii. TIFLIS. – *Academy of Sciences of the Georgian S.S.R.* – *Institute of Zoology.*

Trudy kafedry obshchego yazykoznaniya. TIFLIS. – *Tiflis State University.*

Trudy po Vostokovedeniyu. Moscow. – *Lazarevsky,* afterwards *Tsentral'ny, Institut Vostochnykh Yazykov,* afterwards *Institut Vostokovedeniya.*

Trudy Tbilisskogo Botanicheskogo Instituta. TIFLIS. – *Academy of Sciences of the Georgian S.S.R.* – *Tiflis Botanical Institute.*

Trudy Tiflisskogo Gosudarstvennogo Universiteta. TIFLIS. – *Tiflis State University.*

Eine tscherkessische Grammatik. DEETERS (G.)

Tschetschenzische Studien. SCHIEFNER (F. A. von).

Tschetschenzisches und Awarisches. USLAR (P. K.) *Baron.*

Tserkov' bliz seleniya Bolnis-Kapanakchi. CHU-BINASHVILI (G. N.)

Tserkov' v Vane, v Imerii, i eya drevnosti. T'A-QAISHVILI (E. S.)

Tserkvi i tserkovnye drevnosti Megrelii. T'A-QAISHVILI (E. S.)

Tsezskie (didoiskie) yazyki Dagestana. BOKAREV (E. A.)

Tsisp'er gzaze. P'ORCHKHIDZE (S.)

Tskhovreba da kanoni. TCHAVTCHAVADZE (I. G.) *Prince.*

Tskhovreba Ivane Machablisa. TCHELIDZE (V.)

Tskhovreba Petre Iverisa. ZACHARIAS, *Scholasticus, Bishop of Mitylene.*

Tskhovreba Sak'art'veloisa. BROSSET (M. F.)

Tubal-kainsky vklad v svanskom. MARR (N. Y.)

T'viuri krebuli. PERIODICAL PUBLICATIONS. – *K'ut'aisi.*

Tvorchestvo A. R. Tsereteli. NUTSUBIDZE (SH. I.)

Tvorenie Merchula v latinskom perevode bel'giiskogo orientalista. DONDUA (K. D.)

Typicon Gregorii Pacuriani. BAKURIANI (GRIGOL).

Typikon de Grégoire Pacourianos pour le monastère de Pétritzos (Bačkovo) en Bulgarie. BAKURIANI (GRIGOL).

Über den Glauben. HIPPOLYTUS, *Saint, of Rome.*

Über die geographische Verbreitung der awarischen Sprache. USLAR (P. K.) *Baron.*

Über die georgischen Handschriften in Österreich. P'ERADZE (G.)

Über ein merkwürdiges Volk des Kaukasus, die Kubetschi. FRAEHN (C. M.)

Über georgisches Heidentum. WESENDONK (O. G. von).

Die Weihnachtsfeier Jerusalems im siebten Jahrhundert. LITURGIES. – Greek Rite. – *Euchologion.*

'Wisdom and lies': variations on a Georgian literary theme. LANG (D. M.)

The Wisdom of Balahvar. A Christian legend of the Buddha. LANG (D. M.)

Works of the Karl Marx State Library of the SSR of Georgia. TIFLIS. – *Karl Marx State Library.*

Yafeticheskie yazyki "shakh-dagskoi podgruppy". SHAUMYAN (R. M.)

Yafeticheskiya elementy v yazykakh Armenii. MARR (N. Y.)

Yafeticheskiya nazvaniya derev'ev i rasteny. MARR (N. Y.)

Yafeticheskoe proiskhozhdenie abkhazskikh terminov rodstva. MARR (N. Y.)

Yafetichesky Kavkaz i trety etnichesky element v sozidanii sredizemnomorskoi kul'tury. MARR (N. Y.)

Yafetichesky sbornik. SAINT PETERSBURG. – *Academia Scientiarum Imperialis.* – Яфетический Институт, afterwards Институт ясыка и мышления.

Yakov Gogebashvili. Obshchestvenno-pedagogicheskaya i literaturnaya deyatel'nost'. T'AVZISHVILI (G. I.)

Yazyk i myshlenie. SAINT PETERSBURG. – *Academia Scientiarum Imperialis.* – Яфетический Институт, afterwards Институт языка и мышления.

Yazyki Severnogo Kavkaza i Dagestana. SERDYUCHENKO (G. P.)

Yury Bogolyubsky. DADIANI (SH. N.)

Zaimstvovanie chislitel'nykh v yafeticheskikh yazykakh. MARR (N. Y.)

Zakon o Kavkazskom Istoriko-Arkheologicheskom Institute. TIFLIS. – *Kavkazsky Istoriko-Arkheologichesky Institut.*

Zakony lezginskogo udareniya. ZHIRKOV (L. I.)

Zametki po sistematike i geografii rasteny. TIFLIS. – *Academy of Sciences of the Georgian S.S.R. – Tiflis Botanical Institute.*

Zametki po tekstam sv. Pisaniya u drevnikh armyan i gruzin. MARR (N. Y.)

Zapiska ob uchenykh trudakh Professora N. Y. Marra. MARR (N. Y.)

Zapiski Kollegii Vostokovedov pri Aziatskom Muzee Rossiiskoi Akademii Nauk. SAINT PETERSBURG. – *Academia Scientiarum Imperialis.*

Zapiski Vostochnago Otdeleniya Imperatorskago Russkago Arkheologicheskago Obshchestva. SAINT PETERSBURG. – *Императорское Русское Археологическое Общество.*

Zarya Kolkhidy. Roman. LORT'K'IP'ANIDZE (K. A.)

Zarya nad El'brusom. SHOGENTSUKOV ('ALĪ A.) *and others.*

Zemel'nye vladeniya drevnegruzinskikh svyatilishch. BARDAVELIDZE (V. V.)

Zhilishche mtiulov. PANEK (L. B.)

Zhitie Agathangela, katolikosa damasskago. AGATHANGELUS, *Saint and Martyr, of Damascus.*

Zhitie i muchenichestvo sv. Antoniya-Ravakha. ANTONY, *Saint and Martyr,* called RAWAḤ.

Zhitie Petra Ivera. ZACHARIAS, *Scholasticus, Bishop of Mitylene.*

Zhitie Petra Novago, muchenika Kapetoliiskago. PETER, *Saint and Martyr, of Capitolias.*

Zhitie Prokhora, much. Luki i much. Nikolaya Dval-i. QIP'SHIDZE (D. A.)

Zhitie sv. Grigoriya Khandzt'iiskago. GIORGI, *Merchule.*

Zhurnal Ministerstva Narodnago Prosveshcheniya. RUSSIA. – *Министерство Народнаго Просвѣщенія.*

'Zima' = 'smert', iz paleontologii rechi. MARR (N. Y.)

Zogadi enat'metsnierebis kat'edris shromebi. TIFLIS. – *Tiflis State University.*

Zoologiis institutis shromebi. TIFLIS. – *Academy of Sciences of the Georgian S.S.R. – Institute of Zoology.*

Zum georgischen Evangelientext. BAUMSTARK (A.)

Zur Geschichte des altgeorgischen Evangelientextes. VÖÖBUS (A.)

Zur vorbyzantinischen Liturgie Georgiens. P'ERADZE (G.)

Zvukovoi sostav tsezskogo (didoiskogo) yazyka. MEGRELIDZE (I. B.)

Zwei Grundsteine zu einer grusinischen Staats- und Rechtsgeschichte. HOLLDACK (F.)

SELECT SUBJECT-INDEX

ARCHAEOLOGY

Antiquités géorgiennes. T'AQAISHVILI (E. S.)

Antiquities of Georgia. T'AQAISHVILI (E. S.)

Aperçu général du voyage de M. Brosset dans la Transcaucasie. BROSSET (M.-F.)

Arkheologicheskaya ekskursiya po kviril'skomu ushchel'yu. TSERET'ELI (G. E.)

Arkheologicheskie pamyatniki Armazis-khevi po raskopkam 1937–1946 gg. AP'AK'IDZE (A. M.) *and others.*

Arkheologicheskie raskopki v drevnegruzinskoi stolitse Mtskheta. LOMT'AT'IDZE (G. A.)

Arkheologicheskoe puteshestvie po Gurii i Adchare. BAK'RADZE (D. Z.)

Armazni. Istoriko-arkheologichesky ocherk. MELIK'SET'-BEGI (L. M.)

Bronzy drevnei Gruzii. T'AVADZE (P'. N.) and SAQVARELIDZE (T'. N.)

Caucasica. BAILEY (*Sir* H. W.)

La culture mégalithique en Géorgie. MELIK'SET'-BEGI (L. M.)

The Date of the Building of the Cathedral "The Living Pillar". KAKABADZE (S. N.)

Description de quelques antiquités géorgiennes. BROSSET (M.-F.)

Dnevnik poezdki v Shavshiyu i Klardzhiyu. GIORGI, *Merchule.*

Drevneishie arkheologicheskie pamyatniki Mtskheta. CHUBINISHVILI (T. N.)

Drevnosti Gulekarskoi tserkvi. T'AQAISHVILI (E.S.)

L'église géorgienne du Clibanion au Mont Admirable. PEETERS (P.)

Ananursky Uspensky Sobor. SADZAGELI (G.) *Iverieli.*

Ekspeditsii na Kavkaz 1892, 1893 i 1895 g. KHAKHANOV (A. S.)

Essai de déchiffrement des inscriptions de l'église de Manglis. BROSSET (M.-F.)

Études sur les monuments géorgiens photographiés par M. Iermakof. BROSSET (M.-F.)

Explication de diverses inscriptions géorgiennes, arméniennes et grecques. BROSSET (M.-F.)

Explication de quelques inscriptions ... au Mont Athos. BROSSET (M.-F.)

Explication de quelques inscriptions géorgiennes. BROSSET (M.-F.)

ARCHITECTURE

pervoi poloviny XIX stoletiya. TSINTSADZE (V. G.)

Tserkov' bliz seleniya Bolnis-Kapanakchi. CHUBINASHVILI (G. N.)

BIBLE AND BIBLICAL STUDIES

À propos de la plus ancienne version géorgienne des Actes des Apôtres. T'ARKHNISHVILI (M.)

Das Adysh-Tetraevangelium. Neu übersetzt ... von Joseph Molitor. BIBLE. – New Testament. – *Gospels*.

Akhali aght'k'ma Up'lisa Chueynisa Ieso K'ristesi. Sakhareba Ioanesi. BIBLE. – New Testament. – *John*.

Altgeorgisches Glossar zu ausgewählten Bibeltexten. MOLITOR (J.)

L'ancienne version géorgienne des Actes des Apôtres. BIBLE. – New Testament. – *Acts*.

Ancient Georgian versions of the Old Testament. BLAKE (R. P.)

The Athos Codex of the Georgian Old Testament. BLAKE (R. P.)

Eine Benutzung des Testamentum Domini nostri Jesu Christi. SCHMIDT (C.)

Biblia. BIBLE.

Chanmetifragmente. Ein Beitrag zur Textgeschichte der altgeorgischen Bibelübersetzung. MOLITOR (J.)

Chetveroevangelie v drevnegruzinskom perevode. BIBLE. – New Testament. – *Gospels*.

Dsigni akhlisay aght'k'misa. BIBLE. – New Testament.

Early Versions of the New Testament: Manuscript Studies. VÖÖBUS (A.)

Evangelienzitate in einem altgeorgischen Väterfragment. MOLITOR (J.)

Le fragment géorgien de l'Évangile de Thomas. BIBLE. – New Testament. – *Apocrypha*.

The Georgian text of Fourth Esdras from the Athos manuscript. BIBLE. – Old Testament. – *Apocrypha*.

The Georgian version of Fourth Esdras from the Jerusalem manuscript. BIBLE. – Old Testament. – *Apocrypha*.

Die georgische Bibelübersetzung. MOLITOR (J.)

Die georgische Bibelübersetzung. A) Alte kirchliche Abhängigkeit Georgiens von Armenien. GOUSSEN (H.)

The Gospel according to S. John, translated from the eleven oldest versions ... By ... S. C. Malan. BIBLE. – New Testament. – *John*.

The Gospels of Bert'ay. BLAKE (R. P.) and DER NERSESSIAN (S.)

Gruzinskie versii apokrificheskikh deyany apostolov. BIBLE. – New Testament. – *Apocrypha*.

Gruzinskie versii Sobornykh Poslany. BIBLE. – New Testament. – *Epistles*.

Hippolyts Kommentar zum Hohenlied ... herausgegeben von G. N. Bonwetsch. HIPPOLYTUS, *Saint, of Rome*.

K'art'uli versiebi apokrip'ebisa motsik'ult'a shesakheb. BIBLE. – New Testament. – *Apocrypha*.

Kat'olike epistolet'a k'art'uli versiebi. BIBLE. – New Testament. – *Epistles*.

Khanmeti palimpsest fragments of the old Georgian version of Jeremiah. BLAKE (R. P.)

Note sur un manuscrit grec des quatre Évangiles. BROSSET (M.-F.)

Notes on the text of the Georgian and Armenian Gospels. BLAKE (R. P.)

Notice sur la Bible géorgienne imprimée à Moscou en 1742. BROSSET (M.-F.)

O kavkazskoi versii Biblii v gruzinskikh palimpsestnykh fragmentakh. MARR (N. Y.)

Oksfordsky fragment drevne-gruzinskoi versii Ieremii. GENKO (A. N.)

The Old Georgian Version of the Gospel of John. BIBLE. – New Testament. – *John*.

The Old Georgian Version of the Gospel of Mark. BIBLE. – New Testament. – *Mark*.

The Old Georgian Version of the Gospel of Matthew. BIBLE. – New Testament. – *Matthew*.

Opisanie persidskago rukopisnago Chetveroevangeliya. BIBLE. – New Testament. – *Gospels*. – *Appendix*.

Les origines de la version arménienne et le diatessaron. LYONNET (S.)

Le "protévangile de Jacques" en géorgien. BIBLE. – New Testament. – *Apocrypha*.

P'salmuni Davit'isi. BIBLE. – Old Testament. – *Psalms*.

Quattuor Evangeliorum versio Georgiana vetus. BIBLE. – New Testament. – *Gospels*.

Recent work on the Georgian New Testament. LANG (D. M.)

Sakhareba Ioanesi. BIBLE. – New Testament. – *John*.

Sakharebay ot'kht'avi. BIBLE. – New Testament. – *Gospels*.

Song of Solomon. BIBLE. – Old Testament. – *Song of Solomon*.

Sur les bénédictions d'Isaac, de Jacob et de Moïse. HIPPOLYTUS, *Saint, of Rome*.

Svanetskiya rukopisnyya evangeliya. KHAKHANOV (A. S.)

Tolkovanie Pesni pesnei. HIPPOLYTUS, *Saint, of Rome*.

Up'lisa chûeynisa Ieso K'ristesi dsmida sakhareba. BIBLE. – New Testament.

La version géorgienne ancienne de l'Évangile de Luc. BIBLE. – New Testament. – *Luke.*

Zametki po tekstam sv. Pisaniya u drevnikh armyan i gruzin. MARR (N. Y.)

Zum georgischen Evangelientext. BAUMSTARK (A.)

Zur Geschichte des altgeorgischen Evangelientextes. VÖÖBUS (A.)

BIBLIOGRAPHY

À propos des travaux de philologie géorgienne de M. G. Garitte. TʻARKHNISHVILI (M.)

Acquisition de livres géorgiens par le Musée asiatique. BROSSET (M.-F.)

Activité littéraire des Géorgiens et des Arméniens. BROSSET (M.-F.)

Bibliografiya: otdelʻnyya izdaniya i statʻi na gruzinskom yazyke, poyavivshiyasya v 1911–1912 gg. SHANIDZE (A. G.)

Bibliografiya izdany Akademii Nauk Gruzinskoi SSR, 1937–1956. TIFLIS. – *Academy of Sciences of the Georgian S.S.R.*

Bibliographia Caucasica et Transcaucasica. MIANSAROV (M. M.)

Bibliographie analytique des ouvrages de Monsieur Marie-Félicité Brosset. BROSSET (L.)

Bibliographie française de la Géorgie. BERIDZE (SH.)

Buchkunst des Morgenlandes. VIENNA. – *National-bibliothek.*

Catalogue de livres géorgiens. (Histoire et littérature de la Géorgie.) BROSSET (M.-F.)

Catalogue des manuscrits arméniens et géorgiens de la Bibliothèque Nationale. PARIS. – *Bibliothèque Royale,* afterwards *Impériale,* afterwards *Nationale.*

Catalogue des manuscrits géorgiens de la Bibliothèque de la Laure d'Iviron au mont Athos. ATHOS, *Mount.*

Catalogue des manuscrits géorgiens de la Bibliothèque Patriarcale Grecque à Jérusalem. JERUSALEM. – *Greek Patriarchal Library.*

Catalogue des manuscrits géorgiens littéraires du Mont Sinaï. CATHARINE, *Saint, of Alexandria.* – CONVENT OF, ON MOUNT SINAI.

A Catalogue of the Armenian Manuscripts in the British Museum ... To which is appended a Catalogue of Georgian Manuscripts in the British Museum. LONDON. – *British Museum.*

Catalogue of the Georgian manuscripts in the Cambridge University Library. BLAKE (R. P.)

La collection "Monuments de l'ancienne langue géorgienne". GARITTE (G.)

Description des manuscrits géorgiens du Musée d'État de Géorgie. TIFLIS. – *Museum of Georgia.*

Dsignebis katalogi kʻ. sh. dsera-kitʻkhvis gamavrtselebelis sazogadoebis dsignis maghaziisa. TIFLIS. – *Society for the Spreading of Literacy among the Georgians.*

Dsignis matiane. PERIODICAL PUBLICATIONS. – TIFLIS.

Georgian Manuscripts in England. PʻERADZE (G.)

Georgian Studies in Oxford. LANG (D. M.)

Gruzinskie rukopisi Instituta Vostokovedeniya. SAINT PETERSBURG. – *Academia Scientiarum Imperialis.* – Институт Востоковедения.

Istoria kʻartʻuli stambisa. TCHITCHINADZE (Z. E.)

Iz istorii russkogo akademicheskogo Kavkazovedeniya XVIII veka. POLIEVKTOV (M. A.)

Izdanie drevnegruzinskikh rukopisei. SHANIDZE (A. G.)

Karl Markʻsis sakhelobis Sakʻartʻvelos SSR sakhelmdsipʻo bibliotʻekis shromebi. TIFLIS. – *Karl Marx State Library.*

Khelnadsertʻa aghdseriloba. KʻUTʻAISI. – *Kʻutʻaisi State Historical Museum.*

Kratky katalog sobraniya gruzinskikh rukopisei priobretennago Imperatorskoyu Publichnoyu Bibliotekoyu v 1896 godu. SAINT PETERSBURG. – Императорская Публичная Библіотека.

Kurzer Überblick über den Stand der georgischen Literaturforschung. TʻARKHNISHVILI (M.)

Liste des travaux de M. Brosset. BROSSET (M.-F.)

Un manuscrit byzantin daté du pontificat du pape Jean XIX. PEETERS (P.)

N. Nikoladzis arkʻivis katalogi. NIKOLADZE (N. I.)

Narodnaya slovesnostʻ Kavkaza. Materialy dlya bibliograficheskogo ukazatelya. BAGRY (A. V.)

Neuere russische Arbeiten zur armenisch-georgischen Philologie. STEGENSEK (A.)

Notice des manuscrits géorgiens envoyés en France par le prince Théimouraz. BROSSET (M.-F.)

Notice des manuscrits géorgiens récemment acquis par l'Académie. BROSSET (M.-F.)

O gruzino-grecheskoi rukopisi s miniatyurami. OKUNEV (N. L.)

Obzor istochnikov po istorii Azerbaidzhana. MELIKʻSETʻ-Begi (L. M.)

Opisanie gruzinskikh rukopisei Gosudarstvennogo Muzeya Gruzii. TIFLIS. – *Museum of Georgia.*

Opisanie gruzinskikh rukopisei sinaiskogo monastyrya. CATHARINE, *Saint, of Alexandria.* – CONVENT OF, ON MOUNT SINAI.

Publications récentes relatives à la littérature géorgienne. TʻARKHNISHVILI (M.)

Putevoditelʻ po khranilishcham drevnikh rukopisei

Gosudarstvennogo Muzeya Gruzii. TIFLIS. – *Museum of Georgia.*

Rustvelologicheskaya literatura, 1712–1956 gody. IMEDASHVILI (G.)

Rust'velologiuri literatura, 1712–1956 dslebi. IMEDASHVILI (G.)

Sak'art'velos SSR metsnierebat'a akademiis gamotsemat'a bibliograp'ia, 1937–1956 dsds. TIFLIS. – *Academy of Sciences of the Georgian S.S.R.*

Sak'art'velos sakhelmdsip'o muzeumis dzvel khelnadsert'a satsavebis gzamkvlevi. TIFLIS. – *Museum of Georgia.*

Sak'art'velos sakhelmdsip'o muzeumis k'art'ul khelnadsert'a aghdseriloba. TIFLIS. – *Museum of Georgia.*

Sakhelgamis gamotsemat'a katalogi. PERIODICAL PUBLICATIONS. – *Tiflis.*

Sobranie gruzinskikh rukopisei Instituta Vostokovedeniya Akademii Nauk SSSR. SAINT PETERSBURG. – *Academia Scientiarum Imperialis.* – Институт Востоковедения.

Das Studium der altgeorgischen Sprache in Georgien. Bibliographische Übersicht. JEDLIČKA (J.)

Über die georgischen Handschriften in Österreich. P'ERADZE (G.)

Works of the Karl Marx State Library of the SSR of Georgia. TIFLIS. – *Karl Marx State Library.*

Zapiska ob uchenykh trudakh Professora N. Y. Marra. MARR (N. Y.)

BIOGRAPHY AND MEMOIRS

Apolon Kobakhidze. KOBAKHIDZE (I.)

Besiki. Roman. BELIASHVILI (A. I.)

Bukhara: mogonebani. 'AINĪ (ŠADR AL-DĪN).

Chemi dsarsuli. – Mogonebani. ZHORDANIA (N. N.) *President of Georgia.*

Davit' Erist'avi. TCHITCHINADZE (Z. E.)

Davit' Guramishvili. NASIDZE (M.)

Davit' Rondeli. LOLADZE (V.)

Didi sakheebi patara charchoebshi. PAPAVA (T'.)

Dva izsledovatelya kavkazskikh yazykov. Akademik A. A. Shifner ... i baron P. K. Uslar. TSAGARELI (A. A.)

Egnate Ninoshvili. SAKHOKIA (T'. T.)

Georgy Leonidze. Kritiko-biografichesky ocherk. GOL'TSEV (V. V.)

Giorgi Merchule, k'art'veli mdserali meat'e saukunisa. INGOROQVA (P. I.)

Ilia Tchavtchavadze. Portretebi da ilustratsiebi. TCHAVTCHAVADZE (I. G.) *Prince.*

Ioseb Besarionis-dze Stalini: mokle biograp'ia. ALEKSANDROV (G. F.) *and others.*

Ioseb Davit'ashvili. TCHITCHINADZE (Z. E.)

Iosif Vissarionovich Stalin: kratkaya biografiya. ALEKSANDROV (G. F.) *and others.*

K stoletiyu dnya rozhdeniya M. I. Brosse. MARR (N. Y.)

K svedeniyam o lichnosti arkhidiakona Gaioza, vposledstvii arkhiepiskopa astrakhanskago i stavropol'skago. PAL'MOV (N. N.)

Mariam, ukanaskneli dedop'ali Sak'art'velosi. PAPAVA (T'.) and (A.)

Mémoires. CHUBINIDZE (V.)

Mep'e Erekles sakhsovari. JANASHVILI (M. G.)

Moghvadse k'alebi revolutsiamdel Sak'art'veloshi. DGEBUADZE-P'ULARIA (P'.)

Mogoneba. CHUBINIDZE (V.)

Mogonebebi. MGELADZE (V.)

N. Ya. Marr i gruzinovedenie. DONDUA (K. D.)

Nikolai Yakovlevich Marr. Ocherk ego zhizni i nauchnoi deyatel'nosti. MIKHANKOVA (V. A.)

Notice biographique sur Marie, dernière Reine de Géorgie. ROTTIERS (B. E. A.)

Nouvelles recherches sur l'historien Wakhoucht, sur le roi Artchil, et sur divers personnages géorgiens enterrés à Moscou. BROSSET (M.-F.)

Perezhitoe. TSERET'ELI (A. R.) *Prince.*

Platon Ioseliani. TCHITCHINADZE (Z. E.)

Saiat'novas vinaoba. MELIK'SET'-BEGI (L. M.)

Shek'spiri. QIASASHVILI (N. A.)

Shot'a Rust'aveli, 1172–1216. TCHITCHINADZE (Z. E.)

Solomon Dodashvili. TCHITCHINADZE (Z. E.)

Solomon Dodashvili, tskhovreba da moghvadseoba. GOTSADZE (M. K.)

Sulkhan-Saba Orbeliani. Tskhovreba de literaturuli mogvadseoba. BARAMIDZE (A. G.)

Svimon mep'e, 1557–1600. KARITCHASHVILI (D. G.)

T'avadi Rap'ael Erist'avi. QIP'SHIDZE (G. T'.)

T'bilisis ghrmad mokhutsebuli adamianebi. SHAP'IRO (I. B.) *and others.*

Tskhovreba Ivane Machablisa. TCHELIDZE (V.)

Ukanasknelni zhamni tskhovrebisa Imperatoris Nikolooz pirvelisa. NICHOLAS I, *Tsar of Russia.*

Vakhtang meek'vse. NASIDZE (M.)

Veliky Mouravi. ANTONOVSKAYA (A. A.)

La Vie et l'oeuvre de M.-F. Brosset. BERIDZE (SH.)

Yakov Gogebashvili. Obshchestvenno-pedagogicheskaya i literaturnaya deyatel'nost'. T'AVZISHVILI (G. I.)

DICTIONARIES

Abkhazsko-russky slovar'. MARR (N. Y.)

Avarsko-russky slovar'. ZHIRKOV (L. I.)

Deutsch-georgisches Wörterbuch. MECKELEIN (R.)

Dictionnaire français-géorgien. MATCHAVARIANI (I. N.) and GVARJALADZE (I. S.)

Le dictionnaire géorgien. SKAMKOCHAISHVILI (S.) and MELUA (M.)

Dictionnaire géorgien-français. OK'ROPIRIDZE (E.)

Dictionnaire géorgien-russe-français. CHUBINOV (D. I.)

English-Svanetian Vocabulary. WARDROP (Sir J. O.) K.B.E.

Georgian-English Dictionary. CHERKEZI (E.)

Georgisch-deutsches Wörterbuch. KLUGE (T.); MECKELEIN (R.)

Germanul-k'art'uli sitqvari. MECKELEIN (R.)

Gruzino-russky slovar'. CHUBINOV (D. I.)

Gruzinsko-osetinsky slovar'. SANAKOEV (P. A.)

Gruzinsko-russko-frantsuzsky slovar'. CHUBINOV (D. I.)

Gruzinsky glossary. TCHQONIA (I. M.)

Gruzinsky (k'art'sky) glossary po imerskomu i rach'inskomu govoram. BERIDZE (V. M.)

Guyrdziag-iron dzyrduat. SANAKOEV (P. A.)

Kabardinsko-russky slovar'. APAZHEV (M. L.) and others.

K'art'ul-germanuli sitqvari. MECKELEIN (R.)

K'art'ul-osuri lek'sikoni. SANAKOEV (P. A.)

K'art'ul-p'ranguli lek'sikoni. OK'ROPIRIDZE (E.)

K'art'ul-rusul-frantsitsuli lek'sikoni. CHUBINOV (D. I.)

K'art'uli enis ganmartebit'i lek'sikoni. CHIK'OBAVA (A. S.) and others.

K'art'uli khatovani sitqva-t'k'mani. SAKHOKIA (T'. T.)

K'art'uli lek'sikoni. SKAMKOCHAISHVILI (S.) and MELUA (M.)

K'art'uli ot'kht'avis simp'onia-lek'sikoni. IMNAISHVILI (I. B.)

Keberdei-urys slovar'. APAZHEV (M. L.) and others.

Kratky gruzino-russko-latinsky slovar' iz trekh estestvennykh tsarstv prirody. ERIST'AVI (R.D.) Prince.

Mat'ematikuri terminebi. AVALISHVILI (I.)

Metallurgicheskaya terminologiya. K'ASHAKASHVILI (N. V.) and GHAMBASHIDZE (R. B.)

Metalurgiis terminologia. K'ASHAKASHVILI (N. V.) and GHAMBASHIDZE (R. B.)

Ort'ograp'iuli lek'sikoni. T'OP'URIA (V. T.) and GIGINEISHVILI (I. M.)

P'rangul-k'art'uli lek'sikoni. MATCHAVARIANI(I.N.) and GVARJALADZE (I. S.)

Rapport sur le dictionnaire manuscrit géorgien-russe-latin de M. D.Tchoubinof. BROSSET (M.-F.)

Russko-abazinsky slovar'. CHERKESSK. – Cherkessky Nauchno-Issledovatel'ky Institut.

Russko-gruzinsky slovar'. CHUBINOV (D. I.); TIFLIS. – Academy of Sciences of the Georgian S.S.R.

Russko-kabardinsko-cherkessky slovar'. KARDANOV (B. M.) and BICHOEV (A. T.)

Russko-svansky slovar'. NIZHARADZE (I. I.)

Rusul-k'art'uli lek'sikoni. TIFLIS. – Academy of Sciences of the Georgian S.S.R.

Simfoniya-slovar' k gruzinskomu chetveroglavu. IMNAISHVILI (I. B.)

Sitqvis-kona Imerul da Ratchul t'k'mat'a. BERIDZE (V. M.)

Sitqvis-kona: Saba-Sulkhan Orbelianis da Davit' Chubinashvilis lek'sikonebshi gamotovebuli sitqvebi. TCHQONIA (I. M.)

Sop'lis meurneobis terminologia. KETSKHOVELI (N. N.) and others.

Tchanur-megrul-k'art'uli shedarebit'i lek'sikoni. CHIK'OBAVA (A. S.)

Tek'nikuri terminologia. BERIDZE (V. M.) and others.

Tekhnicheskaya terminologiya. BERIDZE (V. M.) and others.

Terminologiya sel'skogo khozyaistva. KETSKHOVELI (N. N.) and others.

Tolkovy slovar' gruzinskogo yazyka. CHIK'OBAVA (A. S.) and others.

Urys-keberdei-sherdzhes slovar'. KARDANOV (B. M.) and BICHOEV (A. T.)

Uryshv-Abaza slovar'. CHERKESSK. – Cherkessky Nauchno-Issledovatel'sky Institut.

Vocabulaire et grammaire de la langue géorgienne. KLAPROTH (H. J. von).

DRAMA

Colchidea et la poésie. URUSHADZE (S.)

The Georgian Shakespeariana. QIASASHVILI (N. A.)

Gruzinskaya sovetskaya dramaturgiya. KAKABADZE (P. M.) and others.

Gruzinsky teatr za sto let. BUKHNIKASHVILI (G. V.)

Irines bedniereba. KLDIASHVILI (D. S.)

Iulios Keisari. SHAKSPERE (W.)

Julius Caesar. SHAKSPERE (W.)

K'art'uli Shek'spiriana. QIASASHVILI (N. A.)

K'art'uli t'eatris aghdgenis 100 dseli. GEORGIA. – National Theatre.

K'art'vel dramaturgt'a piesebi. BERDZENISHVILI (G.) and others.

Kolkhidea da poezia. URUSHADZE (S.)

Mep'e Davit' Aghmashenebeli. ORBELIANI (A. V. JAMBAKURIAN-)

Mijatchuli Promet'e. AESCHYLUS.

Mit'ridati Rasinisa. RACINE (J.)

Potoplennye kamni. MOSASHVILI (I. O.)

Rcheuli t'khzulebani khut'tomad. DADIANI (SH. N.)

ECONOMICS, POLITICS AND SOCIOLOGY

EDUCATION

Burji erovnebisa. GOGEBASHVILI (I. S.)

Deda ena. Meore nadsili: anbanis shemdeg sakit'-khavi dsigni. BOTSVADZE (N. I.) and BUR-JANADZE (E. I.)

Deda ena. Pirveli nadsili: anbani. BOTSVADZE (N. I.) and BURJANADZE (E. I.)

Dzirit'adi ukughmart'oba. GOGEBASHVILI (I. S.)

Izbrannye pedagogicheskie sochineniya. GOGE-BASHVILI (I. S.)

O Kavkazskom Universitete v Tiflise. MARR (N. Y.)

T'khzulebani. GOGEBASHVILI (I. S.)

Tp'ilisis sakhelmdsip'o universiteti, 1918–1928. TIFLIS. – *Tiflis State University.*

EPIGRAPHY AND PALAEOGRAPHY

Albanskaya nadpis'. MARR (N. Y.)

Album paléographique. T'AQAISHVILI (E. S.)

Das Alter der georgischen Schrift. DEETERS (G.)

Arabskaya azbuka s drevnegruzinskoi transkrip-tsiei. MEGRELIDZE (I. B.)

Archéographie géorgienne. BROSSET (M.-F.)

Armazis bilingva. TSERET'ELI (G. V.)

Armazskoe pis'mo i problema proiskhozhdeniya gruzinskogo alfavita. TSERET'ELI (G. V.)

Autographie géorgienne. BROSSET (M.-F.)

Das Awestaalphabet und der Ursprung der ar-menischen und georgischen Schrift. JUNKER (H. F. J.)

A bilingual inscription from Armazi. TSERET'ELI (G. V.)

Copie figurée de quelques cachets géorgiens. BROS-SET (M.-F.)

Epigraficheskie zametki. TURCHANINOV (G. F.)

Epigrafika Vostoka. SAINT PETERSBURG. – *Aca-demia Scientiarum Imperialis.*

Garesdzhiiskaya tetralingva epokhi mongolov 1352 g. MELIK'SET'-BEGI (L. M.)

Greek script and Georgian scribes on Mt. Sinai. BLAKE (R. P.)

K gruzinskim nadpisyam iz Meskhii. MARR (N. Y.)

K'art'uli t'vit'-dserileba. BROSSET (M.-F.)

The newly discovered alphabet of the Caucasian Albanians. KURDIAN (H.)

Paleograp'iuli albomi. T'AQAISHVILI (E. S.)

Persidskaya azbuka v gruzinskoi transkriptsii. MEGRELIDZE (I. B.)

Shrifty dlya nadpisei na chertezhakh. MIK'ELADZE (M. D.)

Shrip'tebi nakhatebze dsardserebisat'vis. MIK'E-LADZE (M. D.)

ETHNOGRAPHY

Abkhaziya. GURKO-KRYAZHIN (V. A.)

Abkhazsky kul't i byt, v predelakh Abzhu. JANASHIA (N. S.)

Erinnerungen an einen Aufenthalt bei den Tscher-kessen des Kreises Tuapse. TRUBETSKOI (N. S.) *Prince.*

Ethnographical and Historical Division of Georgia. GUGUSHVILI (A. I.)

Etnografiya Kavkaza. Yazykoznanie, *etc.* USLAR (P. K.) *Baron.*

Et'nograp'ia, p'olklori, kritika, publitsistika, kore-spondentsiebi. VAZHA-P'SHAVELA, *pseud.*

Et'nograp'iuli nadserebi. BOTCHORISHVILI (L. I.)

Les formes d'organisation du travail dans l'éco-nomie sociale de l'ancienne Géorgie. TIFLIS. – *Academy of Sciences of the Georgian S.S.R.*

Das georgische Volk. LEIST (A.)

Georgischer Volkstransport. GEGESHIDZE (M. K.)

Gruzinsky narodny transport. GEGESHIDZE (M. K.)

Ingushy. Populyarny ocherk. YAKOVLEV (N. F.)

Iz kul'turnogo proshlogo ingushei. GENKO (A. N.)

Iz starogo narodnogo byta pshavov. MAKALAT'IA (S. I.)

Die jetzigen Kubätschi. DORN (B.)

K'art'uli khalkhuri transporti. GEGESHIDZE (M. K.)

Kavkazsky etnografichesky sbornik. SAINT PE-TERSBURG. – *Academia Scientiarum Imperialis.* – Институт Этнографии им. Н. Н. Миклухо-Маклая.

Khevsury. GURKO-KRYAZHIN (V. A.)

Kolek'tiuri nadirobis gadmonasht'ebi Ratchashi. ROBAK'IDZE (A. I.)

K'ordsinebis zogiert'i dses-chveuleba dzvel T'bi-lisshi. IT'ONISHVILI (V. J.)

Kubachintsy i ikh kul'tura. SHILLING (E. M.)

Masalebi Sak'art'velos et'nograp'iisat'vis. TIFLIS. – *Academy of Sciences of the Georgian S.S.R. – I. A. Javakhishvili Historical Institute.*

Materialien der Ethnographie Georgiens. TIFLIS. – *Academy of Sciences of the Georgian S.S.R. – I. A. Javakhishvili Historical Institute.*

Materialy po etnografii Gruzii. TIFLIS. – *Academy of Sciences of the Georgian S.S.R. – I. A. Java-khishvili Historical Institute.*

Narody Dagestana. Sbornik statei. NIKOLSKAYA (Z. A.) *and others.*

O religioznykh verovaniyakh abkhazov. MARR (N. Y.)

Obychnoe semeinoe pravo cherkes. LADYZHENSKY (A. M.)

Ocherki po etnografii Kavkaza. KOSVEN (M. O.)

On the Religious Beliefs of the Abkhazians. MARR (N. Y.)

Peoples and languages of the Caucasus. A synopsis. GEIGER (B.) *and others.*

The Religious Beliefs of the Abkhazians. JANASHIA (N. S.)

Religioznyya verovaniya abkhazov. JANASHIA (N. S.)

Rutul'tsy. LAVROV (L. I.)

Shromis organizatsiis p'ormebi dzveli Sak'art'velos sakhalkho meurneobashi. TIFLIS. – *Academy of Sciences of the Georgian S.S.R.*

Sledy rodovogo stroya u mtiulov. PANEK (L. B.)

Sovetskaya etnografiya. SAINT PETERSBURG. – *Academia Scientiarum Imperialis.*

Les survivances de la chasse collective en Ratcha. ROBAK'IDZE (A. I.)

T'edzmis kheoba. Istoriul-et'nograp'iuli narkvevi. MAKALAT'IA (S. I.)

Travaux et mémoires de l'Institut d'Ethnologie. PARIS. – *Université de Paris. – Institut d'Ethnologie.*

Über ein merkwürdiges Volk des Kaukasus, die Kubetschi. FRAEHN (C. M.)

V gornoi Ingushetii. BOROZDIN (I. N.)

Zhilishche mtiulov. PANEK (L. B.)

FICTION AND ROMANCES

Abkhazskie novelly. LAKERBAI (M. A.)

Abkhazskie rasskazy. DROZDOV (A. M.)

Akhali nergi: romani. GOGIAVA (K.)

Akhali tskhovrebisaken. Da-dzma. KVAKHADZE (B.)

Amiran-Darejaniani. MOSES, *of Khoni.*

Arsen iz Marabdy. JAVAKHISHVILI (M. S.)

Arsena Marabdeli. JAVAKHISHVILI (M. S.)

The Book of Wisdom and Fiction. Selections. SAVVA, *the Monk [Prince* SULKHAN ORBELIANI].

The Book of Wisdom and Lies. SAVVA, *the Monk [Prince* SULKHAN ORBELIANI].

Chelovek gor. K'IACHELI (L.) *pseud.*

Chrdili ert'i sinamdvilis. INASARI (I.)

A Christmas Carol. DICKENS (C.)

Contes orientaux. BORIN (A.)

Dagestanskie povesti i rasskazy. SULTANOV (K.)

Dauvidsqari zap'khuli. ZEDGINIDZE (E.)

David Stroitel'. Trilogiya. GAMSAKHURDIA (K. S.)

Davit' aghmashenebeli. Tetralogia. GAMSAKHURDIA (K. S.)

Desnitsa velikogo mastera. Roman. GAMSAKHURDIA (K. S.)

Didi sitsotskhle. Mot'khrobebi. KAKUSHADZE (N. V.)

Didostatis Konstantines marjvena. GAMSAKHURDIA (K. S.)

Dionisos ghimili. Romani. GAMSAKHURDIA (K. S.)

Dsignis sasakhle. KAKUSHADZE (N. V.)

Elissa. QAZBEGI (A. M.)

Ert'tomeuli. BELIASHVILI (A. I.)

Gabzaruli guli. ARAGVISPIRELI (Sh.) *pseud.*

Gadsqvetili zghapari, novelebi. T'URDOSPIRELI (D.)

Garozgili. T'vit'mpqrobelobis droindeli jariskatsis tskhovrebidan. ZURABISHVILI-ELEP'T'ERIDZE (I.)

The Georgian Version of the Story of the Loves of Vis and Ramin. SARGIS, *of T'mogvi.*

Grozny vlastelin. LORT'K'IP'ANIDZE (N. M.)

Gruzinskie novelly. KLDIASHVILI (S. D.)

Gruzinskie povesti i rasskazy. T'VALT'VADZE (P'.A.)

Gvadi Bigva. K'IACHELI (L.) *pseud.*

Izbrannoe. K'IACHELI (L.) *pseud.*; LORT'KIP'A-NIDZE (N. M.); NINOSHVILI (E.) *pseud.*; QAZBEGI (A. M.)

Izbrannoe. Perevod s gruzinskogo. ARAGVISPIRELI (Sh.) *pseud.*

Izbrannye proizvedeniya. KLDIASHVILI (D. S.); TCHAVTCHAVADZE (I. G.) *Prince.*

Kamenité cesty Gruzie. JEDLIČKA (J.)

Ketskhoveli. Roman. LISASHVILI (I.)

Kniga mudrosti i lzhi. SAVVA, *the Monk [Prince* SULKHAN ORBELIANI].

Kolkhet'is tsiskari. LORT'K'IP'ANIDZE (K. A.)

Krov'yu geroev. BAK'RADZE (D.)

Lelo. Roman. TCHEISHVILI (A. N.)

Litsom k litsu. Roman. K'UT'AT'ELI (A. N.)

Machekha Samanishvili, *etc.* KLDIASHVILI (D. S.)

Magharoebshi. Romani. LORIA (P. O.)

Medrosheni. HONCHAR (O. T.)

Miriani. A Georgian romance. MIRI, *King of Egypt.*

Le Miriani, ou histoire du roi Miri. MIRI, *King of Egypt.*

Moranboni. URJUMELASHVILI (I.)

Mot'khrobebi. CHKHEIDZE (B.); GVETADZE (R. M.); LOMIDZE (A.); LOMOURI (N. I.); SHATBERA-SHVILI (G. I.)

Mot'khrobebi da romanebi. QAZBEGI (A. M.)

Mzis amosvlamde, romani. ZEDGINIDZE (E.)

Nicholas Nickleby. DICKENS (C.)

Nikolas Niklbi. DICKENS (C.)

O mudrosti vymysla. SAVVA, *the Monk [Prince* SULKHAN ORBELIANI].

Ok'ros betchedi. DGEBUADZE-P'ULARIA (P'.)

Pirveli talghebi. MEGRELI (D.) *pseud.*

Povesti. GVETADZE (R. M.)

Ras itsini? T'OMAANT' KOBA, *pseud.*

Rasskazy. LOMOURI (N. I.)

Razbitoe serdtse. ARAGVISPIRELI (Sh.) *pseud.*

Rcheuli nadserebi or tomad. LORT'K'IP'ANIDZE (K. A.)

FINE ARTS

Rel'efy Shiomgvime i ikh mesto v razvitii gruzinskoi skul'ptury. VOL'SKAYA (A. I.)

Shuasaukunet'a k'art'uli khis chuk'urt'ma, X–XI saukuneebi. CHUBINASHVILI (N.)

Eine Wanderausstellung georgischer Kunst. BAUM-STARK (A.)

FOLKLORE

Caucasian Folk-Tales. DIRR (A.)

Contes et légendes des Oubykhs. DUMÉZIL (G.)

Contes et légendes du Caucase. MOURIER (J.)

Contes lazes. DUMÉZIL (G.)

Fables de Tsey Ibrahim. TSEY IBRĀHĪM.

Gadmotsema "Khogais Mindize" da poema "Gvelis mtchameli". GACHECHILADZE (A. N.)

Georgian Folk Tales. WARDROP (M. S.)

Eine georgische Ballade von Amiran. BLEICH-STEINER (R.)

Georgische Gesänge. LACH (R.)

Georgische und Mingrelische Texte. BLEICH-STEINER (R.)

Gesänge russischer Kriegsgefangener. LACH (R.)

Gruzinskie narodnye skazki. CHIK'OVANI (M. I.)

Gruzinsky epos. CHIK'OVANI (M. I.)

Guriiskie revolyutsionnye pesni. CHKHIKVADZE (G. Z.)

Iz gruzinskogo revolyutsionnogo fol'klora. MEGRE-LIDZE (I. B.)

Iz guriiskikh narodnykh predany o postroike Zarzmskago monastyrya. MARR (N. Y.)

Kabardinskoe skazanie "Krasavitsa Elena i Bogatyr'-zhenshchina". LOPATINSKY (L. G.)

Kakhetinskie revolyutsionnye pesni. CHKHAIDZE (M. P.)

K'art'uli dialek'tebis k'restomat'ia lek'sikonit'urt'. DZIDZIGURI (Sh. V.)

K'art'uli eposi. CHIK'OVANI (M. I.)

K'art'velt' Mahmadiant' sakhalkho lek'sebi. TCHI-TCHINADZE (Z. E.)

K'art'velt'a udzvelesi sardsmunoebis istoriidan. OCHIAURI (T'. A.)

Kaukasische Forschungen ... Erster Teil. Georgische und Mingrelische Texte. BLEICHSTEINER (R.)

Kaukasische Forschungen im k. u. k. Kriegsgefangenenlager Eger. BLEICHSTEINER (R.)

Kaukasische Märchen. DIRR (A.)

Khalkhuri zghaprebi. AGHNIASHVILI (L.)

Khalkhuri zghaprebi, Kakhet'shi da P'shavshi shekrebili. RAZIKASHVILI (T'. P.)

Khalkhuri zghaprebi, K'art'lshi shekrebili. RAZI-KASHVILI (T'. P.)

Latviuri zghaprebi. LATVIAN TALES.

Mijatchvuli Amirani. CHIK'OVANI (M. I.)

Les Proverbes géorgiens. SAKHOKIA (T'. T.)

Récits oubykh. DUMÉZIL (G.) and NAMITOK (A.)

Revolyutsiya v gruzinskom fol'klore. MEGRELIDZE (I. B.)

Rustaveli i fol'klor. MEGRELIDZE (I. B.)

Die Sagen und Lieder des Tscherkessen-Volks. SHORA-BEKMURZIN-NOGMOV.

Shota Rustaveli i gruzinsky fol'klor. MEGRELIDZE (I. B.)

Sovetsky Fol'klor. SAINT PETERSBURG. – *Academia Scientiarum Imperialis.* – Институт Антропологии и Этнографии.

Textes avar. DUMÉZIL (G.)

Textes populaires Inguš. ǦABAGI (M.)

Thrako-armyansky Sabadios-aswat i svanskoe bozhestvo okhoty. MARR (N. Y.)

Udische Texte. DIRR (A.)

GEOGRAPHY, TOPOGRAPHY AND TRAVEL

Arabel da sparsel mdseralt'a geograp'iuli da istoriuli tsnobebi Sak'art'velos shesakheb. DEFRÉ-MERY (C. F.)

Atcharis A.S.S.R. NIZHARADZE (N. I.) and JIBUTI (N. M.)

Court aperçu sur les frontières de la Géorgie. I. (P.)

Description géographique de la Géorgie. VAKHUSHTI, *Prince of Georgia.*

Eltchek'i da setqvianoba Kakhet'shi. K'URDIANI (I.)

Extraits d'une Topographie de la Géorgie, (traduits) par M. Klaproth. GEORGIA. – *Descriptions and Travels.*

Geografiya Gruzii. VAKHUSHTI, *Prince of Georgia.*

Gheoghrafiuli aghdsera Sak'art'veloysa. VA-KHUSHTI, *Prince of Georgia.*

Grozy i gradobitiya v Kakhetii. K'URDIANI (I.)

Kalmasoba, ili khozhdenie po sboru Ioanna Khelashvili, ipodiakona. JOHN, *Prince of Georgia.*

Mimoslva. GABASHVILI (T.) *Metropolitan of K'ut'aisi.*

Orages et grêle en Kakhétie. K'URDIANI (I.)

Pièces diverses relatives à la Géorgie. BROSSET (M.-F.)

Projet d'un voyage littéraire à exécuter en Géorgie. BROSSET (M.-F.)

Puteshestvie. GABASHVILI (T.) *Metropolitan of K'ut'aisi.*

Quelques remarques sur un livre intitulé: *Reise durch Russland nach dem kaukasischen Isthmus.* BROSSET (M.-F.)

Rapport sur la publication de la Géographie de la Géorgie par Wakhoucht. BROSSET (M.-F.)

Registre des cartes géorgiennes manuscrites, acquises par le Musée Asiatique. BROSSET (M.-F.)

Reisen nach Georgien und Imerethi. GUELDENSTAEDT (J. A.)

Sak'art'velos SSR geograp'iuli sazogadoebis shromebi. TIFLIS. – *Georgian Geographical Society.*

Sak'art'velos sazghvrebi istoriulad da t'anamedrove t'valsazrisit' gankhiluli. JAVAKHISHVILI (I. A.)

Sak'art'velos teritoriis sazghvrebis shesakheb. I. (P.)

Sovetsky Ajaristan. SURMANIDZE (M.)

Sparset'i da ik'auri k'art'velebi. AGHNIASHVILI (L.)

Tbilisi, stolitsa Gruzinskoi SSR. OTAROVA (N. A.)

T'ovlian mt'ebshi. Ialbuzi. KETSKHOVELI (N. N.)

Trudy geograficheskogo obshchestva Gruzinskoi SSR. TIFLIS. – *Georgian Geographical Society.*

GEOLOGY

Les Brachiopodes du Crétacé inférieur de la Géorgie Occidentale. NUTSUBIDZE (K'. Sh.)

Dasavlet' Sak'art'velos k'veda tsartsis brak'iopodebi. NUTSUBIDZE (K'. Sh.)

GRAMMARS

Abazinsky yazyk. Grammatichesky ocherk narechiya Tapanta. GENKO (A. N.)

Alphabetum Ibericum, sive Georgianum, cum Oratione Dominicali, *etc.* IBERIAN ALPHABET.

Ap'sshva anban. Abkhazsky bukvar'. BARTHOLOMAEI (I. A.) *Lt.-General.*

L'Art Libéral, ou Grammaire Géorgienne. BROSSET (M.-F.)

Chechensky bukvar'. BARTHOLOMAEI (I. A.) *Lt.-General.*

Einführung in die georgische Sprache. CHKHENKELI (K.)

Éléments de la langue géorgienne. BROSSET (M.-F.)

Esquisse d'une grammaire du géorgien moderne. VOGT (H. K.)

Grammatichesky ocherk agul'skogo yazyka. SHAUMYAN (R. M.)

Grammatichesky ocherk tabassaranskago yazyka. DIRR (A.)

Grammatik zur altgeorgischen Bibelübersetzung. ZORELL (F.)

Grammatika adygeiskogo literaturnogo yazyka. YAKOVLEV (N. F.) and ASHKHAMAF (D. A.)

Grammatika ch'anskago (lazskago) yazyka. MARR (N. Y.)

Grammatika drevneliteraturnogo gruzinskogo yazyka. MARR (N. Y.)

Grammatika gruzinskago yazyka. QIP'SHIDZE (I. A.)

Grammatika gruzinskogo yazyka. RUDENKO (B. T.)

Grammatika kabardino-cherkesskogo literaturnogo yazyka. NAL'CHIK. – *Кабардино-балкарский научно-исследовательский институт.*

Grammatika kabardinskogo yazyka. TURCHANINOV (G. F.) and TSAGOV (M. N.)

Grammatika khinalugskogo yazyka. DESHERIEV (YU. D.)

Grammatika literaturnogo kabardino-cherkesskogo yazyka. YAKOVLEV (N. F.)

Grammatika udinskago yazyka. DIRR (A.)

Grundzüge einer vergleichenden Grammatik des Ibero-Kaukasischen. KARST (J.)

Gruzinskaya grammatika. CHUBINOV (D. I.)

Guide de conversation français-géorgien. MANVELISHVILI (A. P.)

Kabardinskaya azbuka. ATAZHUKIN (K.)

K'art'ul-p'ranguli saubris t'anamgzavri. MANVELISHVILI (A. P.)

K'art'uli ena. Arak'art'uli skolebis VII klasis sakhelmdzghvanelo. RURUA (P'. I.)

K'art'uli ena, gramatika da mart'ldsera savarjishoebit'urt'. III da IV klasis sakhelmdzghvanelo. RAMISHVILI (V. T'.)

K'art'uli ena. Sakhelmdzghvanelo arak'art'uli skolebis X klasisat'vis. KAKABADZE (I. K.)

K'art'uli ena. Sakhelmdzghvanelo arak'art'uli skolebisat'vis, V–VI klasi. RURUA (P'. I.)

K'art'uli enis gramatika. SHANIDZE (A. G.)

Khelovneba aznaurebit'i, gina k'art'ulis enisa t'vit' masdsavlebeli. BROSSET (M.-F.)

Kratkaya gruzinskaya grammatika. CHUBINOV (D. I.)

Kursy kavkazskikh tuzemnykh yazykov. (Grammatika gruzinskago yazyka.) QIP'SHIDZE (I. A.)

Laksky yazyk. Fonetika i morfologiya. ZHIRKOV (L. I.)

La langue géorgienne. MARR (N. Y.); MARR (N. Y.) and BRIÈRE (M.)

Notice et analyse raisonnée du commencement de la Grammaire géorgienne du patriarche Antoni I. BROSSET (M.-F.)

Ocherk grammatiki chamalinskogo yazyka. BOKAREV (A. A.)

Osnovnye tablitsy k grammatike drevnegruzinskago yazyka. MARR (N. Y.)

Posobie dlya izucheniya zhivogo gruzinskogo yazyka. MARR (N. Y.)

Prilozhenie k tablitsam dlya vzaimnago obucheniya chteniyu i pis'mu ... s perevodom slov i

HAGIOGRAPHY

HISTORY

Nepochaty istochnik istorii kavkazskago mira. Marr (N. Y.)

Note sur le manuscrit géorgien No. 23, de la Bibliothèque Impériale de Paris. Brosset (M.-F.)

Notice historique sur les trois dernières années du règne de Wakhtang VI. Brosset (M.-F.)

Notice sur deux fragments relatifs à l'histoire de la Géorgie, au XIIIme siècle. Brosset (M.-F.)

Notice sur le mari russe de Thamar. Brosset (M.-F.)

Notice sur un document géorgien du XVIIe siècle. Brosset (M.-F.)

Notice sur une lettre géorgienne, du roi Artchil à Charles XII. Brosset (M.-F.)

Novye arkhivnye materialy dlya istorii Gruzii XVIII stoletiya. Tsagareli (A. A.)

Ob odnom anonimnom gruzinskom istorike XIV veka. Javakhishvili (I. A.)

P'eodaluri Sak'art'velos sotsialuri urt'iert'obis istoriidan. Gvritishvili (D. V.)

Plenenie Ierusalima persami v 614 g. Antiochus, *Laurae S. Sabae Monachus.*

Posol'stvo knyazya Myshetskogo i d'yaka Klyuchareva v Kakhetiyu, 1640-1643. Polievktov (M. A.)

Posol'stvo stol'nika Tolochanova i d'yaka Ievleva v Imeretiyu, 1650-1652. Polievktov (M. A.)

Proclamation of General Allenby, *etc.* European War, 1914-1919.

Profesori Patkanovi da k'art'uli istoriis dsqaroebi. Bak'radze (D. Z.)

Prostranny reestr gyurdzhyustanskogo vilaieta. Jik'ia (S. S.)

Rapport à S. E. le Prince Vorontzof, sur les chartes géorgiennes. Brosset (M.-F.)

Rapport à S. E. M. le Ministre ... sur ses recherches dans les archives de Moscou. Brosset (M.-F.)

Rapport sur différents documents géorgiens envoyés à l'Académie. Brosset (M.-F.)

Rapport sur un recueil de documents historiques. Brosset (M.-F.)

Review of 'Histoire du Bas-Empire'. Toumanoff (C. L.) *Prince.*

Revolyutsionnoe proshloe Tbilisi. Sturua (N. I.) *and others.*

Revolyutsiya 1905-1907 godov v Gruzii. Khutsishvili (I. G.) *and others.*

Sak'art'velo XIX saukunis pirvel nakhevarshi. Khatchapuridze (G. B.)

Sak'art'velo sabtchot'a kavshiris did samamulo omshi, 1941-1945. Ioseliani (A. P.)

Sak'art'velos deda-k'alak'i Tp'ilisi. Janashvili (M. G.)

Sak'art'velos istoria. Vakhushti, *Prince of Georgia.*

Sak'art'velos istoria, XIX saukune. Kikvidze (A. I.)

Sak'art'velos mokle istoria. Akhali saukuneebis epok'a. Kakabadze (S. N.)

Sak'art'velos saert'ashoriso urt'iert'obani utskho k'veqnebt'an. Tiflis. – *Tiflis State University.*

Sak'art'velos sidzveleni. T'aqaishvili (E.S.)

Sak'art'velo da ket'ili. Urushadze (S.)

Sakavshiro komunisturi partiis (bolshevikebis) istoria. Russia. – *Российская Коммунистическая Партия.– Центральный Комитет.*

Samok'alak'o omis istoria S.S.R. Kavshirshi. Gor'ky (M.) *pseud.*

Sazogadoebrivi modzraoba Sak'art'veloshi 1821-1921 ds. Uratadze (G. I.)

Second rapport adressé à la Conférence de l'Académie Impériale des Sciences. Brosset (M.-F.)

Shromebi. Khatchapuridze (G. B.)

Sigel' gruzinskago tsarya Bagrata IV, 1027-1072. T'aqaishvili (E. S.)

Sostav i istochniki nachal'noi gruzinskoi letopisi. Khakhanov (A. S.)

Sotsialur-politikuri tskhovrebis gansakut'rebuli pirobebi da glekht'a revolutsiuri modzraobis t'aviseburebani Sak'art'veloshi, 1905-1907 dsds. Katcharava (I. M.)

Les sources des notices du Patriarche de Jérusalem Dosithée sur les rois d'Aphkhazie. T'aqaishvili (E. S.)

Stat'i po istorii i drevnostyam Gruzii. Bak'radze (D. Z.)

Stolniki Tolochanovisa da diaki Ievlevis elchoba Imeret'shi, 1650-1652. Polievktov (M. A.)

Sur un projet d'étude des chartes géorgiennes. Brosset (M.-F.)

T'avadi Mishetskisa da diaki Klucharevis elchoba Kakhet'shi, 1640-1643. Polievktov (M. A.)

T'bilisi 1500. Saiubileo krebuli. Tiflis. – *Tiflis State University.*

Tbilisi 1500. Yubileiny sbornik. Tiflis. – *Tiflis State University.*

Tbilisi v XIX stoletii, 1865-1869. Chkhetia (Sh. Q.)

T'bilisis revolutsiuri dsarsuli. Sturua (N. I.) *and others.*

Tp'ilisis istoriisat'vis. Chkhetia (Sh. Q.)

Traité géorgien du comput ecclésiastique. Abuseridze, of *Tbet'i.*

Tskhovreba Sak'art'veloisa. Brosset (M. F.)

Variétés géorgiennes. Brosset (M.-F.)

LAWS

Le Code de Vakhtang VI. Georgia. – *Laws.*

Corpus Juris Ibero-Caucasici. Georgia. – *Laws.*

Détails sur le droit public arménien, extraits du Code géorgien ... par M. Brosset. VAKHTANG VI, *King of Georgia.*

Laws of King George V, of Georgia, surnamed "The Brilliant". GIORGI V, *King of Georgia,* called *The Brilliant.*

Notice du Code géorgien, manuscrit de la Bibliothèque Royale. BROSSET (M.-F.)

Obozrenie Gruzii po chasti prav i zakonovedeniya. DAVID, *Prince-Regent of Georgia.*

Sabtchot'a sotsialisturi respublikebis kavshiris konstitutsia. RUSSIA. – *Laws, etc.*

Sak'art'velo da saert'ashoriso up'leba. LE FUR (L.)

Sak'art'velos samart'lisa da kanont'mtsodneobis mimokhilva. DAVID, *Prince-Regent of Georgia.*

Zwei Grundsteine zu einer grusinischen Staats- und Rechtsgeschichte. HOLLDACK (F.)

LITERARY HISTORY, LITERATURE AND BELLES-LETTRES

L'activité littéraire des moines géorgiens au monastère d'Iviron, au Mont Athos. P'ERADZE (G.)

Die alt-christliche Literatur in der georgischen Überlieferung. P'ERADZE (G.)

Altgeorgische Chrestomathie. SHANIDZE (A. G.)

Die altgeorgische Literatur und ihre Probleme. P'ERADZE (G.)

Amiran-Darejaniani: a Georgian romance and 'its English rendering. LANG (D. M.) and MEREDITH-OWENS (G. M.)

Analyse du Roman géorgien Amiran Daredjaniani. BROSSET (M.-F.)

Die Anfänge der schriftstellerischen Tätigkeit des hl. Euthymius und der Aufstand von Bardas Skleros. T'ARKHNISHVILI (M.)

Caucasus Polyglottus. SHANIDZE (A. G.)

Ch. Rousthawéli: sa vie, son poème, ses maximes, sa philosophie. BERIDZE (Sh.)

Chota Rousthavéli, poète géorgien du XIIe siècle. MOURIER (J.)

Chrestomatie [*sic*] de la littérature géorgienne ancienne. QUBANEISHVILI (S. I.)

De la littérature romanesque géorgienne. BROSSET (M.-F.)

Dsigni "Sibrdzne sitsruisa" da k'art'uli khalkhuri makhvilsitqvaoba. TSANAVA (A. B.)

Dzveli k'art'uli literatura. K'restomat'ia sashualo skolis VIII klasisat'vis. SHANIDZE (A. G.) *and others.*

Dzveli k'art'uli literatura: V–XVIII ss. KEKELIDZE (K. S.) and BARAMIDZE (A. G.)

Dzveli k'art'uli literaturis k'restomat'ia. QUBANEISHVILI (S. I.)

Dzveli k'art'ulis k'restomat'ia. SHANIDZE (A. G.)

Essays. GAMSAKHURDIA (K. S.)

Estructura social y costumbres de la sociedad en el Epos Heroico ... "El Caballero de la Piel de Tigre". NOZADZE (V.)

État actuel de la littérature géorgienne. BROSSET (M.-F.)

Etiudebi dzveli k'art'uli literaturis istoriidan. KEKELIDZE (K. S.)

Gankit'khvani Vep'khistqaosanisa. NOZADZE (V.)

Georgian secular literature, epic, romantic and lyric. BLAKE (R. P.)

La Géorgie et les lettres françaises. BERIDZE (Sh.)

Geschichte der kirchlichen georgischen Literatur, auf Grund des ersten Bandes der georgischen Literaturgeschichte von K. Kekelidze bearbeitet. T'ARKHNISHVILI (M.)

Gruzinskaya parallel' k drevne-egipetskoi povesti "O dvukh brat'yakh". FRANK-KAMENETSKY (I. G.)

Gruzinskaya poema "Vityaz' v barsovoi shkure" Shoty iz Rustava. MARR (N. Y.)

Gruzinskaya povest' ob Aleksandre Makedonskom i serbskaya Aleksandriya. KHAKHANOV (A. S.)

Gruzinskaya povest' ob Amirane, syne Daredzhana i ostatki skazany o nem v Kartvel'skoi narodnoi literature. GREN (A. N.)

Gruzinskoe krasnorechie. KANDELAKI (N.)

Gruzinsky poet XII veka Sh. Rustavelli i ego poema "Barsova kozha". KHAKHANOV (A. S.)

Histoire et littérature de la Géorgie. BROSSET (M.-F.)

Ilia Tchavtchavadze. Saiubileo krebuli. TCHAVTCHAVADZE (I. G.) *Prince.*

Il'ya Chavchavadze. Yubileiny sbornik. TCHAVTCHAVADZE (I. G.) *Prince.*

Istoriya gruzinskoi literatury. Kratky ocherk. BARAMIDZE (A. G.) *and others.*

Iz gruzino-persidskikh literaturnykh svyazei. MARR (N. Y.)

Iz knigi tsarevicha Bagrata o gruzinskikh perevodakh dukhovnykh sochineny. MARR (N. Y.)

Iz poezdki na Afon. O gruzinskikh rukopisyakh Ivera. – O sv. Varlaame. – O drevne-gruzinskikh perevodakh s armyanskago. MARR (N. Y.)

K Rusthaveliana. MARR (N. Y.)

K voprosu o vlianii persidskoi literatury na gruzinskuyu. MARR (N. Y.)

K'art'uli enisa da mdserlobis istoriis sakit'khebi. JAVAKHISHVILI (I. A.)

K'art'uli k'ristomatia. CHUBINOV (D. I.)

K'art'uli literatura. K'restomat'ia arak'art'uli skolebis XI klasisat'vis. KAKABADZE (V. M.)

LITURGIES

hundert. LITURGIES. – Greek Rite. – *Eucho-logion.*

Zur vorbyzantinischen Liturgie Georgiens. P'ERADZE (G.)

MEDICINE

Akad. Iv. Beritashvilis sakhelobis p'iziologiis institutis shromebi. TIFLIS. – *Tiflis State University.*

Avadmqop'oba Pappataci da kogho Phlebotomus'i Sak'art'velosa da mis mezobel k'veqnebshi. KANDELAKI (S.)

MUSIC

Drevneishie instrumental'nye osnovy gruzinskoi narodnoi muzyki. STESHENKO-KUFTINA (V. K.)

Gruzinskaya muzykal'naya kul'tura. CHKHIKVADZE (G. Z.) *and others.*

Gruzinskie narodnye tantsy. JAVRISHVILI (D. L.)

K'art'uli khalkhuri simgheris ostatebi. GEGETCHKORI (L.)

K'art'uli musikaluri kultura. CHKHIKVADZE (G. Z.) *and others.*

"Otello" A. Machavariani. ORJONIKIDZE (G. S.)

Les plus anciens fondements instrumentaux de la musique populaire géorgienne. STESHENKO-KUFTINA (V. K.)

NUMISMATICS

À propos du livre intitulé: "Essai de classification des suites monétaires de la Géorgie". BROSSET (M.-F.)

Aperçu sur les monnaies russes. CHAUDOIR (S. de) *Baron.*

Dissertation sur les monnaies géorgiennes. T'EIMURAZ GIORGIS-DZE, *Prince of Georgia.*

Documents numismatiques du Royaume de Géorgie. BARATAEV (M. P.) *Prince.*

Essai de classification des suites monétaires de la Géorgie. LANGLOIS (V.)

Gruzinskaya numizmatika. KAPANADZE (D. G.)

Iz istorii monetnogo dela v Gruzii XIII veka. JALAGHANIA (I. L.)

Lettres numismatiques et archéologiques, relatives à la Transcaucasie. BARTHOLOMAEI (I. A.) *Lt.-General.*

Lettres sur la numismatique géorgienne. BARTHOLOMAEI (I. A.) *Lt.-General.*

XIII–XIV ss. dasavlur-k'art'uli p'uli, kirmaneuli. ABRAMISHVILI (T'. I.)

Monety Gruzii. PAKHOMOV (E. A.)

Neizdannyya gruzinskiya monety XI veka. PAKHOMOV (E. A.)

Note sur quelques monnaies géorgiennes. BROSSET (M.-F.)

Notes on Caucasian Numismatics. LANG (D. M.)

Notice sur une médaille de l'an 1790. BROSSET (M.-F.)

Numizmaticheskie fakty gruzinskago tsarstva. BARATAEV (M. P.) *Prince.*

Précis de numismatique géorgienne. KARST (J.)

Réponse à M. de Bartholomaei. BROSSET (M.-F.)

Some Byzantine accounting practices illustrated from Georgian sources. BLAKE (R. P.)

Studies in the numismatic history of Georgia in Transcaucasia. LANG (D. M.)

Versuch einer Erklärung von drei Münzen mit Sasaniden-Gepräge. DORN (B.)

Ves i dostoinstvo mednoi monety Tiflisa XVII–XVIII v. v. PAKHOMOV (E. A.)

PERIODICALS AND PUBLICATIONS OF LEARNED SOCIETIES

Akad. N. Maris … institutis moambe. TIFLIS. – *Marr Language Institute,* afterwards *Institute of Linguistics.*

Akhali nakadi. PERIODICAL PUBLICATIONS. – *Tiflis.*

Analecta Bollandiana. BRUSSELS. – *Société des Bollandistes.*

Ap'khazet'is enis, literaturisa da istoriis institutis shromebi. SUKHUMI. – *Abkhazian Linguistic, Literary and Historical Institute.*

Aspirantt'a da akhalgazrda metsnier mushakt'a IX sametsniero konp'erentsia, 1958. TIFLIS. – *Academy of Sciences of the Georgian S.S.R.*

Bedi K'art'lisa. PERIODICAL PUBLICATIONS. – *Paris.*

Bibliothèque du Muséon. PERIODICAL PUBLICATIONS. – *Louvain.*

Bulletin de l'Académie des Sciences de l'URSS. SAINT PETERSBURG. – *Academia Scientiarum Imperialis.*

Bulletin de l'Académie Impériale des Sciences. SAINT PETERSBURG. – *Academia Scientiarum Imperialis.*

Bulletin de la Classe Historico-Philologique. SAINT PETERSBURG. – *Academia Scientiarum Imperialis.*

Bulletin de l'Institut Caucasien d'Histoire et d'Archéologie à Tiflis. TIFLIS. – *Kavkazsky Istoriko-Arkheologichesky Institut.*

Bulletin de l'Institut Marr. TIFLIS. – *Marr Language Institute,* afterwards *Institute of Linguistics.*

Bulletin de l'Université de Tiflis. TIFLIS. – *Tiflis State University.*

Bulletin du Musée de Géorgie. TIFLIS. – *Museum of Georgia.*

Bulletin of the Academy of Sciences of the Georgian S.S.R. TIFLIS. – *Academy of Sciences of the Georgian S.S.R.*

Bulletin of the School of Oriental Studies (of the School of Oriental and African Studies). LONDON. – *University of London. – School of Oriental and African Studies.*

Bulletin Scientifique publié par l'Académie Impériale des Sciences. SAINT PETERSBURG. – *Academia Scientiarum Imperialis.*

Βυζαντινὰ Χρονικά. SAINT PETERSBURG. – *Academia Scientiarum Imperialis.*

Caucasian Review. MUNICH. – *Институт по Изучению СССР.*

Caucasica. Zeitschrift für die Erforschung der Sprachen und Kulturen des Kaukasus. PERIODICAL PUBLICATIONS. – *Leipsic.*

The Caucasus. PERIODICAL PUBLICATIONS. – *Munich.*

Chveni drosha. PERIODICAL PUBLICATIONS. – *Paris.*

D. Gulias sakhelobis Ap'khazet'is enis, literaturis da istoriis institutis shromebi. SUKHUMI. – *Abkhazian Linguistic, Literary and Historical Institute.*

Le Destin de la Géorgie. PERIODICAL PUBLICATIONS. – *Paris.*

IX nauchnaya konferentsiya aspirantov i molodykh nauchnykh rabotnikov, 1958. TIFLIS. – *Academy of Sciences of the Georgian S.S.R.*

Drosha. K'art'uli sotsialuri gazet'i. PERIODICAL PUBLICATIONS. – *Paris.*

Eris dideba. PERIODICAL PUBLICATIONS. – *Paris.*

Ert'oba. PERIODICAL PUBLICATIONS. – *Tiflis.*

Georgica. A journal of Georgian and Caucasian studies. LONDON. – *Georgian Historical Society.*

La Géorgie. PERIODICAL PUBLICATIONS. – *Paris.*

La Géorgie, organe de défense nationale. PERIODICAL PUBLICATIONS. – *Paris.*

Grandeur de la Nation. (Eris dideba.) PERIODICAL PUBLICATIONS. – *Paris.*

The Harvard Theological Review. CAMBRIDGE, Mass. – *Harvard University.*

Iveria. PERIODICAL PUBLICATIONS. – *Tiflis.*

Iveria. K'art'uli erovnuli politikis organo. PERIODICAL PUBLICATIONS. – *Paris.*

Izvestiya Akademii Nauk SSSR. SAINT PETERSBURG. – *Academia Scientiarum Imperialis.*

Izvestiya Gorskogo Instituta Narodnogo Obrazovaniya. VLADIKAVKAZ. – *Gorsky Institut Narodnogo Obrazovaniya.*

Izvestiya Imperatorskoi Akademii Nauk. SAINT PETERSBURG. – *Academia Scientiarum Imperialis.*

Izvestiya Instituta Yazyka, Istorii i Material'noi Kul'tury. TIFLIS. – *Marr Language Institute,* afterwards *Institute of Linguistics.*

Izvestiya Kavkazskogo Istoriko-Arkheologicheskogo Instituta v Tiflise. TIFLIS. – *Kavkazsky Istoriko-Arkheologichesky Institut.*

Izvestiya Tiflisskogo Universiteta. TIFLIS. – *Tiflis State University.*

Jejili. Saqmadsvilo nakhatebiani zhurnali. PERIODICAL PUBLICATIONS. – *Tiflis.*

Journal Asiatique. PARIS. – *Société Asiatique.*

The Journal of the Royal Asiatic Society. LONDON. – *Royal Asiatic Society of Great Britain and Ireland.*

Kavkaz. PERIODICAL PUBLICATIONS. – *Paris.*

Khristiansky Vostok. SAINT PETERSBURG. – *Academia Scientiarum Imperialis.*

Komunisti. PERIODICAL PUBLICATIONS. – *Tiflis.*

Kooperatsia. PERIODICAL PUBLICATIONS. – *K'ut'aisi.*

Krebuli. K'art'uli literaturisa, istoriisa da khelovnebis qoveldsliuri organo. PERIODICAL PUBLICATIONS. – *New York.*

Kvali. PERIODICAL PUBLICATIONS. – *Tiflis.*

Mat'rakhi da salamuri. PERIODICAL PUBLICATIONS. – *Tiflis.*

Mdsqemsi. PERIODICAL PUBLICATIONS. – *K'ut'aisi.*

Mélanges Asiatiques. SAINT PETERSBURG. – *Academia Scientiarum Imperialis.*

Meotsnebe niamorebi. PERIODICAL PUBLICATIONS. – *Tiflis.*

Mnat'obi. PERIODICAL PUBLICATIONS. – *Tiflis.*

Moambe. T'viuri zhurnali. PERIODICAL PUBLICATIONS. – *Tiflis.*

Le Muséon. PERIODICAL PUBLICATIONS. – *Louvain.*

Musha. PERIODICAL PUBLICATIONS. – *Tiflis.*

Nobat'i. PERIODICAL PUBLICATIONS. – *Tiflis.*

Nouvel Orient. MOSCOW. – *Nauchnaya Assotsiatsiya Vostokovedeniya S.S.S.R.*

Novy Vostok. MOSCOW. – *Nauchnaya Assotsiatsiya Vostokovedeniya S.S.S.R.*

Oriens Christianus. ROME. – *Collegium des deutschen Campo Santo.*

Orientalia Christiana Periodica. ROME. – *Pontificio Istituto per gli Studi Orientali.*

Palestinsky Sbornik. SAINT PETERSBURG. – *Православное,* afterwards *Российское Палестинское Общество.*

P'oni. PERIODICAL PUBLICATIONS. – *K'ut'aisi.*

Pravoslavny Palestinsky Sbornik. SAINT PETERSBURG. – *Православное,* afterwards *Российское Палестинское Общество.*

PHILOLOGY AND LINGUISTICS

Yafeticheskiya nazvaniya derev'ev i rasteny. MARR (N. Y.)

Yafeticheskoe proiskhozhdenie abkhazskikh terminov rodstva. MARR (N. Y.)

Yafetichesky Kavkaz i trety etnichesky element v sozidanii sredizemnomorskoi kul'tury. MARR (N. Y.)

Yafetichesky sbornik. SAINT PETERSBURG. – *Academia Scientiarum Imperialis.* – *Яфетический Институт,* afterwards *Институт языка и мышления.*

Yazyk i myshlenie. SAINT PETERSBURG. – *Academia Scientiarum Imperialis.* – *Яфетический Институт,* afterwards *Институт языка и мышления.*

Yazyki Severnogo Kavkaza i Dagestana. SERDYUCHENKO (G. P.)

Zaimstvovanie chislitel'nykh v yafeticheskikh yazykakh. MARR (N. Y.)

Zakony lezginskogo udareniya. ZHIRKOV (L. I.)

'Zima' = 'smert'', iz paleontologii rechi. MARR (N. Y.)

Zogadi enat'metsnierebis kat'edris shromebi. TIFLIS. – *Tiflis State University.*

Zvukovoi sostav tsezskogo (didoiskogo) yazyka. MEGRELIDZE (I. B.)

PHILOSOPHY

Dialek'tikuri da istoriuli materializmis shesakheb. STALIN (I. V.)

Ilia Tchavtchavadze: p'ilosop'iuri da sotsialurpolitikuri shekhedulebani. RATIANI (P. K.)

Ilia Tchavtchavadzis p'ilosop'iuri da est'etikuri shekhedulebani. T'AVADZE (A. G.)

Ioann Petritssky, gruzinsky neoplatonik XI–XII veka. MARR (N. Y.)

Istoriya gruzinskoi filosofii. NUTSUBIDZE (SH. I.)

K'art'uli p'ilosop'iis istoria. NUTSUBIDZE (SH. I.)

K'art'uli sazogadoebrivi da p'ilosop'iuri azris istoriidan. KHIDASHELI (SH. V.)

Logikuri kavshiris dialek'tikuri bunebis shesakheb. TSERET'ELI (S. B.)

Prak'tikis shesakheb. MAO (Tsê-TUNG).

Ratsionaluri martsvali Hegelis daskvnis t'eoriashi. TSERET'ELI (S. B.)

POETRY

Akhundi. Dzveli ambavi. VAZHA-P'SHAVELA, *pseud.*

Anthology of Georgian Poetry. URUSHADZE (V.)

Antologiya darginskoi poezii. ABAKAROV (AḤMAD-KHĀN).

Antologiya gruzinskoi poezii. ABASHIDZE (I. B.) *and others.*

Archiliani. ARCHIL, *King of Imeret'i.*

Arsenas lek'si. ODZELASHVILI (A.)

Boshebi. Poltava. PUSHKIN (A. S.)

La chanson du réfugié. TOGONIDZE (G.)

Chveni simgherebi. GEORGIA. – *Georgian Legion.*

Da budet mir! Stikhi. MARGIANI (R. A.)

Dabadeba da aghzrda Erekle Batonishvilisa. RAZIKASHVILI (N.) *known as* BACHANA.

Dagestanskaya narodnaya lirika. GREBNEV (N.)

Dakarguli samot'khe. MILTON (J.)

Dargala poeziyala antologiya. ABAKAROV (AḤMAD-KHĀN).

Davit'iani. GURAMISHVILI (D.)

Davitiani. Stikhotvoreniya i poemy. GURAMISHVILI (D.)

Davit'iani. (T'khzulebat'a sruli krebuli.) GURAMISHVILI (D.)

Dideba Stalins. ABASHELI (A. B.) *and others.*

Drevnegruzinskie odopistsy XII v. MARR (N. Y.)

Dsigni lek'sebis. T'EVZADZE (A. R.)

Ert'tomeuli. ABASHELI (A. B.); GABESKIRIA (V.I.); GRISHASHVILI (I. G.); RURUA (P.)

Ert'tomeuli. Rcheuli. VAZHA-P'SHAVELA, *pseud.*

Ert'tomeuli. (Rcheuli lek'sebi, baladebi da simgherebi.) KALADZE (K. R.)

Fialki na skalakh. RAMAZANOV (B.)

Gabaaseba T'eimurazisa da Rust'velisa. ARCHIL, *King of Imeret'i.*

Gamardzhveba. Stikhi gruzinskikh poetov, 1941–1944. ABASHELI (A. B.) *and others.*

La Géorgie et le Bien. URUSHADZE (S.)

Georgische Dichter. LEIST (A.)

Georgy Shestoi. Poema. ABASHIDZE (G. G.)

Ghrublian dgheebshi. Lek'sebi da poemebi. GELAZANIA (G.)

Govorit Selim. Skazanie o Chechne. MUZAEV (N.)

Gruzinskaya sovetskaya poeziya. ABASHIDZE (G. G.) *and others.*

Gruzinskaya vesna. AKOBIA (SH.) *and others.*

Gruzinskie liriki. PASTERNAK (B. L.)

The Hermit: a legend. TCHAVTCHAVADZE (I. G.) *Prince.*

L'Homme à la peau de léopard. RUST'AVELI (SHOT'A).

L'hymne au monde harmonieux. URUSHADZE (S.)

Izbrannoe. Perevod s abkhazskogo. GULIA (D. I.)

Izbrannoe. Perevod s gruzinskogo. CHIK'OVANI (S. I.); TSERET'ELI (A. R.) *Prince.*

Izbrannoe. Perevod s kabardinskogo. SHOGENTSUKOV ('ALĪ A.)

Izbrannye perevody. TSAGARELI (G. K.)

Izbrannye pesni i stikhi. STAL'SKY (S.)

RELIGION, THEOLOGY, CHURCH HISTORY, DEVOTIONAL AND PATRISTIC LITERATURE

SCIENCE, TECHNOLOGY AND NATURAL HISTORY